VINTAGE *Classics*

VOL.2

SUSAN NAPIER

MICHELLE REID

SANDRA MARTON

MILLS & BOON

VINTAGE CLASSICS: VOLUME TWO © 2022 by Harlequin Books S.A.

THE MISTRESS DECEPTION
© 2000 by Susan Napier
Australian Copyright 2000
New Zealand Copyright 2000

First Published 2000
Fourth Australian Paperback Edition 2022
ISBN 978 1 867 25999 2

GOLD RING OF BETRAYAL
© 1996 by Michelle Reid
Australian Copyright 1996
New Zealand Copyright 1996

First Published 1996
Third Australian Paperback Edition 2022
ISBN 978 1 867 25999 2

THE BRIDAL SUITE
© 1998 by Sandra Myles
Australian Copyright 1998
New Zealand Copyright 1998

First Published 1998
Third Australian Paperback Edition 2022
ISBN 978 1 867 25999 2

Published by
Mills & Boon
An imprint of Harlequin Enterprises (Australia) Pty Limited
(ABN 47 001 180 918), a subsidiary of HarperCollins
Publishers Australia Pty Limited (ABN 36 009 913 517)
Level 13, 201 Elizabeth Street
SYDNEY NSW 2000
AUSTRALIA

FSC
MIX
Paper from
responsible sources
FSC® C001695
www.fsc.org

® and ™ (apart from those relating to FSC®) are trademarks of Harlequin Enterprises (Australia) Pty Limited or its corporate affiliates. Trademarks indicated with ® are registered in Australia, New Zealand and in other countries. Contact admin_legal@Harlequin.ca for details.

Printed and bound in Australia by McPherson's Printing Group

CONTENTS

The Mistress Deception

Susan Napier

Susan Napier was born on St Valentine's Day, so it's not surprising she has developed an enduring love of romantic stories. She started her writing career as a journalist in Auckland, New Zealand, trying her hand at romantic fiction only after she had married her handsome boss! Numerous books later she still lives with her most enduring hero, two future heroes—her sons!—two cats and a computer. When she's not writing she likes to read and cook, often simultaneously!

More titles by the same author:

THE REVENGE AFFAIR

CHAPTER ONE

'EXCUSE ME—Mr Riordan...?'

Matthew Riordan's dark head jerked up at the interruption and he directed an impatient frown at the middle-aged woman hovering in the doorway of his borrowed office.

'I'm sorry to disturb you...' she said, undeterred by the scowl on his narrow, long-boned face. She advanced towards his desk, a large manila envelope held out between her fingertips. 'I know you asked me to deal with your father's personal correspondence until he's well enough to do it himself, but—well... I think this is probably something that you would prefer to handle yourself...'

Matt's abstraction was banished as he rocked back in his leather chair, his thick eyebrows rising at the sight of his father's unflappable secretary looking so ill at ease.

Was that a *blush* on those leathery cheeks? he wondered incredulously, his dark brown eyes sharpening behind the lenses of his round gold and tortoiseshell spectacles.

For over three decades—since before Matt was born—she had serenely guarded his father's Auckland office, more than a match for Kevin Riordan's rough-and-tumble personality and the raffish nature of many of his employees and customers in the early years of his company. The former rubbish-man turned scrap-dealer and recycling mogul, now owner of New Zealand's largest waste-disposal conglomerate, had rewarded her mental toughness and unflagging loyalty with his boisterous respect, smugly boasting to all and sundry that nothing could fluster his redoubtable Mary.

His confidence had proved justified two days earlier, when Mary had investigated a thud from his office and discovered her employer in the throes of a heart attack. Instantly conquering her shock, she had phoned for an ambulance and proceeded to calmly administer CPR until the medical team arrived. Then she had busied herself telephoning his wife and son, faxing his second-in-command, who was in Tokyo on business, and discreetly fending off speculation and rumours as she postponed appointments and rearranged meetings.

Now, she gingerly placed the neatly slit foolscap envelope on the desk in front of Matt and scuttled backwards. 'What is it—a letter-bomb?' he commented drily, and Mary regained enough of her steely poise to give him a stern look, admonishing him for his flippancy.

Matt laid down his pen and pulled off his glasses, tossing them onto the blotter. His eyes felt gritty with fatigue as he picked up the envelope, noting the plainly typed address with the words 'Strictly Personal' thickly underlined several times. He tipped it up by one corner and three glossy photographs slid face-down across the desk.

He flipped one over and his eyebrows scooted up in puzzled surprise.

The glossy black and white photograph had been taken at a party two weeks ago—a profile shot of Matt leaning over the hand of a tall, voluptuous woman whose long, strapless glittering white gown looked as if it had been applied to her pneumatic curves with a spray gun.

He and the woman were both holding champagne glasses and smiling brilliantly, but the flattering picture didn't tell the full story.

The photograph didn't show the long, painted nails digging painfully into his skin, punishing him for the parody of a kiss he had just planted on the back of her hand. Nor did it reveal that Matt had been dangerously drunk, sullen and obstreperous.

He hadn't been aware that there was anyone taking photographs that night, although in the circumstances that was hardly surprising, but he doubted that Merrilyn Freeman, their over-anxious hostess, would have jeopardised the exclusivity of her private dinner party by inviting a professional photographer along. The harsh contrasts and grainy texture suggested the print had been blown up from a much smaller negative.

It was also perfectly innocuous—nothing to give Mary Marcus reason to treat the envelope as if it was an unexploded bomb.

In the course of his business and social life Matt had been photographed in similar poses with numerous women of his acquaintance. He could see no reason why anyone would want to mail this one to his father, except, perhaps, as an attempt to curry favour...

Matt flipped over the other photographs and his complacent assumption exploded in his face. He stiffened, the breath hissing between his clenched teeth.

To his intense chagrin he could feel the warmth flooding into his face. Although he didn't look up he was excruciatingly aware of Mary's disapproving gaze as she made good her escape, closing the door behind her with a definitive snap that sealed him in with the smoking ruins of his reputation as a gentleman.

Thank God he could rely on her to keep her mouth shut!

His mouth compressed into a thin line, Matt studied the evidence of his betrayal.

In the first photograph Matt was sitting bare-chested on the edge of a rumpled bed, facing towards the camera, his smooth torso sculpted by the soft light from a bedside lamp. The woman in the strapless dress was kneeling on the floor between his splayed legs, the white sequins of her gown a glittering contrast to the black fabric of Matt's formal trousers where his knees pressed against her flanks, trapping her in the quintessential pose of female sexual submission. He was looking down at her bent head, his palms cupping her skull, fingers threaded into her feathery, short-cropped hair, while hers were out of sight of the camera's intrusive eye…from the position of her bent elbows, obviously busy in his lap!

God!

Matt's flush deepened, his blood pressure spiking as he transferred his stunned gaze to the second picture. Here the roles of submission and domination were dramatically reversed. This time Matt was lying flat on his back on the bed, the muscles of his deep chest straining against the pull of his arms stretched over his head, his crossed wrists bound to the head of the brass bedstead with the narrow silk cummerbund he had been wearing in the earlier photo. Straddling his lower belly was the Valkyrie, flaunting a vast expanse of smooth, creamy skin unmarked by tan-lines, her knees digging into his lower ribcage, her spectacular breasts hovering invitingly above his pillowed head as she arched up to secure his bonds. The crowning salacious touch was the thin black leather whip which lay coiled on the bed beside them.

Matt cursed, his alcohol-hazed memories warring with the erotic images before him. His expression tightened as he shifted uncomfortably in his chair, trying to ease the treacherous tautening in another part of his anatomy.

He was furious, and aroused—and furious at himself for being aroused. He had been manipulated—his pride scraped raw, his privacy violated—and instead of being disgusted he was getting turned on!

He raked his fingers inside the empty envelope, grimly unsurprised to find that there was no accompanying message.

No message was needed. Matt knew exactly what form the blackmail would take.

The bitch had set him up!

And to think that he had sent her flowers afterwards, to thank her for preventing him from making a complete drunken ass of himself at the party...an expensive sheaf of yellow roses and a polite, handwritten note which had skilfully disguised his chagrin that *she* should be his rescuer and, later in that guest-house bedroom, sole witness to his humiliating weakness.

Except it was now painfully obvious that she had *not* been the sole witness!

Matt pinched the narrow bridge of his nose, castigating himself for his gullibility. How could he have allowed himself to trust her? He had been suspicious of her from the first day they had ever met, and even tanked to the eyeballs he had recognised the cool antipathy she had exuded when Merrilyn had anxiously thrust them into each other's company. It had been partly the desire to smash through that frigid aloofness which had goaded him into baiting her the way that he had.

And now she thought she had it within her grasp to extract the perfect revenge.

Well, he might have been an easy target drunk, but—sober— he was going to show her how very difficult he could be!

He glanced at the smudged date-stamp on the manila envelope, his eyebrows snapping together when he realised what it meant. He leaned forward and punched in Mary's extension number on his telephone.

'Mr Riordan's office—'

'Mary, when did this envelope arrive in the office?' he demanded, his abrupt urgency overriding any potential embarrassment.

'The day before yesterday—in the morning,' Mary replied, after a small hesitation to think out the sequence of events. 'I always slit open Mr Riordan's personal mail for him as soon as it arrives, and put the stack on his desk…but of course I never look at the contents unless he expressly asks me to—'

'So this has just been lying around—open—on Dad's desk for the past two days?' interrupted Matt, sweating bullets.

'Well, yes…but with Mr Stiller not due back from Tokyo until later in the week, only the cleaners and I have had access to Mr Riordan's office,' Mary pointed out.

Matt's tension eased a notch at the reminder of his cousin's absence. Both only children, he and Neville Stiller had spent a lot of time in each other's company while growing up, but as adults their relationship was far from cordial. Neville, who had worked at KR Industries ever since he'd left high school, had been appointed Chief Executive five years ago, and was generally expected to take over as General Manager when his uncle retired. Matt, on the other hand, had been actively discouraged from following directly in his father's footsteps. Instead he had been educated, guided and groomed for the job which now consumed most of his waking hours—chairman of the family's holding company, which controlled multimillion-dollar investments in both the local and international share markets. Matt had long accepted that there was no place for him in the flourishing business which had been the cornerstone of his father's fortune, but Neville remained intensely protective of the power-base he had carved out for himself, quick to resent any advice or expression of interest in the firm as an attempt to undermine his position as Kevin Riordan's successor.

If this pivotal deal had not demanded Neville's continuing presence in Tokyo, Matt didn't doubt that he would have rushed back to commandeer the General Manager's office.

Firmly ensconced in the seat of power, Neville would have had few qualms about nosing through his stricken uncle's private correspondence, and if he *had* come across the photos how he would have gloated over the knowledge that his cousin had been caught, quite literally, with his pants down!

Matt cringed at the thought. As it was, Neville had had little choice but to grudgingly accept Matt's offer to hold the fort until he had concluded his complex negotiations with a Japanese industrial waste management company with whom KR Industries was planning a joint venture.

Suddenly Matt was hit by another, even more devastating worry.

'Do you know if Dad had time to look at his private mail before he had his heart attack?' he grated.

Mary's sharply indrawn breath recognised the ugly implication. 'I suppose he may have done,' she admitted slowly. 'We went through the business mail together first, as usual, and he dictated a few urgent letters, but...yesit's possible that he started going through his own mail while I was typing up the letters. But since that envelope was the largest, I would have put it at the bottom of his pile...'

They both knew that that was little consolation. The brash personality shaped by Kevin Riordan's poverty-stricken childhood viewed size as an important indicator of status. 'Restraint' was not a word which figured large in his vocabulary. If he had decided to read his mail he was likely to have reasoned that the bigger the envelope the more interesting the contents.

In this case he would have been right!

Matt's dark eyes narrowed to glittering black slits, a faint tic pulsing on the hard temple above his left eyebrow. His left hand clenched on the receiver, the spare flesh whitening over his knuckles and around the broad gold band on his ring finger.

'Mary—bring me a plain foolscap envelope!' he ordered, and slammed down the phone.

He dragged a blank writing tablet towards him and picked up his fountain pen to scrawl a slashing message in his trademark green ink across the page.

When Mary appeared with his request he transferred the photographs and the folded message into the new envelope and addressed it in aggressive block letters.

'See that it goes out immediately,' he said, pushing the sealed envelope across the desk.

'By courier, or post?'

His smile was unpleasant.

'Courier.' He wanted the blackmailer's mental suffering to start as soon as possible.

Mary looked at the address, her poker-face breaking up as she raised concerned grey eyes to his. 'Don't you think you should—'

'Just do it!'

Her mouth snapped shut at his unprecedented rudeness. Her chin lifted and she turned on her heel, her rigid, bony back a silent reproach. Matt was irresistibly reminded that her staunch loyalty to his father had always also extended to himself.

'I'm sorry, Mary,' he apologised swiftly, his deep voice resonant with sincerity as he ran his fingers through his thick wavy hair, disciplined into a conservative cut that flattered the long bones of his face. 'I didn't mean to shout. I'm not angry at *you*. What with keeping my mother company at the hospital and trying to juggle things here, as well as my own job, I haven't had much sleep over the past two nights and I'm afraid my temper's suffered accordingly. But as you said before—this is something that I need to handle myself...'

As a boy he had always been quick to admit fault and offer amends, thought Mary, and as a man he was equally ruthless with his failings. In fact sometimes she felt he took too *much* responsibility upon himself...

'I just hope you know what you're doing,' she murmured.

'Oh, I know exactly what I'm doing,' he told her with a savage smile. 'I'm turning the tables on an extortionist.

'I have a feeling that I may turn out to have a gift for blackmail!'

CHAPTER TWO

RACHEL BLAIR SAT at the kitchen table sipping her morning coffee and glowering at the letter in her hand.

'Hello, what are you doing up so early?' Her elder sister came bustling through the door, dressed in her nurse's uniform and carrying an armful of crumpled sheets and damp towels. 'I thought you were going to leave it one more day before you went back to work.' She vanished into the adjacent laundry and Rachel could hear her lifting and closing the lid of the temperamental washing machine and cranking the dial around.

'I felt perfectly fine when I woke up so I changed my mind,' Rachel called to her through the archway. The mild headache niggling at her consciousness she preferred to attribute to the letter in her hand rather than the lingering after-effects of her ailment.

'Hmm.' Robyn reappeared in the doorway and gave her a professional once-over. 'Just make sure you don't overdo it. Your immune system's probably still not back to full strength.'

'It was only a virus,' Rachel pointed out. 'I've finished my course of antibiotics and my cold is pretty much gone—see?'

She sniffed to show that the clogged airways of the past few days had cleared.

Robyn shook her blonde head in bafflement. 'I don't know how you managed to catch the flu in the middle of Auckland's hottest summer on record. No one else we know has it...'

With an effort Rachel managed not to blush.

'I guess I'm just ahead of my time,' she said airily. 'The doctor said I have the type they'll be offering a vaccine for this winter.'

Fortunately Robyn was easily diverted from her speculation on the source of the infection.

'Maybe if you're lucky they'll name it after you,' she grinned.

Rachel could think of someone far more deserving of the honour of being commemorated as an irksome germ!

'Type-Rachel flu? Do you think I could ask for royalties?' She grinned back, and the resemblance between the sisters was suddenly pronounced, even though, superficially, they looked as different as chalk and cheese.

At forty, Robyn was still as slim and petite as she had been as a teenager, her ash-blonde hair and big blue eyes lending her a doll-like air of feminine fragility which was belied by her job as a hard-working practice nurse.

Ten years her junior, Rachel towered over her sister, and most other women of her acquaintance. Her wide shoulders and full bust would have made her top-heavy if it hadn't been for the broadly rounded hips flaring below her neat waist, and her long, firmly muscled legs. Her triangular face, framed by a spiky, razor-cut cap of hair the colour of burnt toffee, thickly lashed hazel eyes and thin, determined mouth possessed strength of character rather than beauty...but unfortunately people often tended to judge her from the neck down!

She knew that her curvy, hour-glass shape rendered her almost a cartoon-figure of female pulchritude, the living embodiment of countless male fantasies.

It had been rough coping with the unwonted sexual attention

when she was young, but she had determined very early on not to let her overtly sexy body image dictate the path of her life. She had fought hard to be her own person, and with maturity had perfected subtle strategies to control the perceptions and prejudices of those around her—dressing casually, in loose, multi-layered clothing, and cultivating a robust good humour which was the opposite of seductive. Fortunately her height and superior strength gave her a physical edge whenever her defensive strategies proved too subtle for over-active male libidos.

'I doubt it—though you'd probably have hordes of guys clamouring to be personally infected,' chuckled Robyn. Thanks to the considerable age gap between them, and the fact that she had been happily married to Simon Fox for over twenty years, she had never been jealous of her sister's effect on men.

A rattling mechanical hiccup sounded behind her and she darted through to give the washing machine a well-practised kick of encouragement.

Rachel rolled her eyes and returned her brooding attention to her unwelcome letter.

She was getting fed up with this petty campaign of harassment. At first she had dismissed the escalating stream of annoyances as an unfortunate run of back luck, but too many coincidences had piled up, and now her suspicions condensed into certainty.

It was typical of her unknown harasser to hide behind a faceless bureaucracy. Whoever had it in for her was a coward—but very a clever one, initiating trouble but never following it through to a point where Rachel might have a chance to identify the source.

A low growl of frustration purred in the back of her throat.

'What's the matter?' asked Robyn, drifting back to the accompaniment of noisily hissing water pipes.

'The council has received a tip that I'm running a business from this address,' Rachel paraphrased in disgust.

'They're warning me that they're going to investigate and I could be prosecuted for carrying on a non-complying activity.'

'It must be some mistake,' said Robyn, tucking a shoulder-length strand of hair back into the smooth French twist she wore at work.

'You think so? And was it also a mistake when the phone company was told the same thing and tried to charge me a higher line rental? And when the tax department decided to audit me because someone phoned their hotline and told them I had an undeclared second income? Or when I didn't get any mail for two weeks and suddenly discovered that the post office had been advised to redirect my mail to a house which just happened to be the residence of a motorcycle gang?'

Robyn put a hand to her mouth. 'Oh! That reminds me—Bethany said something arrived for you yesterday afternoon by courier. You were having a bath and she was just leaving for basketball practice so she just signed for it and took off with it in her bag. She forgot all about it until this morning.'

She crossed the small, sunny kitchen and fetched the bubble-wrapped plastic courier bag which had been tucked with some other papers behind the telephone on the bench, handing it to her sister.

She glanced at the watch pinned to her breast and let out a little huff. 'I hope Bethany's out of that bathroom—I'm sure when you offered to put us up for a few weeks you didn't expect to have to put up with a teenager who showers twice a day for twenty minutes at a time! I do wish you'd let us pay something towards the water and power, as well as the groceries.'

Rachel paused in the act of ripping into the zip-locked seam of the bag. 'Don't be silly. Just be thankful that Bethany's into cleanliness, not some ghastly grunge kick. It's not as if I have to pay rent, or a mortgage. I've loved having you to stay.' There was a hint of wistfulness in her hazel eyes. Since David had died two years ago there had been no one special in her life, no one who was critical to her happiness—or she to theirs. Usually she kept herself looking resolutely to the future, but these last few days of enforced rest had given her time to dwell on all the 'might have beens.'

She shook off the cruelly unproductive thoughts. 'I just wish that Simon wasn't coming back so soon and whisking you both so far away,' she said lightly.

'We're only moving to Bangkok—not the moon,' Robyn chided her bracingly. Simon, who worked for a multinational chemical company, was being transferred to Thailand to help build a new manufacturing plant. While he had flown out there to meet his new boss, choose their company-paid accommodation and register Bethany to attend the local International School, his wife and daughter had been packing up and selling their Auckland home and arranging to ship their belongings.

'We get an annual home-leave, and, anyway, I hope you'll come up and have a holiday with us. You did say that Westons had some huge contract in the offing that might let you give up your day job!'

Rachel gave a rueful laugh. Her work as a massage therapist and fitness trainer was actually carried out in the early morning or late afternoon and evening, so that she could devote the business hours to the security company which she had inherited from David. No one had been more astonished than herself when she had discovered that her fiancée of six months had altered his will to leave her not only his townhouse but also his fifty-one percent share of the security company which he and his brother Frank, a fellow ex-policeman, had bought.

Although Weston Security Services had possessed a loyal core of clients at the time of David's death, it had also been carrying a heavy debt-load, and at first, woefully aware of her ignorance, Rachel had been content to remain a silent partner. But as the business had continued to struggle she had realised that it would be a betrayal of David's trust to watch his cherished dream die without lifting a finger to help.

It hadn't been an investment that he had given her in his will so much as a part of himself. *She* might doubt herself, but David had always had faith in her ability to tackle new challenges. To that end she had used her stake in the company to persuade Frank to give her an active role in managing the business. She had waived a salary, preferring to see the money invested in new staff and equipment, and lived off her freelance earnings from two city gyms and a physiotherapy practice.

It had been a steep learning curve, and although Rachel had made plenty of mistakes, her hands-on method of training wasn't proving the disaster that Frank had feared it would be. In the last few months the company turn-over had shown a promising improvement, but a balloon repayment was looming on the loan, and meeting the debt was largely reliant on a major corporate contract which Frank seemed to be confident was already in the bag. Rachel was not so sanguine.

'I think it'll be a while before I can afford to do that,' she sighed. 'Frank says that trust and respect build slowly in the security business, and being a woman in a maledominated industry makes it that much more difficult to get accepted—'

She was interrupted as her sister took another surreptitious look at her watch and dashed for the door with a squawk of dismay.

Rachel returned to ripping open the zip-lock bag. Her birthday wasn't far away, and she wondered with a lift of her spirits whether someone had sent her an early present.

Her eager anticipation drained abruptly away as she withdrew some photographs paper-clipped to the back of a scrawled note in green ink which slanted across the page, arrogantly ignoring the ruled lines. She washed down her disappointment with her rapidly cooling coffee as she scanned the jolting words.

Did you really think I would let you use me as your free ride to riches?

Of the two of us you're obviously the more photogenic—a fact which I'm sure the tabloid press will be quick to exploit if these, or any even more explicit, are put into circulation. I always knew you were centrefold material, but while the resultant notoriety might well annoy me, it won't destroy me. Unlike you. What will happen to Westons' reputation for probity and discretion when your corporate clients find out that their security rests in the whip-hand of a blowsy, over-blown dominatrix who looks as if she'd be more at home in a brothel than a boardroom?

Sorry, doll.

You lose.

A mouthful of lukewarm coffee was stranded in her mouth as her throat clogged with shock. Her cup crashed down into its saucer as she unclipped the photographs and fanned them out in her hands like oversized cards.

'Oh, God!' She choked, spewing coffee droplets across the table in her spluttering horror, dropping the photographs as if they were hot coals.

'Oh, *God*!' Rachel's horror deepened to bone-bruising humiliation, the outrageous insults in the note suddenly making sickening sense. There was no signature, but she didn't need one. She knew instantly who to blame for the outrage.

She shuddered, pressing her shaking hands to hot cheeks as she looked down at the shameful photographs. Yes, she had knelt between his legs to unfasten his trousers...but this picture gave the impression that she had been—that she had done it in order to *pleasure* him. The heavy-lidded smile on his face certainly seemed to suggest that she'd been succeeding, whereas in reality she had been cursing a blue streak that his formal trousers had buttons rather than a zip—which she would have cheerfully used to castrate him! If he had gained any pleasure from what she had been doing, then it was purely his own warped mind that had created it.

And the other one—*God!*...that didn't look anything *like*

the way it had actually happened, either. Why—these pictures made her look as if she had been a willing participant in some kind of disgusting sexual perversion, rather than the good Samaritan which she had been dragooned into playing.

But good Samaritans didn't roll around naked on a bed with those they rescued, the devil whispered in her ear.

Rachel shook her head, still dazed by the shock of seeing herself portrayed in the role of sexual predator. It was so fundamentally at odds with her character that it would almost be funny if it wasn't so humiliating. The photographs were slanderously misleading. The circumstantial evidence might trumpet otherwise, but the situation had actually been completely innocent.

Well, perhaps not *completely*, she forced herself to admit as her mind replayed the images of that night. It had definitely not been her finest hour, but Matthew Riordan was to blame for everything that had happened. The whole unsavoury incident had been entirely his own fault!

So how dared he? How *dared* he now turn around and threaten to slander *her* with the evidence of *his* indiscretion! She had never said a word to anyone—not even Frank or Merrilyn—about what had happened that night after they had left the party. In spite of the pressure to gossip she had uttered not a single, solitary syllable. For *his* sake!

And this was how he repaid her for her kindness! One feeble bunch of flowers and this…this *outrage*!

The blood boiled in her veins as she looked at the note and one word suddenly jumped out at her. Blowsy. *Blowsy?*

Her hazel eyes turned a ferocious green. She could shrug off his groundless accusation that she belonged in a brothel as sheer malice, but how dared he call her blowsy? He hadn't had any objections to her *over-blown* 'centre-fold' of a body when he'd been begging her to make love to him, had he?

She was infuriated to feel her breasts tighten at the memory of his words, of the uninhibited way that he had expressed his desire as they had wrestled on the bed. As drunk as he'd been she had thought that he would be incapable of physical arousal, and hadn't he taken great delight in proving her wrong! But then, maybe he hadn't been quite so drunk as he had made out. Maybe it had all been a big act in order to lure her into just such a compromising position while some sleazy photographer snapped away from the closet.

Her eyes went unwillingly back to the most explicit photograph and hot chills fizzled in her belly. It was her body which was flaunted centre-stage, but no one could deny that Matthew Riordan made a pretty impressive supporting act. He wasn't quite as tall as Rachel, but with his clothes off he had been larger than she had expected, in *all* ways... His lean body had a ripped quality, all muscle with little softening body fat, and the raw strength in the muscle-dense arms and thighs had taken her by surprise. At Westons she was used to seeing security guards shaped like weightlifters, but Matthew Riordan's smooth, sleek body had an understated elegance that merely hinted at the power that lay sheathed beneath his skin.

The dirty rat! What a hypocrite he was—the cool, cultivated, highly respectable Matthew Riordan, scion of his wealthy family and controller of a substantial chunk of the New Zealand economy...

Well, the arrogant pig needn't think he could control *her*. She mentally tossed her head. Let everyone find out that the real Matthew Riordan was a sleazy manipulator, without a scrap of moral conscience or a shred of human decency.

She looked at the photo of them lying on the bed and groaned, covering her hot face with her hands. In the end, would it matter which one of them was exposed as the liar? Any mud she threw was going to stick to both of them, and, while he had unlimited resources with which to whitewash himself clean, she had virtually none.

He had already proved as cunning as a snake and as lucky as the devil, she thought, peeking through her fingers again. He couldn't have arranged that pose better if he had employed a Hollywood director to choreograph the sexy scene. The way they were posed made the most of her abundant breasts, her jutting nipples almost brushing his parted lips as she stretched above him to tighten his bindings. He needed only to lift his head slightly and…

Oh, no! She clamped down on the unruly urge to wander down *that* tortuous memory lane. She wasn't going to be made to feel more of a sexual deviant than she did already. She struggled to fix her mind on more important matters. The most threatening implication in the note as far as she was concerned was that there were even *more* explicit photographs in existence.

Her eyes fell on the whip and she gave a little hiccup of hysteria. Admittedly she hadn't been exactly alert to her wider surroundings while their tussle had been going on, but how could she have missed noticing *that*? The whole tenor of the scene implied that she was about to use it once she had rendered her victim helpless. As if she would ever use a whip against another human being! she thought hotly. Although, come to think of it, at the moment the idea did have a certain sadistic appeal. Her pale pink lips pulled unconsciously back from her white teeth as she savoured the vengeful notion. Oh, yes, she mused—if Matthew Riordan and a handy whip should present themselves to her right now she might well take a great deal of pleasure in lashing the gloating smirk off his face.

So he thought he had won this dirty little game of one-up-man-ship, did he…?

'Hi, Rachel, whatcha looking at?'

Rachel gave a frightened little yelp as Bethany bounced into the kitchen, her freckled face scrubbed squeaky clean, her budding breasts thrusting against her dark green school tunic as she leaned over the table.

'Mum said you were opening the courier's package.

What was in it? Photos? Can I see?'

As Rachel frantically tried to push the prints back into the bag Bethany hooked one away. Fortunately for Rachel's madly thundering heart it was the innocuous shot from the party.

'Hey. Wow!' Bethany's green-gold eyes rounded in admiration. 'What a babe! Who is he?'

'No one.' Rachel tried to grab the photograph back, but Bethany danced out of reach with a chuckle.

'You look pretty hot, too. Nothing like your usual maiden-aunt get-ups. You look as if you're about to explode out of that dress! Were you trying to vamp him? He looks pretty vamped to me.'

'Bethany—' Rachel's protest held a breathless note of desperation that only egged her tormentor on.

'So, who is he?' Bethany teased, her face splitting on a grin, her long blonde ponytail dancing across her slender shoulders as she tilted her head. 'A new boyfriend?'

Rachel fired up. 'Definitely *not*!'

Bethany evidently thought her violent rejection a bit overdone. 'He looks a bit younger than you,' she said slyly. 'Is he your secret toy-boy…?'

Rachel bristled with all the dignity of her thirty years. 'Hardly. I *believe* he's about twenty-six!' she snapped. Certainly old enough to have learned more respect for women. Perhaps she would be the one to teach him some manners!

'Mmm. A pity he wears glasses, but I guess you can't have everything, huh? At least his bod is nice, and he has that eat-you-up smile. And I don't suppose he wears his glasses in bed… or haven't you got him that far yet?' Rachel went hot all over. '*Beth-a-ny!*'

Thank God those other photos were safely out of sight! 'Oops, I forgot—personality is more important than looks, right?' The girl giggled. 'At least, that's what you and Mum are always telling me. So—how sexy is his personality?'

'Somewhat less than a slug's,' Rachel blurted out through her gritted teeth.

Bethany laughed in disbelief. 'Oh, yeah? Then why are you looking at him as if you'd like to take a bite out of him?'

'Appearances can be deceptive,' she warned. 'For instance, you look like an innocent fifteen-year-old schoolgirl, when we both know you're actually the devil incarnate.'

Bethany raised and lowered her eyebrows. 'Sounds kinky. Does that have anything to do with being carnal?'

Rachel bit back a reluctant smile. 'You know it doesn't, you evil child.'

Not only was Bethany highly intelligent, but thanks to her frank upbringing she also had a lively understanding of the world around her. Although Rachel sometimes found her so-phistication unnerving, in her heart she thanked God that Beth-any wasn't as naive and wretchedly vulnerable as Rachel had been at her age.

'So, are you going to tell me all about your pin-up boy?' asked Bethany, finally handing the photograph back and clat-tering from cupboard to fridge to fix herself a large bowl of cereal and milk.

'He's no pin-up, believe me,' Rachel said darkly, ramming the resealed bubble-pack deep into her capacious shoulder-bag, hop-ing the contents would be creased into oblivion. 'He's a slimy, spiteful, scum-sucking, foul-minded, flatulent, male chauvin-istic swine with a brain the size of a quark and an ego the size of Mount Everest.'

Bethany's mouth fell open and Rachel flushed as she realised that she had let herself get carried away by her inner rage. But how good it had felt to snarl it out loud! She hastily summoned a weak grin to show that she had only been joking.

'Of course—that's on his *good* days.'

'Uh, sure…' In spite of her evident curiosity Bethany wisely decided not to tease for an answer as to what the mystery man was like on his *bad* days. She crunched on her cereal, sending sidelong looks at Rachel as she got up and absently washed out her coffee cup, her mind still shellshocked by Matthew Riordan's underhanded attack.

'Um, Rachel... I—we get on really well together, you and I...don't we?'

'Mmm?' She couldn't just ignore his vicious threat and expect it to go away. He had the potential to make her life a misery. 'Oh—yes, of course we do,' she said warmly.

'And you know how you always say how much you like having me around—you know, when Mum and Dad go away on holiday and I come and stay here with you...?'

Rachel shook out a tea-towel. She knew what it was like to be a helpless victim and she had no intention of ever letting it happen again. 'What?' She struggled to make sense of what Bethany was saying. 'Oh, yes, I do—you're great company.'

'Well...how would you feel if I was—you know—around a lot more. Like...maybe...all the time...'

Rachel's attention snapped fully back to the young girl at the table.

'All the time?' Her voice sharpened as she realised what her niece was asking. 'You mean, you living here...with me? Permanently?' Her heart expanded tightly in her chest so that she could hardly breathe as Bethany nodded. 'But, Beth,' she protested weakly, 'you're going to be living in Bangkok—'

Bethany abandoned the table, eager to argue her case.

'Just because Dad has to work there doesn't mean I have to be dragged away from all my friends—I mean, what if I don't like the school?' she said in a rush. 'I won't know anyone, I don't know the language—'

'Beth, it's an English-speaking school,' Rachel pointed out gently. 'There'll be teenagers like you there from all around the world. They're all in the same boat, and you'll soon make new friends—'

'But I like my old ones! I love the school I go to now...and what about my yachting? I bet I won't be able to bike down to the harbour and go sailing on my own in Thailand!'

'Oh, Beth, if you feel like this you should talk to your parents—'

'I have,' she gulped. 'But they don't listen. They keep telling me I'll adjust. But what if I *can't*? What if I really, really, *really* hate it over there? Mum and Dad wouldn't let me come back on my own, but if I was coming to live with you, then they couldn't say no, could they?' She bit her lip and her voice wavered. 'Unless you don't want me to…you think I'd be in the way…'

A lump rose in Rachel's throat and she had to swallow hard to stop herself bursting into tears. She longed to let her emotions rule, to sweep Bethany fiercely to her breast and assure her that of *course* she wouldn't be in the way, that she would *always* be welcome into Rachel's home and heart.

But she knew she couldn't. There were bigger issues at stake. She took a deep breath.

'Oh, darling, I know how you're feeling.' She cupped Bethany's long face with her strong fingers and smiled brightly into her woeful eyes, hoping to phrase her rejection in a way that wouldn't irreparably damage their very precious relationship. 'I know you're scared about stepping out into the unknown, but you're not alone. Don't you think that your parents are finding this move a bit scary, too?'

Bethany blinked at the sudden shift in her perspective. 'Mum and Dad?'

'Of course—they're leaving behind all their friends, too. It's going to be especially tough for your dad—he has to step into a new job in a new country with colleagues he doesn't know, while displaying the confidence and authority that people expect of his new position. And your mum—she has to give up a job she really loves and revert to being a full-time housewife in a community where she doesn't know a soul. But together you'll get through it. The three of you are a *team*…'

Bethany was quick to pick up the underlying message. 'So you won't let me come and live with you, even if I'm horribly homesick?' she said in a thin, high voice.

Rachel braced herself against the mixture of hurt and resentment glowing in the reproachful green eyes. 'If you go over there expecting to be able to do that, you're just setting yourself up for failure, and you're too intelligent for that. When you want to succeed at something you know you have to put your whole heart into it. Your mum and dad *need* you to be there for them, Beth. Don't disappoint them.'

'I don't have much choice, do I?' said Bethany stiltedly. 'If *you* don't want me...'

Rachel forced her voice to remain steady, although she felt clawings of panic shredding at her control. 'You have a choice about the way you behave—whether you accept with grace or try and make everyone around you feel guilty because life isn't perfect. You take your mum and dad's unconditional love and support for granted, but a lot of kids grow up without that kind of emotional security to back them up when things get rough.' Her eyes were clear as she picked her words carefully. 'I only wish your grandparents had been as protective of Robyn and I as Robyn and Simon are of *you*. It's difficult to have any confidence in yourself when you hear nothing but criticism and condemnation from the people you love...'

Bethany looked away, scuffing her thick-soled school shoes on the tiled floor, the freckles standing out on her pale skin. 'I guess...' She lifted her chin and said with a totally false brightness, still avoiding Rachel's eyes, 'I suppose I'd better get my bag, or I'm going to miss my bus.'

Ignoring her half-eaten cereal on the table, she grabbed her lunchbox off the bench and rushed out of the kitchen. Rachel closed her eyes, letting out a ragged sigh as she sagged against the sink.

'Thanks.'

She opened her eyes to see her sister hovering in the doorway, her sweet face grave.

Rachel smiled wanly. 'For what?'

Robyn came into the kitchen, her eyes shadowed with relief and redolent with sympathy. 'For simply being an aunt.'

'You're my sister,' said Rachel. 'What else would I be?' They looked at each other, a world unspoken in the glance.

'She didn't really want to stay with me, anyway,' Rachel dismissed. 'It isn't a rejection of you and Simon. She's just temporarily got cold feet.'

'I know. But, still, if you'd given her the choice she was asking for it could have made things very difficult for us over the next few years.'

'Well,' said Rachel, 'I do have a pretty crammed life already. God knows I don't need the added complication of trying to cope alone with daily doses of teenage angst!'

Robyn wasn't fooled by her flippancy. 'Oh, Rachel, you would have got on famously, and you know it. If you were only thinking of yourself you would have said yes to her in a New York minute! I know you hated to hurt her, but she'll get over it. From what I heard she was trying to manipulate you with a sneaky form of emotional blackmail.'

So...she was the victim of two separate blackmail attempts in one day, Rachel thought with an unexpected sting of humour—and it was still only breakfast!

'Do you think she'll ever forgive me for letting her down?' she couldn't help asking.

Robyn crossed to give her the hug she so badly needed. 'You haven't let her down. You love her and want the best for her. You always have. She knows that.'

'I'm going to miss you all horribly,' she admitted gruffly. Up until now she had been careful not to let them see how shattered she had been by their decision to move abroad.

'I know.' Robyn responded to the rib-crushing fierceness of her hug with a little gasp. 'But we're only going to be an e-mail away, and at least I'll have plenty of spare time to keep you up to date with our doings. We can even send each other photos over the Internet!'

A short while later, when Robyn and Bethany had departed for school and work, Rachel dragged the abused package out of her handbag, grappling with the awful spectre that her sister's innocent words had raised.

There were worse things than having yourself splashed all over the tabloids. What if Matthew Riordan decided to go global and posted those frightful pictures on the Internet!

She smoothed out his loathsome note and forced herself to go over it again, word by horrible word.

In places the slashing green down-strokes almost seemed to dig through the page, as if they'd been written in a rage. Having seen the reputedly buttoned-down Riordan heir in the raw, both literally and figuratively, Rachel could well believe he was not as cold-blooded as his reputation made out, but this outpouring of contempt made him sound dangerously reckless.

What did he really *mean* by his threats? They were actually rather vague. Should she wait for him to deliver more specific demands...or was he assuming that she knew what they were?

Perhaps he intended to broadcast the photographs regardless of her response—or lack of it? How could she defend herself if he started sending copies to the press, to Westons' clients? Her family and close friends might believe her explanations, but to everyone else she would be reduced to an obscene joke. As Frank was constantly drilling into her, reputation was everything. He was so proud of the Westons name. If he found out that there was the slightest possibility of Rachel being involved in a scandal he would be furious. In order to protect the business she might well have to resign.

Rachel bit her lip, battening down her fear. She mustn't let herself be panicked into doing anything stupid. She should be thinking damage control, not capitulation.

She had heard Kevin Riordan boast that his son intended to run for City Council in this year's local body elections, with an eye to contesting the Mayoralty sometime in the future. Logically, that meant Matthew Riordan had almost as much of a vested interest in keeping compromising photographs out of the public eye as Rachel did.

It was that *'almost'* which gave him his ruthless edge. He was prepared to subject himself to public humiliation and rely on his PR clout for damage control afterwards...but surely only as a last resort. At the moment the primary value of the photographs to him must be as a weapon to hang over her head.

All Rachel had to do was keep cool and try to exercise some damage control of her own.

If only she had known what she was getting into she would never have taken on the job of watching over Merrilyn Freeman's wretched dinner party!

CHAPTER THREE

'*YOU'VE GOT TO do something!*'

Rachel jumped as Merrilyn glided up behind her and hissed urgently in her ear.

'About what?' Relaxed yet alert, Rachel thought everything was going swimmingly. A string quartet played exquisitely civilised Baroque on the terrace, the champagne was flowing, the caviare circulating, the conversation buzzing, and there had not been a hint of a problem with gatecrashers, light-fingered guests or suspiciously wandering staff.

Merrilyn's fingernails bit into her bare arm as she tugged her out of the way of a passing white-jacketed waiter. A slim red-head in an arresting green taffeta dress, she vibrated with nervous anxiety. 'He's going to ruin everything, I just know it!' she whispered frantically. 'I've spent months planning this! My first big formal dinner party and it's going to end up a total disaster!'

Rachel had been Merrilyn's fitness trainer for a year, and she was well acquainted with the young woman's propensity for worrying over trifles. The exclamation mark might have been invented with Merrilyn in mind.

'What on earth are you talking about?' she murmured sooth-ingly, transferring her dangerously tilted champagne glass to her free hand. 'Everyone's having a great time.'

'I'm talking about *him*!'

Rachel followed her agonised gaze to the archway between the huge lounge and the sunken dining room, expecting to see some ill-bred, loutish interloper dipping his fingers into the caviare bowl.

'*Matthew Riordan?*' she said incredulously.

'Oh, God, just look at him...' Merrilyn moaned.

Rachel looked, ignoring the shivery frisson that lifted the fine hair on the back of her bare neck. She always instinctively bristled when she saw Matthew Riordan, and had learned not to take any notice of the uncomfortable sensation, which was normally a harbinger of trouble.

Viewed from the side, in formal black he looked leaner than usual, but otherwise impeccable, his knife-sharp profile tilted down as he poured champagne into the glass of a young soci-ety matron from a bottle which he had produced from under his arm. Whatever he was saying made her blush, and her middle-aged husband stiffen at her side.

'You see!' hissed Merrilyn, her nails stabbing at the nerve in Rachel's elbow. 'He's at it again.'

'At what?' asked Rachel reluctantly, easing her arm out of her clutches. She had done a sterling job of avoiding Matthew Riordan so far tonight, and would prefer to keep it that way.

'Saying wickedly provocative things to people.' She sounded on the verge of tears.

'Matthew Riordan?' Rachel said again, just to check that they were indeed discussing the same person. The man who was re-nowned for his cool reserve and deadly civility?

'Yes, Matthew Riordan,' moaned Merrilyn, her hand flut-tering up to pluck at her diamond choker. 'Oh, God, John will never forgive me if he starts a *fight*—'

'Matthew *Riordan*?' gaped Rachel, beginning to feel like

a maniacal parrot. 'For goodness' sake, Merrilyn, take a deep breath and *calm down*,' she said astringently. 'He's a merchant banker, not a lager lout. I've met the guy—he's intelligent and articulate, but abnormally controlled; I bet he knows exactly how far he can go.

'He would no more get into a stupid fight than he would pick up the wrong fork at dinner. He's certainly not going to insult his hostess or make a fool of himself by creating a scene. And none of your other guests are going to risk offending someone so influential—certainly not to his face.'

'You haven't heard the shocking things he's been saying!' Merrilyn despaired.

'Come on, Merrilyn. Give the guy a break.' Rachel couldn't believe that she was actually defending the man who was directly responsible for Weston Security Services losing two lucrative corporate contracts within the past month, but the important thing right now was to curb her client's hysteria. 'Everyone lets their hair down a bit at parties. Don't you *want* him to enjoy himself?'

'But he's *not* enjoying himself; that's the whole *point*!' Merrilyn's exquisitely made-up face was a mask of tragedy. 'He's *drunk*!'

Rachel almost laughed at the ludicrousness of the idea. 'I doubt it. He hasn't been here long enough to have had more than a couple of glasses of champagne—'

'No. You don't understand!' Merrilyn moaned. 'He was drunk when he *arrived*. And to think I was panicking because he hadn't turned up. Now I almost wish he *hadn't*…!'

The disgusted admission was tantamount to heresy from a dedicated social climber like Merrilyn, and Rachel registered a surge of alarm.

She reappraised him. 'He looks quite steady on his feet to me.'

'Trust me, he disguises it well, but he's on the brink of being bombed out of his skull,' said Merrilyn grimly. Once, on the massage table after one of their sessions in the gym, she had confided to Rachel that her brother was an alcoholic. 'And another thing—he's turned up solo! He was *supposed* be coming with Cheryl-Ann Harding. I've spent a fortune on the table settings—if his girlfriend's not here it's going to wreck the symmetry!'

'His *girlfriend*?' Rachel was startled. 'I thought he was married?' She had noticed the plain gold band he wore on his left hand.

'He *was*... Oh, hell, what's he going to do now?' Merrilyn was distracted by the sight of the ruffled young matron being hustled away by her stiff-jawed escort. 'If Cheryl-Ann isn't here he's going to be roaming around like a loose cannon all night,' she muttered. 'They've been going out for yonks—it's common knowledge that Matthew's father is putting on the pressure for him to get married again, and everyone agrees they'd make a perfect couple. If they've had an argument, why on earth couldn't they have saved it until *after* my party?'

She planted a hand in the small of Rachel's back, propelling her forward. 'Quick! Let's get over there while he's still by himself and see if you can keep him diverted long enough to sober him up for dinner.'

Rachel almost stumbled over her white slingbacks. '*Me?*'

'Well, that's why you're here, isn't it? To mix and mingle and stop minor problems escalating into major embarrassments?' declared Merrilyn. 'I can't tell you how much I appreciate you being here, Rachel. I'm so *glad* you persuaded me to go with Westons rather than some other firm. You're right, it's *so* much better having someone I *know* handling potentially sensitive matters like these. I'll be sure and tell all my friends what a classy personal protection service you run!'

Sensing she was overdoing the gushing flattery, she altered her tone to a panicky plea. 'Look, just stick to him like glue and do what you can to cover for him, OK? And be *discreet*! The fewer people who realise what's going on, the better.'

'Why don't you just politely ask him to leave?' murmured Rachel as they approached their target.

'Throw him out? Are you *mad*?' Merrilyn's whisper was scandalised. 'He's one of my most important guests. It would be social suicide!'

She raised her voice on a fluttering laugh. 'Matthew! Look who I've brought to see you! I know I don't have to introduce you two—Rachel was just telling me she thinks you're the most intelligent and articulate man she's ever met!'

He had been topping up his own glass, and now he tucked the champagne bottle under the potted plant at his elbow with a casual disregard for his surroundings which made Rachel blink.

'Really? How delightfully flattering of her.'

He held out his hand, and although Rachel mistrusted his honeyed drawl, allied as it was with a mocking disbelief in the dark brown eyes, she automatically reciprocated. But instead of the cool, impersonal shake he had delivered when they had been first introduced to each other in his office, he raised her hand to his mouth and placed a string of tiny kisses across her long fingers, letting her feel the faint sting of his teeth.

'I shall endeavour to return the favour.' Bowed over her hand, his eyes were licensed to rove, and made the most of their freedom. 'Your breasts are truly in magnificent form this evening, Miss Blair,' he purred. 'What a pity they're so much more impressive than your IQ—but I suppose a woman can't have everything.'

Hearing Merrilyn's choked whimper of horror, Rachel gulped down her shock and pinned on a blinding smile.

'Can't she? What a woefully limited little world you must inhabit, Mr Riordan.'

His eyes flickered, the only indication that she had pinked him with her quick riposte.

'But I'm forgetting. One should never trust to appearances, particularly where women are concerned,' he continued smoothly, his gaze openly caressing the bounteous curves which plumped above the beaded edge of the gown. 'Perhaps it's your dressmaker or plastic surgeon who should be accepting my compliments...'

'With compliments like yours, who needs insults?' murmured Rachel, resisting the urge to hitch up her fitted bodice.

Merrilyn had shrieked with outrage when she had seen the subdued, off-the-rack black dress which Rachel had originally planned to wear.

'You can't wear that—it's not glamorous enough! You'll stand out like a sore thumb, which is exactly what we want to *avoid*. Give me your measurements and I'll arrange for my dressmaker to send over something more suitable.'

It had been Rachel's turn to be horrified when she had gone up to the bedroom where she was to change and found the strapless, figure-hugging sequinned dress hanging on the closet door. Unfortunately it fitted like the proverbial glove, giving her no excuse to demur.

'Oh, I do apologise...am I being insulting?' Matthew Riordan oozed with silky insincerity, making her stiffen as he twisted her wrist to rest his lips against her pulse-point.

By now Rachel could perfectly understand Merrilyn's panic. His diction was nearly perfect, but his words were stunningly uninhibited and his spectacles could not hide the hot, restless look in the hooded brown eyes. Apart from a streak of colour on his high cheekbones his face was noticeably pale in contrast to his sleeked-back hair and the dark stubble that graced his chin. His sultry air of controlled recklessness bore little resemblance to the grimly reserved chairman of Ayr Holdings whom Rachel had encountered when she had accompanied Frank to re-pitch for a couple of corporate contracts.

The companies, for whom they had run fraud prevention training programmes and provided security patrols, preemployment vetting and confidential investigations in litigation support, had been involved in a series of mergers orchestrated by the majority shareholder—Ayr Holdingsand, having attained a controlling interest on several new boards, Matthew Riordan had been seeking to centralise their security arrangements.

At the meetings, although it had been made clear from the outset that Rachel was attending as co-owner of Weston Security Services, Matthew Riordan had virtually ignored her, addressing all his queries and remarks to Frank. When Rachel had taken it upon herself to answer or make an informed comment, he had given her minimal responses in a tone of clipped courtesy that had barely concealed his impatience with her interruption. Frank had claimed she was being over-sensitive, but Rachel had come away from their ultimately unsuccessful series of meetings steaming with frustration at being treated more like a glorified secretary than an equal partner.

'No, just unbelievably crass,' she replied, striving for just the right note of crushing boredom. She could feel his lips move against her skin as he smiled, the blood thumping through her artery his proof that she wasn't as calm as she looked. She tried to slip her hand free, but to her surprise she discovered his grasp was unexpectedly strong. A brief, almost invisible power struggle ensued, and Rachel finally resorted to the feminine trick of curling her angry fingers over the edge of his palm and digging her fake nails into the sinewy back of his hand. He didn't even flinch.

'What else did you expect?' he taunted. 'A woman like you wearing a dress like that...you're obviously not aiming to appeal to a man's *intellect*...'

Even though she knew full well she was being deliberately provoked Rachel couldn't help snapping at the bait. 'A woman like me?'

She had narrowed his hostility to a specific focus, and now she was paying the price. His smile was insolent in the extreme. 'Big, bold and brassy.'

The thin gold rim around her hazel irises glowed incandescently bright as she spluttered, '*Brassy—?*'

'It means flashy, strident, showy...' he elaborated, his eyes sliding from her breasts, heaving in outrage, to the tightness of her dress across her round hips and the slit in the side of the clinging skirt which revealed her leg to midthigh. 'I knew the first time you walked into my office what you really were— window-dressing...a showgirl trying to do a man's job...'

Rachel dug her fingernails deeper into his flesh and he gave an exaggerated wince.

'Uh, Rachel...' Merrilyn's voice fluttered anxiously to her ears and Rachel suddenly remembered the role she was supposed to be playing. She should be pacifying him, not prodding him into even worse behaviour.

She batted her eyelashes and adopted a girlishly meek tone. 'May I please have my hand back now, Mr Riordan?'

'It depends what you're planning to do with it,' he challenged, and she couldn't stop her eyes flickering to his temptingly exposed cheek. Unexpectedly he laughed, a purring sound that ruffled the nerves along her spine, and kissed her fingers again, releasing her hand with a slow, stroking motion that made it clear that it was purely his own choice.

'A toast,' he said, lifting his champagne glass and leaning forward to brush it against hers. 'To the unfair sex, who resort to seduction when all else fails.'

'If it was a man you would call it clever use of available resources,' Rachel responded tartly. 'And if you imagine this is a seduction you have some very odd opinions. You don't like women very much, do you, Mr Riordan?'

His eyes glittered darkly. 'I like *certain* women very much.'

'Let me guess...small, fluffy-headed, delicately built females who constantly defer to your superior intellect and would never dream of challenging your masculine superiority?'

His face tautened. 'What a sharp-tongued bitch you are!'

Her mouth curved smugly. She had obviously guessed right. She had probably just described Cheryl-Ann Harding to a T. She tossed back her champagne, forgetting that she had simply been holding it as a prop. 'Not your type, Mr Riordan?'

He looked her over, blatantly undressing her with his hot black eyes. 'I don't know—bedding you could have its…compensations,' he drawled insolently. 'As long as you kept your mouth shut. Except to scream at the appropriate moment, of course.'

'You mean the moment of my supreme disappointment?' she said sweetly, and had the pleasure of seeing his ears turn red. She could almost envisage the steam issuing forth. 'It must get very noisy in your bedroom, Mr Riordan.'

Merrilyn uttered a choked groan, overridden by Matthew Riordan's sneer. 'There's only one way for you to find out, isn't there?'

'Why, is this a proposal, sir?' Rachel simpered.

'Miss Blair, the *last* thing you'd ever get from me would be a marriage proposal,' he snarled.

'Good. Because being married to a chauvinist like you would make me feel suicidal!'

His face went stony-blank, his voice as vaporous as dry ice, and just as freezing as it bled from his pale lips. 'You wouldn't get the chance. I'd have murdered you beforehand. In fact, I'd be hard put to control my homicidal impulses until after the wedding!'

With that he yanked up the champagne bottle from under the plant and stalked off.

'Oh, God, oh, God, oh, God…' Merrilyn was chanting the horrified mantra under her breath, her face as white as milk under the professional coating of make-up.

'He insulted me first!' said Rachel shakily, knowing that it was no excuse. She had been thoroughly unprofessional. How many times had she heard David say that to successfully subdue a volatile opponent you had to remain emotionally detached from the situation?

'You don't understand…his first wife, Leigh, *did* commit suicide,' said Merrilyn. 'They'd only been married a few years…'

'Oh, *no*...' Rachel breathed. She closed her eyes, her own spiteful words ringing in her ears, lacerating her conscience.

'You've seen the kind of mood he was in, now he's going to be even *worse*,' Merrilyn fretted. 'I *told* you this was going to end up a disaster.'

'Look, don't worry, I'll handle it,' said Rachel, with far more confidence than she felt. 'I'll go and find him again—you just concentrate on looking after your other guests.'

'But we're sitting down to dinner soon! How can I concentrate on anything else? It'll be like having an unexploded bomb at the table!'

'Change the seating. I'm in a suitably obscure corner—put Matthew Riordan next to me.'

'After what just happened—are you kidding? That would really light his fuse!'

'There won't be any fireworks,' vowed Rachel grimly. 'If he won't co-operate I'll think of something else, but I won't let him create a disruption.'

To Rachel's relief Merrilyn appeared to accept her assurances although she still looked dubious as she hurried off to resume her hostessing duties.

Rachel didn't need a bloodhound to track down her quarry; all she had to do was follow the trail of nervous smiles and negative energy which Matthew Riordan had left scattered in his wake.

She found him outside, wandering down the terrace steps, having bypassed the glass dangling from his fingers in preference to swigging champagne straight from the bottle. The evening was so warm and humid that stepping from the air-conditioned comfort of the house into the velvety night was like being enveloped by a smothering blanket. The mingled scent of the jasmine which cloaked the walls of the large courtyard below the terrace and the Mexican orange blossom shrubs set in tubs around the kidney-shaped swimming pool was heavy in the air.

Approaching his brooding back as he prowled restlessly along the edge of the salt-water pool, Rachel decided that the grovelling approach would probably only invite his further contempt.

'Looking for a small dog or a child to kick?' she asked, and when he swung around to face her she didn't give him a chance to open his mouth.

'Don't you think you've had enough of that?' She nodded at the champagne bottle.

His mouth twisted, the lenses of his glasses reflecting the dancing light from the flaming torches decorating the fluted columns in the courtyard.

'What are you? My conscience?'

'Since you apparently don't have one of your own, I felt constrained to volunteer,' she said acerbically.

'Like to live dangerously, do you?' He prowled back towards her, his voice thick with menace, but Rachel stood her ground. Let him know that she was far more than merely the sum of her curvaceous parts!

'Merrilyn's afraid that you're going to get totally smashed and run amok, insulting all her guests and ruining her chances of making it onto the social register.'

Her shrewdly judged frankness arrested the flaring animosity in his face. 'So she asked *you* to stop me?' he asked incredulously.

'Something like that.'

He took a long swallow of champagne and slowly licked his lips, taking one final step that brought him close enough for her to feel the heat from his body. 'You and whose army?'

Rachel jerked her eyes away from his mouth. It was a highly inconvenient time to notice that his lips were sensuously full, casting a sexy shadow over the intriguing indentation in his chin. 'I thought I'd start off by appealing to your better nature.'

'You're so sure I have one? It didn't sound as if you thought so back in there...' He jerked his head towards the partying buzz, tilting himself momentarily off balance before quickly adjusting his stance. A tiny slip but a betraying one.

'Back in there I was operating under a slight misapprehension,' she murmured.

He cocked his head. 'Oh, and what was that?'

'Merrilyn told me you were drunk, but I didn't believe her. I apologise for my stupid mistake.'

He gave a crack of reluctant laughter. 'You're taking a hell of a chance, aren't you?'

She didn't pretend to misunderstand. 'If you're going to take it out on anyone, take it out on me. Merrilyn issued her invitation in good faith. She wasn't to know that you'd have a tiff with your girlfriend and try and drown your sorrows.'

He paused with the bottle halfway to his mouth. 'Is that what she thinks happened?'

'Well, Cheryl-Ann's not here, and you are—distinctly the worse for wear, so...'

She watched him up-end the bottle again, her fingers itching to snatch it away from his lips. But she knew from their earlier encounter that he was a lot stronger than he looked, and stubborn as the devil. Cunning rather than brute force was the best way to handle him.

'Actually it was vice versa,' he said, catching her frustrated look and defiantly refilling his glass, toasting her with an exaggerated flourish before knocking it back.

'I beg your pardon?'

'It was *because* I'd been drinking that Cheryl-Ann refused to come along with me tonight...'

'Oh...' Rachel was disconcerted by his sudden revelation. Merrilyn had acted as if his behaviour was totally unprecedented, but perhaps he was a closet alcoholic.

'Cheryl-Ann likes everything in life to be pleasant and predictable. Particularly her men.'

'Are there so many of them?' she asked curiously. 'I thought you two were a big item.'

'And I thought you didn't believe everything Merrilyn tells you. More champagne?' he said, and splashed some into her glass from the carelessly offered bottle. Most of it slopped over the edge and onto her fingers.

'Sorry,' he said as she sucked in a gasp at the sudden chill. 'Would you like me to lick it off for you? No free hands.' He extended his arms wide in explanation, his unbuttoned jacket splitting wide over his snowy pleated shirtfront, now lightly frosted with bubbles.

'No, thank you,' she said primly, pushing away the unsettling thought of his tongue stroking across her skin. 'But if you'll hand me the bottle I'll pour myself some more—I don't trust your aim.'

He laughed again, and tucked the bottle under his arm. 'I may be drunk, but I'm not stupid.'

She shrugged. 'It was worth a try. You *could* be a bit more co-operative.'

'Why should I?' His mouth turned down, making him look wilful and determined to be difficult. She was reminded that while he seemed preternaturally mature, and commanded a lot of power in his position, exuding an air of intimidating and apparently effortless authority, he was still four years her junior. She should be able to handle him with one hand tied behind her back!

'Well, surely you don't want people to think that you're a lush?' she wheedled.

'I'm rich enough not to have to care what people think,' he said, with breathtaking arrogance and unfortunate accuracy. 'But, as it happens, I have none of the usual vices.'

'Just the unusual ones?' hazarded Rachel unwisely.

'What would you classify as unusual?' he murmured in a sultry undertone, his dark eyes suddenly uncomfortably curious. She was acutely aware of his closeness, and the restless energy that seethed through his body, creating an invisible charge that made her exposed skin feel supersensitive to the sultry air.

'Never mind,' she said hurriedly, running her hand nervously through her hair. At this rate she would soon be tearing it out! 'Look, can we just agree that you'll moderate your behaviour for Merrilyn's sake?'

'Not for yours? After all, you seem to be the only one willing to brave my drunken wrath. Why is that, by the way?' Cynicism coated his voice as he speculated. 'What's in this for you?' His eyes narrowed as he leapt from cynicism to suspicion. 'In fact, what are you doing here at all? Merrilyn's guests are all from the ranks of Auckland's social élite, the movers and shakers—on what grounds do *you* qualify?'

Rachel hesitated.

'I happen to be her personal trainer,' she said, but she had spoken a heartbeat too late. Even steeped in alcohol Matthew Riordan's brain was unnervingly quick.

'My God, could it be that you're not really here as a guest at all?' he murmured, with the beginnings of a goading smile. 'That you're just the hired help! I saw a car with Weston Security markings in the driveway—is that why you're here? Helping make sure that we movers and shakers aren't slyly pocketing the silverware?' He began to laugh, uninhibitedly.

'Could you please keep your voice down?' she snapped, looking over her shoulder at the people watching from the terrace.

His laughter abated to a taunting grin. 'I'm right, aren't I? You and that bulky young man on the door are playing on the same team.'

'WSS is supplying the security coverage here tonight, yes,' she admitted stiffly.

He rocked on his heels, shaking his head. 'I just don't believe it!'

Rachel had had enough of being the target for his amusement. 'What? That we're capable of doing a first-rate job? *You* may have chosen to think otherwise, but Westons has a string of very satisfied private and corporate clients who are extremely impressed with the services we deliver—'

'And what little service are you, *personally*, delivering this evening?' he wondered, with a mocking leer at her exposed skin. 'A "relief" massage for the stressed-out cat burglar?'

Even though she'd thought she was inured to sly jokes about being a masseuse, Rachel found herself blushing.

'I'm in charge!' she threw at him, and when his eyebrows climbed above the frames of his glasses she sucked in a furious breath at his provoking scepticism. 'You know damned well from reading our bids that I'm a qualified security guard—'

'With the ink barely dry on your certificate,' he charged.

'*And* a licensed private detective—'

'Ditto...both of which only serve to prove that you passed a police vetting of your background.'

'And in monitoring private functions like this, where there's a lot of valuable art on display and expensive jewellery around people's necks, it's standard practice to have operatives working undercover,' she finished grittily.

'Or, in your case, *un*covered!' he drawled, toasting her tight bodice with his glass. 'You've certainly perfected the art of distraction. With a *body*guard like you around, few men would be likely to find anything else worth pinching...'

'Is that why you stopped Westons winning those contracts we quoted on?' she burst out, the suspicion having haunted her ever since those abortive meetings. 'Not because we didn't present the best bid, but because of some stupid macho prejudice you have against *me*? Because of the way I *look* you presume I can't possibly be a competent professional. Is *that* why you've been whispering to your father and Neville Stiller, warning them against choosing us for the KR Industries job?'

'You think I'm *macho*?' His wandering attention was snagged by the diverting notion.

'Just answer the questions!' she rapped out.

'I thought they were rhetorical,' he responded blandly. 'In view of the sex discrimination act, if it *were* true I'd be stupid to admit to it…and we've both already agreed that I'm merely drunk.'

He crooked his elbow at her in a parody of politeness. 'I think I just heard the call to dinner. Shall we go in? No doubt Merrilyn's already arranged for us to sit cosily together, so that her pet Amazon can keep me firmly on the leash!'

CHAPTER FOUR

'I THINK A choke-chain would be more appropriate,' muttered Rachel as she reluctantly linked her arm with his. 'Are you going to behave during dinner?'

'Probably not...'

There was an angry bleakness in the laconic answer that made her heart sink. She halted, forcing him to swing around to face her, his back to the pool.

'*Why?*' She braced herself for yet another sarcastic, evasive response.

He shook off her hand and fortified himself with another mouthful of bubbles, uttering a sound of disgust when he discovered he had drained the bottle. He cast it with a reckless arm into the pool. It hit with a loud splash and bobbed briefly on the surface, then spiralled down through the ripples of light as the water poured in through the narrow neck.

He watched it sink with an intense fascination, waiting until the rippling surface of the water settled back into reflective smoothness before he spoke. 'You know...it was a night just like this; a perfect, romantic, cloudless, starry summer night...'

His lyrical tone gave Rachel an ominous tingling at the base of her skull. 'What night?'

'The night my wife killed herself,' he said casually, and Rachel's breath stopped in her throat.

'She—didn't...*drown*?' she stammered, alarmed by the fixed intensity with which he was staring into the pool.

He pivoted unsteadily on the coping stone to give her a sardonic look. 'No, she wanted to make it neat and tidy for both of us. She took a handful of pills washed down with half a bottle of vodka...exactly four years ago tonight.'

Oh, God, no wonder he was in such a black fugue! On each anniversary of David's death Rachel, too, was a mass of raw nerves as she coped with the onslaught of painful memories, re-experiencing the angry sense of helplessness she had suffered at the time. But for Matthew the pain must be multiplied tenfold. At least Rachel had the comfort of knowing that the man she'd loved had died for a positive purpose—to save the life of the child his car had successfully swerved to avoid.

'Perhaps she expected to be found...' she offered tentatively, hampered by her ignorance.

'And saved? By me?' His laugh was bitter. 'Then I obviously failed her, didn't I? Her death was *my* fault...'

'That wasn't what I meant—'

'Even though she was married to *me*?' he lashed out. 'Grounds for suicide in itself. Wasn't that what you said?'

'When I said that, I didn't know about your wife—'

'You were just taking a lucky guess?'

She swallowed. 'I was angry. I was trying to think of the worst insult I possibly could.'

'Congratulations. You succeeded admirably!'

'Matthew, I'm sorry.' She reached out, unconsciously using his first name in an effort to re-establish their tenuous emotional connection.

He recoiled violently.

'Go to hell!' He struck her hand away and in that moment

she knew that it would be sheer madness to let him sit down in polite company.

His self-control was too precarious. The alcohol had already stripped away far too many of his inhibitions, freeing him to express thoughts and feelings which would normally be taboo to a man of his pride and emotional reserve. He had gone beyond the point where he was willing, or even able, to exercise reasonable judgement.

Which meant that Rachel would have to fall back on her risky plan B.

While he was still swaying from the momentum of his action she surged forward with a little cry of alarm.

'Look out!' She caught his padded shoulders in a bunching grip. 'Don't move—' Her body bumped softly into his as he instinctively stiffened. '—or you'll trip over—'

He teetered on the brink of the pool as something firm slid against the back of his ankles, preventing him from shifting his feet to re-establish his centre of gravity over his arching back.

'The—' She snatched her hands back, her eyes flying wide with horror as he continued to topple backwards, his arms now windmilling wildly.

'Cat!' Her hands clapped over her mouth as he crashed down into the water, sending a small tidal wave spilling over the tiled edges.

'Oh, no!' she cried as the string quartet on the balcony craned to see what had happened in a cacophony of discordant strings. 'Matthew, are you all right?'

For one awful instant when he went under she thought he might not be able to swim, but he almost immediately resurfaced and began to swim clumsily towards the side, hampered by his waterlogged clothes.

'I could see it was going to happen but I couldn't do anything to stop it!' she cried apologetically.

A waiter and a few other guests hurried down the steps to assist, and she waited for them to reach her before she risked offering Matthew her helping hand. While one person falling in the pool could be dismissed as an accident, two would be serious grounds for gossip.

Merrilyn fluttered to the fore as he was hauled to his dripping feet. 'W-what *happened*?' she stammered.

'He tripped over the cat and fell into the pool,' Rachel told her succinctly.

Merrilyn's smooth brow wrinkled. 'But we don't have a—' She caught Rachel's eye. 'Oh, you must mean the *neighbour's* cat. That wretched tom is *always* prowling over here—one day I'm going to ring the SPCA...' She trailed off as Rachel's tight smile warned her not to overdo the descriptive colour.

'Unless I get my hands on it first and wring its damned neck!' growled Matthew Riordan, removing his fogged glasses and raking his hand over his wet head, sending little rivulets streaming down into the back of his collar. 'I didn't even see it!'

'It's coal-black,' Merrilyn said quickly. 'I'm most *frightfully* sorry, Matthew. How awful! *Naturally* we'll pay for dry-cleaning. Oh, dear, you're so *wet*!' she finished feebly.

'Water tends to do that to people,' he said blithely.

'And we were just about to sit down to our individual herb soufflés!' Merrilyn shrilled, clenching her beringed fingers over her heart.

There was a little pause, and Rachel could see her obsessive need to be the perfect hostess warring with her fervent desire be swiftly rid of her unexpectedly awkward guest.

There was an audible squelch as he shifted on his feet. 'Since I don't have my car with me, I can't drive home...and I can hardly get into a taxi like *this*,' he said impatiently, moving his arms and sending water cascading out of his sleeves.

Rachel noticed with alarm that his consonants were now definitely blurred and he was visibly unsteady on his feet. Instead of sobering him up, as she had half hoped, the adrenalin shock of his dunking had evidently speeded up the absorption of alcohol into his already saturated system.

'You can't let all those soufflés go flat, Merrilyn,' she said pointedly. 'Shall I show Matthew somewhere to dry off while the rest of you go ahead with dinner? Preferably somewhere that he doesn't have to trek back through the house—like your guest quarters, perhaps? He might like to have a shower, as well as a change of clothes...'

'Of *course!*' Merrilyn eagerly fell on the immediate solution to her dilemma. 'The guest-house would be perfect!' It was tucked well out of sight and sound of the main house. 'I'll send a maid along shortly with some suitable clothes.' But not shortly enough to interfere with dinner, she silently communicated as she added, 'Uh, do you need any help, Rachel...?'

Rachel had received the silent message. 'No thanks.' She wedged her shoulder discreetly under a dripping arm. 'I'm sure I can manage.'

'You will see that he has everything he needs?' Merrilyn couldn't help pleading.

'Of course I will,' said Rachel confidently.

She wasn't so sure of her ability to manage ten minutes later, as she was faced with the task of manhandling a fullygrown male out of his clinging wet clothes. Although Matthew Riordan had meekly allowed her to guide his listing body along the cobbled path around the house, once they had reached the guest-house he had turned infuriatingly passive.

'If you don't get out of those things soon you're going to get a chill,' Rachel repeated as he stood motionless in the middle of the big bedroom, creating a small puddle on the polished wooden floor.

He merely gazed at her blankly and she sighed, taking the spectacles out of his limp hand and placing them on the table beside the king-sized bed, with its wrought iron bedhead topped with shiny brass.

'Look, you're shivering already.' She put a hand on his chest to confirm her point and was taken aback at the heat burning through his wet shirt. Even given the warmth of the night it seemed unnatural, particularly in view of the visible tremors which were shaking his torso.

'I'm hot,' he said helpfully, and she moved her hand to lay it across his flushed forehead. That, too, felt uncomfortably warm. She frowned as he sighed and turned his face to rub it against her soft palm. 'Mmm... That feels so good...'

She flushed and hastily circled around behind him to collar his drenched jacket and ease it down his uncooperative arms. She carried it into the bathroom and dropped it into the expansive marble spa-bath. While she was there she turned on the pulsating shower in the transparent glass cabinet, hoping that the inviting sound would lure him in, but when she returned to the bedroom, carrying a towel with which to mop the water from the floor, he was still standing in exactly the same place, his bedraggled shirt hanging twisted and loose, his expression darkly frustrated.

'What's the matter?' she asked, averting her eyes from the drops of water sliding down his chest and pearling on his peaked brown nipples. She excused her momentary fascination as professional interest—his firm upper body suggested that he must work out, since he wouldn't retain that kind of muscle definition just sitting around in boardrooms.

'It won't come off,' he complained, plucking at the wet fabric on his shoulder.

'That's because you haven't undone your tie or cufflinks,' she said in exasperation.

Silk-shaded table lamps beside the rattan couch and the shiny brass bedhead had sprung to soft life when Rachel had keyed in the alarm code in the electronic panel by the door. Now, trying to read the expression in his eyes, she was sorry that she hadn't bothered to also flick on the overhead lights. Without the protection of his glasses his eyes seemed larger, their pale lids heavier, but in the muted shadows of the room it was impossible to guess what he was thinking as he stared at her with that strange, unblinking concentration.

'Matthew?'

'Matt. My friends call me Matt.'

'We're not friends, remember? We're practically strangers.'

'Rachel…'

At least he knew who she was, she thought humorously, and he didn't *sound* as if he bore a grudge…

Tossing the towel on the cream bedspread, she dealt briskly with the gold links in his sleeves and reached up to unsnap the studs which fastened the black tie. As she pulled it free from his wing collar his hands came up to settle heavily on her waist, and she stiffened as he swayed forward, his damp chest pressing against her breasts.

'What are you doing?'

'The room is moving,' he protested thickly, sliding his arms further around her body.

'It's not the room; it's your head,' she told him, pushing at his chest.

'It hurts.'

'What? Your head? Did you hit it when you fell?' Fears of delayed concussion swirled in her head. She ran her hands up the nape of his neck and sifted her fingers through the silky strands of wet hair, but could detect no flaws in the smooth symmetry of his skull.

'Not there,' he muttered, and took one of her hands and pressed it back across his forehead. 'Yes, there…' He sighed with satisfaction. 'Your hands feel nice…so cool…'

In fact they were quite warm. He was running a slight fever, guessed Rachel. He wasn't only drunk, he was also ill. Which might explain why he was so *very* drunk. '

Are you taking any pills or painkillers?'

'Doctor says I don't need anything. Just mild flu. Hate pills. Never take them.' He shivered, his eyes closed, his voice hoarse. 'They don't kill pain, they cause it. That's how Leigh died. Too many damned pills!'

'So you were telling me,' she said cautiously, afraid his wife's name would be the trigger for another angry outburst.

'She shouldn't have done that,' he murmured. 'I loved her.'

'I'm sure you did,' she soothed. She noticed that the arm around her waist had relaxed and drifted southwards, his hand curving down the slope of her buttock, and hurriedly detached herself.

'You should be able to take off your shirt now,' she said, stepping back. She deliberately made her tone brusque, placing her hands on her hips to reinforce the distance she was consciously creating between them.

Unfortunately he appeared blind to the subtleties of her body language...but not to her body. His eyes dilated as they roved down the shimmering column of white sequins standing before him.

'I can't,' he said, in the same vague, unfocused voice. He shrugged helplessly, creating an intriguing interplay of muscle across his upper chest. *Trapezius, deltoid, pectoralis major, latissimus dorsi,* Rachel charted silently, forcing herself to see the biomechanical entity rather than an attractive man.

He was watching her from under his lashes, and she was abruptly aware that, drunk or ill, he was still a consummate male. '*You* do it, Rachel.'

His suddenly sweet and beguiling smile made heat pool in the pit of her stomach. 'You haven't even *tried.*'

He pouted, and to her horror she found herself wondering what it would be like to suck on that sullen lip. 'I'm cold.'

She immediately felt a surge of guilt. What if his enforced swim had a further ill effect on his weakened immune system?

'You were hot only a minute ago,' she protested weakly.

He gave a dramatic shiver and she caved in, refusing to acknowledge the forbidden pleasure she took in removing his shirt, peeling the thin silk away from his damp body. His chest and upper arms were hard and smooth, the muscles twitching with tension as she picked up the thick peach-coloured towel and briskly blotted him down, trying not to notice the tingling in the tips of her fingers whenever they brushed his overheated skin.

As a masseuse, her sense of touch had become highly refined and her tactile skill made her very aware of the subtle changes in his body as his muscles began to relax. She instructed him to bend his head and vigorously attended to his hair, and when she moved around to deal with his back and shoulders he sighed with contentment, flexing his spinal column and rotating his shoulder-blades, purring like a big cat.

'I like being rubbed,' he told her, his ability to communicate apparently reduced to simple expressions of sensory acknowledgement.

'Most people do. It stimulates the blood supply which in turn helps removes toxins at cellular level,' she said clinically, with a final dust down his lumbar vertebrae.

'It feels good, too,' he insisted, pulling the bunched towel back towards his abdomen, which was already perfectly dry. She let go of the plush folds and he staggered, the back of his knees hitting the edge of the bed. He sat down, letting the towel flop onto his squelchy shoes.

'For goodness' sake, you're going to make a watermark on the covers!' With a huff of annoyance Rachel knelt to slide his custom-made shoes off his feet and remove his wringing black socks. His feet were long and narrow, his toes straight and marvellously even. He wriggled them sensuously in her sequinned lap and she pushed them back to the floor, and sat back on her haunches, looking up at him expectantly.

He looked expectantly back, and she finally accepted the fact that he was so plastered that he wasn't going to do *any-* thing for himself.

'Perhaps I should get a man to do this...' she said, even as she knew she wouldn't. There was something too elementally satisfying in having the man who was causing such strife at Weston Security virtually helpless in her hands. On a personal level there was an even more primitive response operating, one that Rachel didn't wish to dwell on too deeply.

He clenched his hands on his splayed knees, glowering at the suggestion. 'No—no one else. Only *you*.'

'You're the boss,' she said wryly, her conscience somewhat quieted by the arrogance of his plea.

His narrow white silk cummerbund had twisted on his hips when he had pulled out his shirt-tails, giving her easy access to the fastenings. Undoing the small silver hooks, she pulled it off and draped it over the edge of the brass bedhead, taking a deep breath as she reached out for the top of his trousers. Discovering the succession of tiny buttons was a shock, but she struggled on valiantly, even when it became obvious that the delicate bump and brush of her busy fingers was having an enlivening effect on his depressed nervous system. She heard him groan, and nearly leapt out of her skin when he cupped his hands on either side of her bowed head and began massaging the sensitive skin behind her ears with his thumbs.

'Matthew—'

His hands tightened on her scalp. 'Oh, Rachel...' He whispered a phrase that made her hasten hysterically to her task. Her fingers became more and more clumsy as they negotiated the changing contours of his lap, and as soon as the last button yielded to her feverish persuasion she scrambled to her feet and tugged off his sopping trousers with a final, punishing jerk that sent him sprawling back on the mattress.

His white designer briefs were moulded transparently to his form, and the sight of his still burgeoning arousal was indelibly printed on her brain in the few seconds that it took to scoop up the towel and toss it across his lap.

If she'd thought the most awkward part was over she was wrong, for, freed of the constriction of his clothes, Matthew experienced a burst of hyperactivity and decided that Merrilyn would be furious at them for missing her dinner. It took some fast talking, combined with body-blocking techniques learned from years of self-defence classes, to stop him from marching out of the guest-house, virtually *au naturel*, to deliver his apologies to the party at large.

Dismissing the shower as a practical impossibility, Rachel tried to convince him that he needed to lie down and rest while he waited for his change of clothes to arrive, hoping that once his head was on the pillow he might lapse into a natural stupor. She coaxed him back onto the bed by turning down the covers and slyly offering to give him a massage, but her cleverness backfired and turned into a physical tussle during which he became feverishly amorous.

She had figured that it would only take a few minutes of slow, gentle kneading for her to induce a sense of such physical wellbeing that he would doze off, and when she had informed him that he must lie absolutely still for his massage he had meekly lain back on the cool white sheets. But when she had knelt at his side and tried to get him to turn onto his stomach he had stubbornly refused.

'I want to watch,' he said huskily. 'I've never had a massage before.' He pulled her hand from under his shoulder and placed it on his chest, covering it with both of his as he pressed her fingers into the skin over his rapidly beating heart. 'What big hands you have,' he discovered in surprise, lifting his captured prize to inspect it.

Once upon a time such comments had used to hurt.

She gave her standard tart response. 'All the better to slap you with.'

His eyes sparkled darkly with innocent curiosity. 'Are you into spanking? Is that one of your 'unusual vices'?'

His brain might be partially on hold, but there was evidently nothing wrong with his short-term memory. 'Certainly not!'

'Oh.' He had the nerve to sound slightly disappointed. 'Look,' he murmured, meshing their fingers together to measure their length. 'We're both the same size.'

'No, we're not,' she refuted. 'I'm taller, stronger and fitter than you are.'

But not smarter. His darting smile was the only warning she got before he pulled her sharply across his chest, sweeping one lean leg around the back of her knees and trapping her legs together within her narrow skirt as he rolled them both over until she was squashed beneath him, her hands pinned on either side of her head. She felt a brief shudder of sick panic as her mind slipped back into the distant past, and then her superb conditioning kicked in and they were rolling back and forth in a brief struggle for ascendancy.

Brief, because Rachel almost instantly realised that, whatever strength Matthew Riordan possessed, his stamina was sorely depleted and his alcohol-impaired motor skills made it simple to speedily counteract his clumsy moves. Never having wrestled with a semi-naked man before, she was seriously distracted by the slippery threshing of his limbs and the sinful pleasure that came from riding his squirming body, feeling all that latent male power quivering beneath her bare hands.

A dampness that had nothing to do with his fever bloomed on his skin, exuding a musky scent and belatedly making her realise that he wasn't fighting for victory so much as enjoying the arousing effects of a full body-to-body massage. The threat of physical harm, which had never been very real, was now eclipsed by a far more insidious menace.

'What on earth do you think you're doing?' she hissed as he slowly rotated his hips against the crush of her belly and uttered a sexy little moan.

'This is so fantastic...' he dreamed with closed eyes, his lower body undulating, his hand insinuating itself into the parted slit in her skirt, sliding up the back of her crooked leg towards the fullness of her bottom. 'You feel so different than I'd imagined...firm, yet so deliciously soft where you're most a woman...'

'Stop that!' she elbowed his arm away and straightened her

leg with a jerk, and he groaned again as her knee dragged heavily across his swollen groin.

His hands moved over her sequinned back. 'Oh, yes...do that again. I like it when you're rough with me...'

'*Matt!*'

He opened his eyes and gave her a glazed smile. 'Are you going to take all your clothes off now, so we can have sex?'

The suggestion almost blew off the top of her head. '*No!*'

His sultry certainty didn't waver. 'When we're both nude I'll be able to feel every part of you against me...' His voice was thick with excitement 'Feel and see everything while we're making love—'

'We're *not* going to *be* making love!'

'Why?' He regarded her with heavy-lidded confusion. 'We're already in bed together—'

'We're *on* a bed, not in it,' she clarified. 'You're supposed to be resting—'

'But I don't want to rest. I want you to make love to me—'

To? Not *with*? Rachel's imagination ran riot even as she choked out, 'You can't always have what you want.'

'But you want it too,' he insisted. 'I know you do. I can *feel* it— I can see the way you look at me.'

He knew and felt and saw too damned much for a man who was supposed to be drunk and incapable!

It had been two years since she had experienced any sexual stirrings, and Rachel was unprepared for the sudden reawakening of her dormant feelings. She lashed herself with the knowledge that her carnal curiosity was shamefully inappropriate: he was too young; he wasn't in the full possession of his senses; he was, if not her enemy, then at the very least a serious opponent of her professional interests; and he was already involved with another woman. To succumb to his drunken seduction she would have to be both mad *and* bad...

'Stop it—Matthew, I'm serious! I don't want to have to hurt you,' she threatened, fending off his wandering hands.

'You won't hurt me…it's only women who sometimes find it painful,' he murmured bemusingly, his eyes hot and smoky. 'But I'm ready for you, Rachel. You can do whatever you like to me—I promise I'll like it.'

She felt a deep, erotic thrill. 'For God's sake, Matthew,' she whispered. 'You don't know what you're *doing*—'

'So? You can show me. Please… I'll be a good lover. I'm a very quick study and it won't take me long to figure out what you like best.' The phrases tumbled over one another, each word slurring into the next. He tried to slither clumsily on top of her, and in a flurry of sequins she pinned his back to the bed, hitching up her gown to straddle his hips with a pincer movement of her strong thighs, bracing herself above him on stiffened arms, her hands flat against his shoulders.

'I said *no*!'

'But Merrilyn told you to make sure I had everything I wanted,' he reminded her soulfully.

'She said *need*, not *want*.'

'But I *do* need you, Rachel.' His black eyes burned with passionate conviction. 'I need you *now*.' He dug his heels into the mattress and arched his hips, pushing himself up between her spread thighs in an attempt to demonstrate just how urgent was his desire. The swollen hardness barely contained by his damp underwear nudged at the gauzy lace covering the core of her feminine being, sending a secret tingle shooting along the cluster of exposed nerve-endings.

'You have to help me…you're the one she chose to soothe the savage beast.'

'Breast,' Rachel corrected automatically, and inwardly groaned at her stupidity as his steamy gaze obediently sank to her cleavage, brandished almost under his nose. 'It's savage breast, not beast,' she explained quickly. 'People often misquote that line.'

His mind did not appear to be improved by her informative little lecture.

'Your breasts don't look savage to me,' he told her gravely, his flattened hands creeping up her sides. 'They look like velvet pillows, all big and plush and soft.' He lifted his head from the pillow and drew in a deep, sighing breath. 'They smell nice, too...sweet and warm and spicy...'

His head sank back as his questing hands slid the final distance to cup the ripe fruit dangling so tantalisingly within his reach, cupping their overflowing weight in his hot palms. 'And they make an incredibly sexy handful...'

As Rachel looked down in shock he pressed a gentle, exploratory finger against one springy mound and watched in fascination as it sank deep into the creamy, resilient flesh. She sagged onto one arm, her biceps bulging with the effort of supporting her whole weight, and caught hold of his wrist in her strong fingers. 'Don't—'

'Why not? Don't you like me playing with them?' he asked huskily. 'I'll be very gentle...'

She felt a hot flush sweep over her body. 'Just keep your hands to yourself.'

The fingers of his other hand curled over the top of her gown. 'But I can *prove* that you like it...' He yanked down strongly and Rachel let out a little screech as a warm wash of air flowed across her freed breasts.

'I knew it was too low-cut for you to wear a bra,' he crowed smugly, shoving the tight bodice clear down to her tapered waist. 'See...your nipples are already excited.' He touched one ruffled raspberry peak. 'Would you like me to suck them?' he offered dreamily. 'I think I'd like to do that more than anything...'

Gasping at his audacity, and appalled by the sizzling temptation of his touch, Rachel reared up and gathered both his wrists in one hand, slamming them forcefully up over his head.

He laughed feverishly, treating it as a teasing new game, kicking his legs and bucking and twisting his body so that her breasts bounced against his sweaty chest. Desperate to control both him and the wayward desires still pulsing through her veins, Rachel snatched the cummerbund hanging from the shiny top rail of the bedhead and looped it tightly around his straining wrists, threading the free ends through one of the wrought-iron bars and securing it with a rough knot. As she did so her flushed breast brushed his cheek, and she felt his head turn and the hot, wet lash of his tongue...

Rachel's hands were shaking when she rolled off his body and dragged her bodice up to cover her sensitised breasts, shielding them from his regretful gaze. To her relief their final bout seemed to have left him weak and lethargic, and he made no attempt to escape from the bond which he could have quite easily pulled free with a little concentrated effort. Instead he lay quietly beneath the sheet that she tucked over him, following her around with his dark, brooding eyes until she agreed to release him on a vow of good behaviour.

He was still shivery, still feverish and disorientated, and Rachel managed to extract the name of his doctor from him and looked up the medical listings in the phone book by the bed.

Fortunately his physician was at home, and not so overcautious or fee-conscious to think that a house-call to his wealthy patient was essential. He listened to Rachel describe the symptoms and cheerfully informed her that a short dousing was not going to turn a slight case of flu into galloping pneumonia.

'It's probably more the excess of alcohol he's suffering from than anything else,' he said. 'Just make sure there's plenty of fluids on hand to counteract the dehydrating effects and let Matt sleep it off. He'll probably have a king-sized headache in the morning, but you can tell him from me that from the sound of it he deserves the hangover!'

Rachel had no intention of doing anything of the kind. Having always been the type to learn well from her mistakes, she waited only until he slipped into a restless doze before sneaking out to order one of the security guards to patrol his door. Then she breezed back to the party, bearing the convenient news of Matthew's medically confirmed illness with which to disarm the gossips.

She had basked in Merrilyn's profitable gratitude and had privately congratulated herself on her handling of an extremely tricky situation.

Until now.

CHAPTER FIVE

RACHEL FLIPPED DOWN the sun visor at the top of her windscreen and scrunched down behind the steering wheel as Matthew Riordan came down the steps from the restaurant, his lean body already at an impatient angle as he stepped onto the footpath.

She stuffed the remainder of her sandwich in her mouth and looked at her watch, noting the time in the spiral notebook lying open on the passenger's seat. Only half an hour for lunch, and a business lunch at that, she thought as she watched him briskly shake hands with the two business suits who were with him before striding off in the direction of his car.

For the past two days, ever since she had received his torrid threat, Rachel had been investigating her blackmailer, and amongst other things she had learned that he was not a man who liked to waste his time or energy on inessentials.

She watched him circle to the driver's side of his gleaming black Porsche, pausing to shrug off the jacket of his lightweight grey suit before sliding behind the wheel. She had been surprised when she had discovered the kind of car he drove. Somehow she had assumed that he would travel as his father did, in a chauffeur-driven limousine with a fax and a phone so that he could work while he travelled. But then, as she had already learnt to her cost, Matt Riordan was full of surprises.

In retrospect Rachel was extremely glad that she hadn't given in to her first impulse yesterday morning, which had been to storm straight over to his office and confront him with his moral depravity. As she had left the house and slammed her way angrily into her car she had been mentally composing a blistering lecture on his disgusting lack of ethics, vile cowardice and base ingratitude!

Then it had struck her that that was probably what he was *expecting* her to do...that he might be banking on provoking her into a panic reaction rather than a carefully considered response, and if she didn't go in extremely well-armed for a fight then she could be setting herself up for another lesson in humiliation.

She had forced herself to calm down as she'd driven to work. She needed hard facts rather than wild theories before she decided what action it was safe to take. Whatever happened she had to keep a lid on things until Robyn and Bethany were safely gone.

She had still been debating whether to come clean with Frank as she'd parked her car and walked into the low-rise commercial building which Weston Security Services shared with a fax bureau and a firm of accountants.

'You're late,' had been his blunt words of welcome as she'd walked through the door, and she was instantly on the defensive.

'Things were a bit hectic at home,' she told him, regretting the unproductive half-hour she had spent simmering over the photographs, now stashed in her briefcase. She paused to greet Lannie, their receptionist, and accept a small pile of mail.

Frank frowned. With his stocky build, wheat-blond hair and blue eyes he sometimes reminded her joltingly of David, but he possessed little of David's personal warmth. Frank was an abrasive type A personality, who was driven, rather than inspired, to succeed.

'When you rang you said you'd be in by eight-thirty, so I arranged a debriefing on the Johnson insurance case. Everyone else was on a tight schedule so we had to go ahead without you. I know your sister's leaving in a few days but we still have a business to run here,' he grunted.

'I'm sorry. It's just that something came up after I rang...'

She knew how much she owed Frank. He could have made it impossible for her to work alongside him, but although he had been originally reluctant, and had constantly tried to fob her off with make-work tasks, she felt he had grudgingly come around to accepting her right to the partnership.

'Are you sure you're OK to come back to work?'

'Just a bit of a headache,' she said, adjusting her nervous grip on her briefcase and its explosive contents.

Frank gave her a hard look. His naturally suspicious nature had made him a good detective, and as David's only surviving relative he had been very protective of his younger brother. He hadn't much liked Rachel when she and David had started dating, and even after they'd got engaged the relationship had never been particularly relaxed. Frank was divorced himself, toughened by his profession and cynical about marriage.

'If you're not well enough, you shouldn't be here.'

'I'm fine,' she insisted. Frank was so hard-bitten himself that he had little respect for the weakness of others. She hated it when he condescended to understand that she might not feel up to the job.

She decided in that instant that she wasn't going to tell Frank about her humiliating problem—not while there was any chance she could quietly handle it herself.

'OK, that's good, because we have a major problem looming,' said Frank, following her into her small sunny office.

'What kind of problem?'

'Matthew Riordan!'

'W-what?' Rachel's briefcase slipped from her nerveless hand

and crashed against the side of a filing cabinet. 'Why? What's he done now?' she asked with brittle casualness.

'It's not what he's *done*, it's what he's *going* to do,' fumed Frank. 'His father's had a heart attack.'

'Kevin Riordan?' Rachel was genuinely upset. She had liked the brash and ebullient head of KR Industries, who had shown a flattering admiration for 'feisty' women. He had been a welcome surprise after his infuriating son. 'When? Is he all right?'

'Keeled over at his desk on Monday. All I know is that he's in hospital and likely to be there for a while.'

'Oh, no, how *awful*...' she said, thinking of his boastful plans for an energetic retirement. 'He isn't even sixty-five yet...'

'Yeah—awful for *us*.' Frank dismissed her unselfish concern with a scowl. 'Because Matthew Riordan's stepped in to effectively run KR Industries, just when our fraud prevention package is on the table for a final decision, and so far he's got a one hundred percent kill-rate on our deals!'

Rachel was confused. 'But—I thought he had no official standing at KR—surely Neville—'

'Neville is away in Japan—I got a fax from him last night,' Frank said, drumming stubby fingers on top of the filing cabinet. 'He'll obviously take over when he gets back, but at the moment he's out of the loop. With him pushing our case the old man was bound to have approved our bid, now with Junior minding the store we might not get it signed by the deadline. That would mean having to go through the bid process all over again.'

'But Matt Riordan's not going to make any major decisions if he knows he's only keeping the chair warm.'

Frank's paranoia was running rife. 'Don't you believe it. Neville told me that he doesn't trust the bastard an inch. If Riordan has overall power of attorney for his father he can virtually do whatever the hell he likes. With his position and influence he could do a lot of damage in a few days. I wouldn't put it past him to try to sabotage our bid...'

Rachel thought of the contents of her briefcase and felt her stomach lurch as Frank plunged on. 'I think we need to face the fact we may not be able to make that balloon payment after all...'

'I could mortgage the townhouse—'

'No!' Frank rejected the offer as forcefully as he always had before. 'David gave that to you free and clear and it's going to stay that way. Anyway, it would put your equity in the company at more than the whole is worth right now. If the worst comes to the worst we can maybe try downsizing, or even selling our client base...

'We have to be realistic, Rachel,' Frank told her. 'We were banking on that KR contract coming through and without it our chances don't look good. I'll sort through our options and try and figure out something, and, in the meantime, why don't you do some personal digging around on Riordan himself? See if you can come up with anything that might be useful.'

His tone doubted that she would. If he had seriously believed that an investigation was likely to be productive he would have put one of their senior men on the job, but unknowingly Frank had provided Rachel with the perfect excuse to devote the rest of the next few days to stalking her prey and plotting his downfall.

Wanting to make the most of her fast-dwindling time with Robyn and Bethany, she had used her illness as an excuse to cancel the rest of the week's gym appointments and several massage bookings at the physiotherapy clinic, so she had no other demands on her time until the following Monday.

Now, Rachel softly depressed the accelerator, rolling her car slowly forwards past the row of parked cars as Matt Riordan began to ease his Porsche out of his parking space further down the road.

She pulled down her baseball cap and adjusted her sunglasses. She didn't know exactly what she expected to achieve by tailing him around, but it was better than doing nothing. David had always believed that dry fact-gathering was no replacement for personal observation when trying to guess what a suspect's next move might be.

After spending all of the previous day delving into the microfiche files of old newspapers at the central library, checking property and legal records and making numerous phone calls under a variety of names, Rachel had been chafing to take some *real* action.

After calling to check that he was still in the building, she had driven over to KR Industries head office and waited until dusk in order to find out which of the three Riordan-owned Auckland properties Matthew was currently calling home. If it did come down to forcing a confrontation, she'd rather it was well away from the public eye.

His destination had turned out to be not his own city apartment, but the family's three-storeyed modern mansion on Auckland's millionaires' mile. Rachel had followed the black Porsche's tail-lights through the city streets, careful to change lanes irregularly and hang one or two cars back, and had felt a little thrill of triumph when she'd seen Matt Riordan finally swing in through the electronically operated iron gates which guarded the estate, still unaware of her presence. Her hands had been sweaty on the steering wheel and her heart had fluttered with exhilaration as she'd continued on past and parked further up the street, in the inky shadows of an overhanging pohutukawa tree, and savoured the small victory—her first solo tailing job!

Using her company cellphone, she'd checked her voice messages, then rung Robyn to let her know that she was on her way home. As she'd been saying goodbye she was startled to see the gates reopen and the black Porsche sweep out again and purr off into the night. He must have only called in to drop something off or say hello to his mother, she'd thought in dismay.

By the time she had got her engine restarted and fumbled her gears it had disappeared around the corner, and at the next intersection it had been only a wink of a brake-light at a distant curve, heading back towards the city. Rachel had pursued the streak of black metallic paint pulsing under the orange street lights on the straight stretch ahead as fast as she'd dared, and had actually believed she was catching up when she'd been flagged down by a uniformed police officer standing by her unmarked car, and handed the indignity of a speeding ticket and an on-the-spot breath test.

'What about that Porsche ahead of me? He was going just as fast—why didn't you stop him?' she'd complained.

'Because he had the sense to slow down as soon as he spotted me and not register over the speed limit on my radar,' the female officer had said drily.

Flushed with annoyance, Rachel had tucked the ticket in her notebook and set off again at a sedate pace, resigned to the fact that she had no chance of catching up with her quarry. She had driven past Matthew's apartment building, noting the darkened windows of his top floor corner eyrie, and vowed not to be taken off guard so easily the next day.

Now, pulling into the heavy lunchtime traffic behind the gleaming Porsche, Rachel thought that at least there would be no chance of breaking the speed limit today!

Expecting him to head to another business meeting, or go back to the office, she was intrigued when he turned off towards a leafy suburb—until she remembered that it was where the city's newest private hospital was located. She had looked it up in the telephone book the previous day when she had wanted to find out Kevin Riordan's medical condition.

Rachel drove into the open car park and surfed into an empty spot on the waves of heat which shimmered off the surface of the new black seal. She nibbled on her lower lip as she watched Matthew lock his leather briefcase into the boot of his car and shoulder back into his jacket as he made for the double glass doors of the hospital. What she wouldn't give to be able to rifle through the contents of that briefcase!

A thick-set uniformed security guard—unfortunately not

one of Westons'—was strolling between the cars, and Rachel thought he might think it suspicious if she remained lurking in her car rather than seeking the air-conditioned coolness of the hospital. Besides, a comfort stop was a growing imperative. Rachel was already suffering from sitting for too long in a small metal box under the blazing sun. Her short-sleeved silk tunic top was sticking to her back, and while the car was stationary the fan blowing air around her sweeping skirts was merely recycling the oppressive heat.

The hospital looked big enough and busy enough to provide plenty of cover, she reasoned. Perhaps she might even manage a quick snoop to find out how Kevin Riordan was *really* doing behind the smokescreen of official information. Taking a charitable view, maybe it was the stress and worry over his father that had caused Matthew to flip out. Maybe he had stooped to a sordid act of blackmail while the balance of his mind was disturbed?

She shivered in spite of the oppressive heat. Those had been very the words quoted in a news clipping about twenty-four-year-old Leigh Riordan's tragic death. Most of the details had been suppressed, but not the coroner's final decision—that she had taken her own life 'while the balance of her mind was disturbed'.

But, no, she told herself, the charitable view was difficult to take when the fact was that Matthew had had those sleazy photos taken over a week *prior* to his father's heart attack.

The coronary care wards were on the third floor, and, unwilling to risk being caught in a lift, Rachel ran lightly up the stairs, two at a time, blessing her rapid return to fitness. She wasn't even breathing hard as she peeped around the heavy smoke-stop door on the third floor, reassured by the evidence that lunchtime was a popular visiting hour. Opposite her was a spacious dayroom peopled with a mix of elegantly dressed visitors and bathrobe-attired patients.

Halfway down the polished corridor she could see a T-intersection, where the nurses' station was situated, and more people moving about—the staff distinguishable only by the open white coats they wore over their smart clothes. In her thigh-length sand-coloured tunic worn over her filmy, patterned brown skirt Rachel was confident of blending in.

A logo on a door across the way caught her eye and she darted for the women's restroom with a sigh of relief. While she was in there she took her plastic pump bottle out of her capacious shoulder-bag and refilled it from a filtered water dispenser, and spritzed a dash of refreshing cologne across her throat and wrists.

Replacing her sunglasses, she cautiously exited and walked towards the nurses' station, her eyes flicking over the patients' names posted outside the individual private rooms.

She had almost reached the intersection when she glimpsed a grey suit around the corner of the right-angled reception desk and shied backwards. At the same time that she realised the suit-wearer was a woman, her reversing heel ground down on something soft and uneven.

Her cry of dismay mingled with a similar one of pain as she lurched around, her sunglasses tumbling off her nose to join the cascade of envelopes and the bunch of flowers which her swinging shoulder-bag had knocked out of the clutches of the tiny grey-haired woman woefully flexing one crushed foot.

'I'm most dreadfully sorry. That was entirely my fault. Are you all right?' Rachel burst out, thanking the Lord that she was wearing flat sandals. From her pain-creased features, Rachel judged the woman to be somewhere in her mid-sixties and, knowing how brittle older bones could be, she crouched to inspect the damage, relieved to see only a faint impression of her sole on the reddened top of her victim's foot.

'It looks like you'll just have some bruising. I'm *so* sorry; I know how painful something like that can feel!'

She hastily gathered up her sunglasses, scrabbling together the scattered mail and injured flowers before rising back to her full height. The other woman couldn't have been much more than five feet tall, and Rachel immediately felt like a clumsy giant as she loomed over the tiny figure in the fashionable powder-blue summer suit.

'It's really not that bad,' said the lady bravely. 'And it couldn't have happened in a more convenient place, could it?' She tested her foot gingerly back on the ground and smiled kindly at her sheepish assailant. 'Are you on the staff?'

'Oh, no—I don't work here,' Rachel responded with a weak smile. 'I don't think the hospital would be too keen to employ someone who goes around trampling people down!'

'I don't know—you could generate them some very brisk business.' The woman laughed. Although she was expensively dressed, and the triple strand of pearls around her neck undoubtedly genuine, the vibrant Kiwi twang in her accent bespoke down-to-earth origins.

'Or get them sued *out* of business. I'm afraid your flowers may be a little bit bruised, too.' Rachel smiled apologetically as she handed them back.

'Oh, well, I don't suppose my husband will notice. He'll be too busy complaining I haven't brought him whisky and chocolates.'

Rachel was amused by her expression of loving exasperation. 'In a coronary care unit?'

'He's a very bad patient,' the little lady admitted ruefully. 'He's always been so proud of being as tough as old boots—never had a sick day in his life until this...'

'Is he *very* ill?' Rachel asked warily.

'He had a heart attack, but they've decided it's not his heart that's really the problem—so now they've scheduled him for a triple by-pass.' An age-spotted hand worried with her pearls. 'The surgeon says it's very straightforward nowadays...'

'I'm sure your husband's in the very best of hands,' reassured Rachel firmly. 'Is your family visiting with you?' she asked, beginning to hand over the thick wad of cards and letters she had picked up, waiting patiently as the woman sorted them to fit them in her grasp.

'Well, my son was supposed to meet me here,' the woman confided. 'But he probably arrived early in order to interrogate the doctors to within an inch of their lives and order them not to upset his sweet little old mum by going into too much gruesome detail—never mind that I'd prefer to know everything there is to know. He's a lovely boy, really, but he can be so very *managing*...'

Her irritation showed and Rachel grinned. 'I know the type.'

'But you're so wonderfully *tall*,' admired the older woman, making herself an instant friend for life. 'I wish I was like you. I always get a crick in my neck when I have to argue with my husband or my son. It must be lovely to be able to stand up to bossy men and look them straight in the eye.'

'Or, better still, look down on them,' grinned Rachel.

She found herself on the receiving end of an assessing look as the grey head cocked to one side, soft curls framing the still-pretty face. 'You might be taller than my boy, but not by much...'

Rachel answered the silent question. 'I'm a hair off six foot.'

'Ahh. So you'd have almost a whole inch with which to lord it over my son. He doesn't seem to have cottoned onto the fact that we're really the superior sex. Mind you, that's partly my fault—he was a late baby, you see, and an only child, so he was doubly spoiled. I wasn't in the best of health for a while, so that probably encouraged him to regard women as generally rather fragile beings. Then his father insisted he be sent off to boarding school to toughen him up and acquire the correct degree of polish.' She sighed. 'Unfortunately I think it succeeded *too* well. He was a passionate, sensitive little boy who became a rather introverted adult. He had one or two bad experiences with women—he married once, when he was twenty, but it came to a wretched end—so now he seems to reserve all his passion for his work...'

Rachel was getting a very bad feeling. Her eyes fell to the last envelope she was in the act of passing over—a thin foolscap rectangle whose neatly typed address jumped out and hit her in the face.

Her fingers unconsciously tightened on the envelope, preventing it from leaving her hold as she blurted, 'You're Mrs *Riordan*. Mrs *Kevin* Riordan?'

'Why, yes—I'm Dorothy...do you know my husband?'

Of all the ghastly coincidences!

'Only slightly. My firm has quoted for some business with him. When I heard yesterday that he was ill I rang the hospital to see how he was but all they would tell me was that he was in a stable condition.' Rachel heard herself babbling while her brain screamed at her to get out of there as fast as she could!

'And now you've come down to make a personal enquiry?' Dorothy Riordan's small face lit from within. 'That *is* kind of you. Kevin's not having visitors yet, but I'll tell him you called, Miss...?'

As Rachel dithered over whether to lie a cool voice denied her the chance.

'Blair. Rachel Theodora Blair.' A grey-clad arm reached between them and plucked the envelope out of her white-knuckled hand. 'Thank you, Rachel, I'll take that!'

Rachel spun around to stare in guilty horror at the man who had prowled silently up behind her. There was a muted fury in the chocolate-brown eyes as he looked from the envelope in his hand to her stricken face.

'Oh, Matt, there you are!' said his mother happily. 'Do you know Miss Blair, too?'

Matthew showed his teeth. 'Intimately.'

His mother looked startled at the throaty purr, and Rachel flushed, edging back as he deliberately invaded her personal space.

'She was just telling me she's come to see how your dad is...'

'Was she?' Matthew's cynical murmur made Rachel scramble to correct Mrs Riordan's flattering misconception.

'Actually, I'm—I was—'

'Making a special delivery?' Matthew suggested, saluting her with a taunting flick of the envelope now in his possession. In the austere grey suit and plain blue shirt and tie he presented a picture of civilised menace that made her nerves twitch.

'Just passing…' she finished lamely, casting Mrs Riordan an unconsciously pleading look.

'I've brought all the morning mail from home, Matt.' His mother showed him the rest of the collection in her hand. 'I thought it might give your dad a nice boost to see some of the cards and letters that people have sent, wishing him well.'

'Is that what this is, Rachel?' asked Matthew silkily, turning over the envelope in his manicured hands. 'Greetings from a fond well-wisher?'

'I have no idea,' she said, grateful for his mother's restraining presence.

Her gratitude was premature.

'Really? I thought you were a woman who liked to always be *on top* of everything,' he said in that same low drawl. 'A lady who prefers to be in a *controlling* position in all her dealings—holding the *whip hand* over the rest of us, so to speak…'

Rachel glared levelly at him, her firm jaw clamped shut to contain her outrage. He was blatantly admitting it! He was virtually *boasting* about what he had done, in front of his own mother!

Thankfully Mrs Riordan was looking curious but unenlightened by his innuendo-laden comments.

'Goodness, it sounds positively frightening,' she said innocently. 'What is it you do, exactly, Miss Blair?'

Rachel told her about Weston Security. Trying to keep her attention on the conversation was extremely difficult with Matthew subtly crowding her on the physical as well as psychological front. Her skin goose-pimpled where the polished fabric of his jacket sleeve brushed her bare arm too often for it to be accidental, and if she turned her head even slightly in his direction her senses swam with a heady masculine scent which struck a disturbing chord in her memory.

'How fascinating! It must be a very exciting field.' Mrs Riordan's enthusiasm had the ring of genuine interest. 'I suppose you need a lot of experience?'

'Oh, Rachel is a highly experienced woman,' supplied Matthew laconically. 'She omitted to tell you that she also works as a masseuse, and I can personally testify that she's *extremely* exciting in the field!'

This piece of loaded sexual innuendo did not slip by unnoticed. 'Matt!' His mother's pained surprise was a parental rap across the knuckles.

'It's all right, Mrs Riordan.' Rachel seized the chance to get some of her own back. 'I'd already come to the conclusion before today that your son wasn't spanked enough as a child.'

His eyebrows rose above the wafer-thin tortoiseshell frames. 'Are you offering to put me over your knee, Mistress Blair?'

'Matt!'

This time they both ignored his mother's faint protest.

'It would be a wasted effort—you're obviously beyond any hope of redemption,' snapped Rachel.

'Is there ever any redemption to be gained through violence? And isn't spanking considered a form of child abuse these days? Some mother *you'd* make...'

Her eyes became molten pools of gold as his casual thrust penetrated deep into her guarded heart. Her hands and feet felt icy while her head swam.

I'd make a *wonderful* mother, she wanted to scream back at him. I *did* make a wonderful mother... I did everything that a mother is supposed to do for her baby—suffered the pain, made the sacrifices, and created something supremely *good* out of a nightmare of hatred and fear...

Shaken by the wounding ease with which he had pierced her

defences, Rachel smothered the painful gush of bitter memories and lifted her chin, offering him a sullen, stoic stare so different from her usual antagonistic challenge that his expression sharpened with predatory interest.

'Mum, why don't you take those letters along to show Dad?' he said suddenly, not taking his eyes off Rachel's pale mask of self-control. 'The cardiac surgeon is still with him, so you can ask him all the questions we were talking about last night...'

Was *this* where he had been off to the previous evening? Rachel lacerated herself for overlooking the obvious. Some detective *she* was!

'Are you ordering me to run along?' Mrs Riordan's wry question showed that she was no fool.

Matthew turned a sweet smile on his mother that made Rachel catch her breath. This was Mrs Riordan's 'sensitive little boy' in the full glory of his maturity. 'Would you mind? I've already had a good chat to Dad. Rachel is too shy to admit it, but she's actually here to see *me*...'

'Oh?' Dorothy Riordan raised pale, pencilled eyebrows. 'Yes, she and I have some...' He paused delicately, sliding his hand down Rachel's forearm and entwining his warm fingers firmly with hers, stiffening his arm in order to hold them shoulder to shoulder as he looked into her flaring eyes. 'Unfinished business...'

'Oh, I *see*...'

'What did you have to say it like that for?' Rachel rounded on him as soon as his mother was out of earshot. 'You know what she thinks now, don't you?'

'That we have some business to conduct?'

'The only business implied by that suggestive little act of yours is *monkey* business!' she snapped.

'Better she thinks that than realises the truth,' he returned with a bite. Jerking her by the hand, he began marching her back down the corridor.

'What *truth*?' Rachel scorned to fight his hold, defiantly matching him stride for stride.

'That you're willing to risk my father's life to make a cheap score!'

'*What?*'

He suddenly stopped, pushed open a door that was slightly ajar and nudged her into a small room lined with crowded shelves. So distracted was she by his outrageous claim that she didn't realise what was happening until it was too late.

'What do you think you're *doing*?' she screeched as he kicked the door shut behind them. Her shoulder bumped against a shelf of folded sheets as she hastily tried to widen the distance between them in the narrowly confined space. The overhead light threw Matthew's grim face into harsh relief as she protested shrilly, 'This is a supply cupboard!'

'I stand in awe of your powers of deduction,' he sneered, leaning back against the door as he tore open the envelope in his hand.

'That was addressed to your father, not you!' she accused.

'And what is it you're so keen for him to see? Ahh, what have we here? Another episode of the *Lifestyles of the Sick and Shameless*?' He flashed her a familiar set of images and she sucked in an appalled breath.

'Oh, my God!' She raised her bewildered gaze to his.

'You bitch!' He exploded away from the door. 'You had to keep turning the screws, didn't you? Even when you knew it wasn't going to get you what you wanted!'

She cracked her elbow on a ledge as he backed her into the nest of shelves in the corner. 'I don't know what you're talking about!'

He brandished the photographs under her nose. 'You were trying to foist these on a sick man—'

She shook her head in confusion. 'I *wasn't*—'

'The hell you weren't!' He slammed his hands flat down on the shelves on either side of her hips, his breath hot on her face.

'I *saw* you handing them to Mum. If I hadn't stopped you she'd probably have taken them in and opened them in front of Dad.'

'But I had nothing to do with those.'

His eyes flamed behind their twin shields of precision glass. 'So you're a liar as well as being malicious!'

The slap resounded as a sharp echo in the small room and Rachel watched in awful fascination as the white outline of her palm on his lean cheek filled up with blood. For a moment there was no sound but their mutually quickened breathing.

'You looking to get physical with me?' he growled, leaning closer.

In the space between one heartbeat and the next his anger ripened into a different kind of passion.

'I thought you only did that with men who were tied down...'

Rachel's body throbbed in recognition of his excitement, her skin drawing tight over her flesh, her breasts aching with the memory of what it felt like to be fondled in his eager hands. She remembered the smooth glide of his glossy skin, the hard flex of his muscles, the soft abrasion of hair on his thighs, the way his hips had surged between her spread legs. A soft, liquid warmth burst inside her belly and she shuddered.

'Take your hands off me!'

'I'm not touching you,' he pointed out hoarsely, and she realised to her mortification that it was true. The tension that had underpinned their every encounter was suddenly laid starkly bare.

She flushed.

'How dare you get all self-righteous with me?' she panted. '*You* were the one who opened up this particular Pandora's box. You can't blame *me* if the evils you let loose have come back to haunt you!'

He was studying her mouth as it moved, and she knew from the sultry, bitter-chocolate gaze that it wasn't her words in which he was interested.

'The only thing that's been haunting me is you,' he mur-

mured. 'The memory of the touch and taste and smell of you...
so real and yet so elusive. If it wasn't for the pictures I might
have believed it was all some wild dream...like the ones that
I've been having nightly ever since...'

His meaning sank like warm honey into her bones. She
thought of all the nights that she had woken, hot and sweaty,
from a faceless demon lover's embrace; but faceless only because she had resolutely refused to see.

'Stop looking at me like that!' she demanded weakly, her bag
sliding unnoticed off her shoulder to slump limply to the floor.

'Like what?'

She turned her head aside from the erotic intensity of his
stare and felt his breath moist in her ear, feathering up into her
hair as he leaned even closer, his legs crowding against hers,
his tie sliding against the front of her tunic, settling lightly between her breasts. 'Like what, Rachel? Tell me...how do I look
at you?' he asked as she tried to hold herself rigidly aloof from
the tumult of fire in her blood.

He nuzzled at the point of her jaw just below her ear and
licked a hot trail back up to her soft lobe.

'How do I look? As if I want to eat you?' He nipped at the
succulent flesh, keeping it captive between his teeth as she
arched her neck away, then releasing it to press his open mouth
into the sensitive hollow between the stem of her neck and her
collarbone and drink in the taste and texture of her skin. 'That's
because I do! God, how can someone so bad taste so damned
good...?' he groaned.

Since she was fifteen Rachel's worst nightmare had been
to find herself pinned down by superior strength, trapped and
helpless against a greedy male assault. But where was the revulsion, the fear and the fury to defend herself now? She was rendered helpless—not by the violence of *Matthew's* sexual need,
but the uncontrollable desires that raced recklessly through her
own veins.

Her hands, which should have been groping for a way to

swiftly incapacitate him, were instead sliding around his waist underneath his jacket, her arms slowly contracting until her breasts were crushing satisfyingly tight against his crisp cotton shirt-front. Her knee, which should have been aimed in a punishing jab between his legs, was instead obeying a more primal instinct, slowly rubbing up and down the outside of his thigh as he worked his lower torso deeper into the fork of her body.

His hair, soft and fragrant with natural musk, brushed her nose and cheek as his marauding mouth strayed over her throat, her chin, her cheekbones, her eyes, everywhere but where she desperately wanted it to be... Reason spun beyond her reach as she relinquished her fragile grasp on reality and cast herself adrift on a storm-tossed sea of pure emotion.

'Matt...' She tunnelled her hands up between his shoulder blades and raked her trim nails all the way down the length of his back, hard enough for him to feel the sharp scrape through the polished cotton.

He arched and shuddered, sensation pooling at the base of his spine and spilling over into his loins. 'Witch...!' His hands, which had been gripping the edges of the shelf in a futile attempt at self-control, swooped down to her flanks, smoothing up her thighs and over her womanly hips, tracing the rounded shape of her full bottom through the filmy skirt, snagging his fingers in the soft gathers as he kneaded her against his growing hardness.

Thready gasps mingled with whispered sighs and the rustle of cloth as their mutual excitement exploded into hungry passion. And still he had not kissed her...!

Matthew's rough-shaven jaw rasped tantalisingly across Rachel's soft lips, and with a stifled sound of frustration she clenched her hands in his thick dark hair, holding his head still so that she could at last find the intimacy that she craved. He resisted only long enough to wrench off his spectacles and shove them blindly into his jacket pocket, then his mouth was settling hotly over hers.

It was everything she had wished, everything her dream had promised...sinfully sweet and deliciously devouring; steamy, wet and wonderful. Her breasts grew heavy and her limbs weighted as his tongue stroked inside her, limber and strong, sliding against the slippery surfaces of her mouth, exploring the ripples in her arched palate and delving into the silky recesses beneath her tongue. He kissed and withdrew, kissed and withdrew, biting and sucking at her lips with each lingering withdrawal and slanting his head to make each invasion different... deeper, slower, longer...more flagrantly erotic...

She revelled in the straining tension of Matthew's body, time ceasing to matter as she felt his hands begin to move up her body, massaging it through the thin silk. When he came to her breasts, and found her nipples barricaded behind a wall of impenetrable lace, he uttered a whispered curse and kissed her with a punishing force that she returned in glorious measure, sinking her teeth into his lower lip and reaching down to draw teasing fingers across the taut bulge at the front of his trousers.

A rattle on the door-handle was all the warning they received as a freckle-faced young nurse suddenly invaded their illusion of privacy. They wrenched apart, far too late for any polite pretence as to what they'd been doing.

'Er... I just came in to get an extra pillow for a patient,' the nurse stammered, her eyes rounding at the sight of their flushed faces and rumpled clothes. Matthew recovered first, reaching up to pull one off the shelf just above them.

'Here, have this one.' His reddened mouth curved sardonically. 'We certainly weren't going to need it.'

He made it sound as if they had been about to make love standing up! Although goodness knows how far things would have gone if they hadn't been interrupted, Rachel was forced to concede. With a muffled sound of horror she noticed the photographs which Matthew had knocked off the shelf face-up under her feet, and bent to snatch them up, shielding them with her bulky bag.

'Thanks.' The nurse hugged the pillow to her breast as she backed towards the door, summoning the courage to venture, 'Umm…you're really not supposed to be doing—uh—what you're doing in here, you know…'

'Honey,' growled Matthew, *we're* not supposed to be doing it *any*where!'

'She probably thinks we're a pair of guilty adulterers,' Rachel complained as they beat a hasty retreat. This time it didn't matter if she took the lift. She had already been thoroughly rumbled.

'Or a brother and sister,' he said, replacing his glasses as they stepped into the empty lift.

She looked at him in disgust, trying not to remember that only minutes ago she had been wax in his arms. 'Trust you to think of something perverted!'

He straightened his tie. 'I'm sure you could match me in perversity. We do seem to be making a habit of being caught *in flagrante delicto*.' He looked at her with a smile of grim satisfaction. 'And this latest incident certainly alters the stakes between us, doesn't it?'

'What do you mean?'

'Well, the blackmail game seems a little unproductive. I think I'm ready to graduate to something more…stimulating.'

'Like what?' asked Rachel, already guessing from his dangerous expression that she was going to hate his answer.

'Like kidnapping!'

CHAPTER SIX

RACHEL'S FINGERS HOVERED over the electronic box set flush into the white plaster wall, itching to try out the keypad. Birthdate? Wedding day?

'Forget it. It's tamper-proof.'

She whirled around as Matthew came up the internal staircase from his triple garage, carrying the by now crumpled photographs he had removed from her bag. She'd thought she had escaped him when she had broken away and made a dash for her car in the hospital car park, cramming her key into the nearside passenger door. But Matthew had foiled her by making an eye-opening leap across the sloping bonnet, sledding across the polished paintwork on his backside to land lightly on the other side and whip himself into the driver's seat in the time it took her to get inside.

'I always wanted to do that!' he had crowed smugly, plucking her keys from her frozen hand.

'You can't do this!' she spluttered, as he drove out of the car park with a cheerful wave of recognition to the amused security guard.

'I just did,' he pointed out, flicking on an indicator as he followed the sign for the motorway.

'But what about your Porsche—'

He shrugged. 'I'll have someone pick it up for me. Right now we have more important things to worry about...'

'Like my having you arrested for abduction?'

'Go ahead. Bring on the cops with their sirens and flashing lights,' he drawled sarcastically. 'Let's get as many people as possible involved in this sordid affair!'

She scowled. 'Where are you taking me?'

'Somewhere we won't be interrupted...'

The place to which he had brought her was certainly secluded. It lay in the rural belt south of the city, surrounded by the flat green fields and timber-railed fences of famous racing studs and training stables. The large white aggressively modern house was well tucked back from the road, on tree-studded land enclosed by a high stone wall and guarded by a state of-the-art remote video and alarm system.

'Not only does disarming it require a double code, but also a fingerprint ID,' Matthew informed her now, as she stood in the bare, white-walled foyer, the intensely coloured light cascading down from the domed leaded-glass skylight high overhead turning her hair into a vibrant cap of jewel-green as she tilted her head to warily monitor his approach. He held up a splayed hand, palm towards her. 'So, unless you're wearing the approved loops and whorls, all hell will break loose if you open a door anywhere in the house.'

She looked at all the closed doors she could see down the wide, straight hallway which passed beneath the graceful white arch of a double staircase leading to the upper floor.

'Then hadn't you better turn it off?' Even speaking softly, her voice echoed clearly in the empty space between the polished hardwood floors and the curving grained timber ceilings.

'I've turned off the sub-network that controls the internal doors and sound and motion sensors; I think I might leave the rest of the bells and whistles in place until you feel a trifle more…secure with my hospitality.'

She tossed her head, drawing herself up to her full height. 'May I at least have my car keys back?'

She fully expected him to refuse. Instead he took them out of his pocket and tossed them over.

'The garage doors are also operated on a code system,' he revealed as she snatched them out of the air. 'Are you thirsty? You look hot.' He turned on his heel and walked into the cool depths of the hallway, shedding his jacket and stripping off his tie. 'Coming?'

Curiosity drove her to follow without further protest. Underfoot the smooth wood changed to plush oriental carpet runners, rich with glowing colours woven into complex geometric patterns. Through half-open doors Rachel glimpsed large white-walled rooms, with more jewelled carpets decorating the wooden floors and only a very occasional piece of furniture. There seemed to be plenty of furniture on the walls, however, and she guessed that the art, rather than an obsession with personal safety, was the reason for the excessive security system.

The huge room into which Matthew turned looked out over a deep blue swimming pool fed by a waterfall and surrounded by pale flagstones and boulders of white rock.

Apart from a floor-to-ceiling bookcase running the length of the back wall, the only furniture was a sinuously curved waist-high cabinet topped with a waxed slab of recycled native timber growing out of another wall, and the long, serpentine ripple of an armless couch facing the glass doors, edged in lead-lights, that opened onto the pool.

He threw his jacket and tie across the top of the cabinet and laid the envelope down on top of them. From a refrigerator concealed in the bottom half of the cabinet Matthew took a bottle of mineral water and one of lager, silently offering her a choice. He poured her requested water into a large goblet of hand-blown glass, pushing it towards her across the intricately veined slab of wood, and did the same with a beer for himself.

'Isn't it a bit early in the day for that?' she attacked. 'If you're going to drink yourself into a stupor again I'd like to leave. In my experience you make an unpleasant drunk.'

He took a long draught of the icy liquid, watching her over the rim. 'Really? That's not what the pictures say.'

Her fingers clenched on her glass. 'You think I *enjoyed* what I had to do that night?' she said icily.

'*Had* to do?' he said, his narrow face hawkishly intent. 'Did someone somehow *force* you to lure me into a compromising position?'

Her glass clashed with the wood as she set it down, glaring belligerently across the bar. 'Of course not! And I didn't *lure* you—'

'But you *did* push me into that pool; there was never any oh-so-convenient *cat*, was there?' He smiled grimly as her face reflected her guilt. 'And I seem to remember *you* were the one who suggested the guest house…'

'Merrilyn was incapable of doing anything but panic; you were bombed out of your mind and threatening to create havoc—*somebody* had to decide what to do.'

'So it really was all your own idea,' he concluded bitterly. 'You still haven't told me *why*—was it some twisted form of revenge for not getting the contracts you wanted? For money? Or just for the sake of some sick head-game?'

He was making no sense. 'You're the one playing the games,' she flung at him. 'You tell *me*!'

He pushed away his unfinished beer and placed his hands flat on the bar. 'You're saying I get to make the first move?' he asked savagely. 'OK. How much?'

'How much what?'

'For the photographs—all prints and negatives. How much?'

She felt a sharp wrench in her chest. Foolishly she had somehow thought that he would relent, that he wouldn't let it go this far...

'You mean...how much money?' Her head whirled. He was asking *her* how much blackmail she was willing to pay?

'What do you think they're worth? Ten thousand?'

'Ten thousand dollars!' she echoed with an incredulous shrill.

'You think it should be more?' he asked sardonically 'How much? Twenty? Fifty grand? A hundred?'

'Don't be ridiculous!' she cried. He might as well ask for the moon. 'You're a *millionaire*, for God's sake. You don't need the money—'

'But you do? Why? To prop up that ailing business of yours?'

His scathing tone made her see red. 'It's not ailing. It's just a matter of smoothing out the cash flows.'

'And the way to do this is by indulging in a spot of blackmail? Hardly a good advertisement for your professional integrity.'

'I don't know what you're talking about—my integrity has never been in question!' she defended herself hotly. 'They're *your* photos. *You're* the blackmailer!'

'The hell I am!' He stared at her, feigning a thunderstruck innocence that made her blood boil.

She fished in her bag for her wallet and held up the green-inked note, now folded and angrily refolded many times. 'Then what's this? And don't tell me that you didn't write it, because—' she took another piece of paper from her wallet and held them side by side '—I compared it to this—the handwriting is identical.'

He looked at the formal apology he had sent with his flowers, briefly diverted. 'You kept this? Did you press one of my flowers, too?'

She flushed. 'Don't flatter yourself.' She withered him with a lie. 'The roses went straight into the bin!'

He reached for the other note and she retracted it sharply. 'Oh, no, you don't—this is evidence. You mailed me those photographs and threatened to release them to the tabloids. You accused me of being a prostitute! And you have the nerve to accuse *me* of being somehow to blame!'

Dark blood began edging along the top of his cheekbones as he began to register the extent his error. 'But you sent them to me first—'

'I never saw them before in my life,' she blazed in righteous indignation. 'Not until you sent them to me with your sleazy note attached. And that envelope I gave your mother at the hospital *she* had just dropped. All I did was pick it up off the floor for her. If you think you can force us to withdraw Westons' bid for the KR contract without you having appeared to have interfered, you can think again! I have no idea where the photos came from, but if you have any more of them—'

'I don't, and I have no idea where they came from, either.'

'You can forget about trying—' She broke off her harangue. 'What did you say?'

He succinctly described the arrival of the envelope, addressed to his father at KR Industries, into his hands. 'There was no message, but I naturally assumed they were from you,' he said, rubbing his lean cheek, as if anticipating another well-deserved slap. 'I thought it was some kind of shakedown—'

'You *naturally* assumed?' Rachel was even more outraged. Her bosom heaved. 'Why was *I* the natural culprit? What made you even *think* I was capable of such a despicable thing?'

'I don't know...maybe it was my subconscious.'

'Your subconscious told you I was a blackmailing bitch?' Her outraged voice bounced off the pitched ceiling.

Instead of flinching, he looked her straight in the eye and said with devastating honesty, 'No, my subconscious was telling me that you were a gorgeous, earthy, incredibly sexy woman to whom I was dangerously attracted. I say "dangerously" because all my logical thought-processes went completely haywire whenever you were in the vicinity. In trying to hide it I guess I might have overcompensated. You may have noticed that I hardly managed to address a single coherent sentence to you whenever we were in a room together...'

Rachel felt as if she had been hit on the head, dazed by this insight—so totally at odds with her own interpretation of his dismissive behaviour.

'If couldn't trust my own instincts or judgement where you were concerned,' he said, seeming satisfied by her stunned silence. 'How could I trust you? I felt furious, betrayed...but I was excited, too. I *wanted* it to be you, because it would licence me to act on my passions in the cause of natural justice...'

'I—you... I don't know what you expect me to say...' she stammered, intensely flustered.

'Should I send you some more roses?' he murmured, removing his spectacles to bare his black-eyed gaze.

'*No!*' She couldn't help thinking of what had happened the last time he had taken off his glasses. 'No...'

'You were equally quick to think badly of me, so in a sense we're even,' he slyly pointed out.

'I had the better reason,' she flashed. 'And Neville said—'

'Ah, *Neville.*' He cut her off, his expression suddenly shuttered. 'I don't doubt my dear cousin cast me in a rather unflattering light...'

The full implications of what he had said were only now beginning to sink in. Rachel stared sightlessly at the notes in her hand. 'I—why are you so willing to trust me now?'

Annoyed by the husky tenor of her voice, she looked up at him, hardening her expression. He needn't think that just because he had confessed to being *dangerously attracted*, she would overlook everything that he had said and done. 'And why should *I* believe what *you* tell me?'

'Perhaps because we both know each other a little better now,' he said, moving around the bar. 'Truce?'

She flushed. 'If you think that a few kisses constitutes knowing someone better—'

He studied her blush. 'Actually, I was talking about our mutual investigations. The man I have watching you says that you have a reputation in your neighbourhood for being a soft touch for those in trouble, but you're scrupulous about old-fashioned principles like honesty and fair dealing.'

'You've had me under *surveillance*?' she bristled. She had been so busy keeping tabs on *him* that it had never occurred to her to look over her shoulder.

'It seemed like a good idea at the time.' He shrugged. 'Of course, if I'd known that you were going to start shadowing *me*, perhaps I could have saved myself the expense.'

'You *knew* I was following you?' She remembered how naively pleased she had been with herself the previous night.

'Well, not until my detective came in with his report while I was visiting Dad—and told me that you had just accosted my mother on the ward,' he admitted.

At least it was some consolation that he hadn't spotted her himself! She knew it would be hypocritical to voice her fierce objection to the invasion of her privacy.

'I hope he's costing you an arm and a leg,' she contented herself with snapping.

'I get a discount—he's with the firm that does the security work for Ayr Holdings. The same one that beat yours out of those contracts,' he said, adding insult to injury.

'I suppose he's the one you'll get to pick up your Porsche—'

'No, actually I told him his input would no longer be necessary, that I'd handle it myself from here on...'

Rachel folded her arms over her chest. 'Did you show him the photographs?'

Matthew's eyes glowed with quiet understanding. 'I haven't shown anyone. I never even mentioned the word "blackmail". As far as he was concerned it was simply a straightforward case of me wanting to find out more about you.'

She stiffened. 'Are you having the bill charged to Ayr Holdings or to a private account?' she asked.

'Privately,' he admitted.

'I see. So he knows it's something you don't want going through the books, then. He probably thinks that you're vetting me as a potential mistress,' she said sourly.

'Lover.'

The soft word caressed her senses like a fur glove. 'What?'

'Just being precise. You could only be my mistress if I was already married. Since I'm not, that would make you my prospective lover rather than my kept woman.' As she scrabbled for a sufficiently devastating answer he added: 'But why set your sights so low? Maybe he thought I was checking out your suitability as a potential wife...'

Her heart gave a sickening thump. She tossed her head. 'What makes you think that marriage to you would be such an elevation? Anyway, men who're contemplating a new marriage generally don't continue to wear their old wedding rings...'

He twisted the thick gold band on his finger. 'Is that a piece of detective school lore?' He slid the heavy ring off his finger and rolled it in his palm. 'I must say it's been very useful for keeping the society she-wolves at bay. You've no idea the offers I was inundated with after Leigh died...'

She could imagine, and for that reason she was sour. 'The rich never have to be lonely for long.'

He slipped the ring into his trouser pocket. 'I never bought into the illusion that sex is an adequate substitute for love, and a love that has to be bought isn't worth the investment. What about you?'

'What about me?' She looked at him wide-eyed, startled by the discovery that beneath the sophisticated shell Matthew Riordan was a romantic.

'After David Weston died did you take up any male offers of comfort?'

'Why are you asking? I'm sure by now you have a full list of my ex-lovers,' she said sniffily.

'I was interested in your present, not past, and at present

there doesn't seem to be any man in your life. Unless you and your partner have a secret thing going…'

'Frank?' Her jolt of incredulous laughter brought a subtle curve of satisfaction to his mouth.

He leaned on elbow on the bar. 'You don't find him attractive?'

'He's handsome enough, I suppose, but we've never particularly hit it off.' She shrugged. 'He's hardly irresistible.'

'Is that what you're looking for? A man whom you find yourself totally unable to resist? That's not very PC of you.'

'Since when has political correctness had anything to do with it? And I'm not *looking* at all. I'm quite content with my life as it is!' she lied, with a fierceness that rang slightly hollow.

'So…what did Weston say when you told him I was blackmailing you?'

'What makes you think I'd automatically go running to Frank? I can handle my own problems.'

He raised his eyebrows. 'You haven't told him? I would have thought you'd value his professional opinion.'

'I haven't told anyone. If Frank knew about those photos there'd be nothing professional about his attitude.' She shuddered. 'He'd go totally ape!'

He straightened, frowning, his shoulders tensing under the tailored blue cotton. 'You mean you're afraid he might get violent. Has he hurt you before?'

'No, of course not! I didn't mean physically. But he'd probably demand I disassociate myself from Westons, and I wouldn't blame him!'

'*I* would. You were his brother's fiancée; surely he'd stand by you?'

'I told you, we're not that close. He'd consider that I'd brought it on myself by being careless. And I was. Someone else followed us to that room and took those photos, and I didn't even notice.'

'Neither did I.'

'Matthew, you weren't in any condition to notice *any*thing, or do anything about it if you *had*.'

Seeing that she was determined to punish herself with the full blame, he was equally determined that she should not.

'I beg to differ. For example, I certainly noticed a great deal about *you*...and if I hadn't been in a condition to do something about it you wouldn't have had to tie me to the bed.'

He had the pleasure of seeing her wrestle with the urge to explode, her self-control only winning by the narrowest of margins as she clipped, 'Dammit, I should have been more careful.'

It was time someone forced her to acknowledge that she sometimes needed help. 'How?'

'I don't know.' She raked her hand through her hair, drawing his attention to the flawless sheen of sun-kissed skin at her temples and the thickness of the lashes that fringed her frowning hazel eyes. The lips he had so recently kissed were compressed into a prim line which he knew was a lie. The lady's disdain was only skin-deep; under that armour of tough self-sufficiency was a passion as reckless as it was strong.

'Don't beat yourself up over it. No one could have planned for things to turn out exactly the way they did that night,' he told her. 'There were too many variables involved, so it had to be a purely spur-of-the-moment thing. Someone saw an opportunity and grabbed it. You were only involved because you were in the wrong place at the wrong time. There's been no demand for money, so this isn't a straightforward case of financial extortion—this is a vindictive act, a smear aimed at the Riordans—specifically *me*.'

So now he was relegating her from starring role in a drama to bit-player in a farce?

'Without a note we can't know that for sure,' she said hotly. 'They might be intended to destroy my character in your father's eyes—make me seem like a danger to his family and thus wreck any chance of anyone associated with me ever getting any business from KR.'

'And who would benefit most from that?'

'Directly? Well, the other security companies who are making competitive bids, I suppose.'

'And are they really likely to use that kind of dirty trick against one of their own, at considerable risk to their own reputations?' he asked. 'A thing like that could boomerang and be as much a threat to themselves as to you.'

Put like that it sounded highly unlikely. Rachel had been so certain of Matthew's guilt that she hadn't bothered to ponder any solid alternatives.

'Well, how many enemies do *you* have?' she challenged.

He shrugged. 'Since Dad has started telling people I'm thinking of standing for local body elections all sorts of cranks have come out of the woodwork. In my opinion anyone who isn't a friend is potentially an enemy.'

She was appalled by such cynicism. 'Why leave out your friends?' she said cattily.

He laughed, and picked up the envelope and his beer. 'Because they're such a rare and precious breed. The only way to have a friend is to be one. Prosperity has plenty of glittering acquaintances—real friendship sticks around for trouble...like now...'

She faced him, arms akimbo. 'I'm not your friend. I'm only here because you didn't give me any choice.'

'A friend in need is a friend indeed—we're both in this together, Rachel, whether you like it or not. Come on, we have some homework to do...'

To Rachel's embarrassment, "homework" consisted of comparing memories with Matthew, who lay on his stomach on the bare floor in a patch of sunlight minutely examining the latest photographs, which he proclaimed as identical to the first three.

'So, we could conclude that there probably are no more—the photographer just managed to get these few shots, not a whole roll of film—otherwise why wouldn't he have sent pictures progressively more explicit and therefore threatening—'

'Because it didn't *get* any more explicit!' Rachel proclaimed, from her lofty perch on the couch.

He rolled on his side and propped his head on his hand. 'Didn't it?'

She looked suspiciously down into his narrow handsome face. 'Don't you *know*?'

'I told you.' He grinned. 'My recollection gets a bit hazy after the bondage bit... My doctor said you told him I was delirious.'

She took a gulp of her water. 'There was no bondage! I *temporarily restrained* you—*gently*—when you tried to pull down my dress—'

'After you had undressed me...'

'Your clothes were wet and you wouldn't take them off for yourself. Your doctor said I did the right thing.'

'So we didn't make love?' he asked wistfully.

All this time he had thought they might have been *lovers*?

'No! What kind of woman do you think I am? No, don't answer that,' she said hastily as he opened his mouth. 'Believe me, Matthew—nothing *happened*.'

'But we wanted it to... I seem to remember—'

'That you were confused—you had a fever,' she reminded him.

'Mmm, you look as if you were pretty hot yourself,' he murmured, returning to his study.

Rachel felt that way now. 'Matthew—'

'Matt.'

She gritted her teeth. 'Is it necessary to use a magnifying glass?'

'How closely did you look at the photos I sent you?'

'I didn't drool over every minute detail with a magnifying glass, if that's what you mean!'

'Then you should have...come down and look at this.' 'I've seen all I need to see—'

'I doubt it. Come on, Rachel, it's a bit too late for false modesty.' He stretched over and laced his fingers around her ankle, giving it a little tug. 'This is important.'

'Oh, all right.' She shook off his hand and reluctantly knelt down beside his prone figure, taking the magnifying glass he handed her.

'Look, there…'

Her face went fiery red as she saw his finger tracing the curve of her bare hip where it joined her torso 'You—'

'Rachel…' His hand clamped around hers on the handle of the glass, forcing it to remain poised over the glossy still. 'Get over it! Try and forget for a moment that this is you and me. This photograph has been altered, so seamlessly it couldn't have been done in a darkroom—it has to have been done on a computer.

'I'm only guessing, but I doubt your bottom is really as slim as it appears to be here—and see the strange angle of your hips in relation to the position of your thighs? Look at the length from hip to knee—those legs don't belong to a woman of your height—and where's the muscle definition of a woman who works out as much as you do in the gym? Then there's the evenness of the skin toning below your waist—is that natural, given the lighting in the room? I bet if you scanned this and looked at it pixel by pixel you'd be able to see the joins…'

'My God—this isn't me!' Rachel realised gratefully, collapsing on her stomach beside him, leaning on her elbows, her hair brushing his cheek as she jostled him for a better look. 'This is all a fake!'

'Well, not *all*…the top half is pretty unmistakably you,' he pointed out. 'And that's definitely me there underneath you…'

She was obeying his advice and concentrating fiercely on the details. 'I didn't *think* my dress had been dragged down that far, but I thought it must have slipped south in the struggle. I remember having to do a lot of wriggling and twisting to get it back up again…'

'So do I,' he sighed reminiscently, earning himself a sharp nudge in the shoulder.

'Why didn't it occur to me that this had to be a fake?' she castigated herself.

'Probably because, like me, you were initially too furious to think rationally, and also because the other two photographs *are* perfectly genuine—if misleading,' he said. 'Whoever did this is clever, and has all the right ingredients: a good digital scanner, some sophisticated computer software, a pile of porn, a lot of patience and a gutful of resentment.'

'And the whip,' she discovered, shifting the thick optic lens, 'that's been scanned in, too. Did you notice, Matt? It's supposedly lying on the sheet, but it's not making any dent in the folds...'

'Well, on reflection, it did seem unlikely that a woman as forceful as yourself would need a whip to keep a man in line,' he said. 'Especially when you already have a tongue far more stinging than any lash.'

She glanced sideways to find his expression teasing. Their eyes met, and for the first time she found herself tempted to laugh over her ghastly predicament.

'I gather you've changed your mind about my being a professional dominatrix?' She referred sweetly to his coruscating note.

His eyelids flickered, and although he steadily held her gaze, his colour rose. 'I doubt you'd want, or expect, abject submission from a man in your bed. I think you're far more likely to demand an equal exchange of passion...'

He imagined she'd be demanding in bed! He probably thought of her as an experienced older woman, Rachel told herself, alarmed at how arousing she found the notion. She'd never been with a younger man—David had been eleven years her senior. She latched onto the memory in a desperate attempt to anchor herself to sober reality.

She cleared her throat and sat up. 'What are we going to do about these?' She indicated the photos.

'I'm glad to hear you say "we",' he said, stacking them up

and helping her to her feet with inbred politeness. 'I take it you're no more keen than I am to have the police involved?'

She shuddered, and shook her head. 'I may as well just tell Frank! The fewer people who know, the less chance of a leak.'

'Then the first thing we need to do is to neutralise the threat those pictures represent by destroying their capacity to create a scandal. That'll give us the freedom to organise a more thorough investigation.'

Rachel tensed suspiciously at the latter statement. 'But no outsiders—and as far as I'm concerned that includes your security people.'

She continued to hammer the point as she followed him out of the room and across the hallway into a stunning white kitchen, where Matthew calmly busied himself making her a snack, after prying out of her that her lunch on stake-out had been a meagre sandwich and an apple.

'Not nearly enough for someone who burns as much energy as you,' he told her, opening the gigantic double-doored refrigerator.

Was that an oblique reference to her size? No—if Matthew wanted to comment on her curves he would do it frankly.

'I haven't really been very hungry the last few days—I'm still recovering from flu,' she protested half-heartedly, her mouth-watering as she watched him skilfully chop chicken, celery and a hard-boiled egg and deftly fold them into sour cream sprinkled with capers, fresh parsley and chives.

'Which I take it is also my fault?' he said, spooning the mixture into a cup of a lettuce and sliding the plate across the tiled breakfast bar where she sat. 'But I can solemnly promise you, Rachel, that's the only kind of infection you risk catching from me in bed.' He smiled at her expression. 'Surely by now you've guessed that's how I hope we're going to end up? By being upfront now we can enjoy the spontaneity later...'

While she was still gaping at his staggering presumption he forked up a morsel of salad and popped it between her parted lips. As her mouth closed and she automatically began to chew he handed her the implement and distracted her from the fact she was eating, with a string of amusing stories about his brash father's cunning machinations to free Matthew from the social stigma of being a *nouveau riche* rubbish-man's son.

Without realising it, Rachel allowed him to draw forth wry recollections of her far less privileged home background, and the impact her unplanned arrival had had on a mother and father who had already discovered the first time around that they were not natural parents. Their love had been strictly rationed according to behaviour; their expectations as low as Kevin Riordan's had been high.

A fragrant cup of spiced tea eventually replaced her empty plate, and Rachel realised they had strayed far from the purpose of her enforced visit. She hurriedly returned to their discussion of tactics, and when he objected to her insistence on pursuing her own separate avenues of investigation, her heated accusations prompted him to frankly spell out exactly why Weston Security had lost its bids.

'It was *not* because of my personal reaction to you.' He refuted her bitter allegation with passionate conviction. 'I wouldn't survive very long at the head of a financial empire if I let my emotions, however intense, dictate my business decisions. Nor was it from any prejudice against women—some of my brightest executives are female.'

He listed a string of salient factors that forced Rachel to acknowledge that perhaps *she* had been the one guilty of prejudice, her hindsight coloured by the disparaging remarks that Neville had dripped in her ear.

She found herself agreeing that she would take no steps without full consultation, but made no promises that she would accept any resulting advice.

'Let's remember that *I'm* the professional in this field; you're just a—'

'Gifted amateur?'

'*Bumbling* amateur,' she corrected.

'Oh, I get it. I'm Watson to your Holmes.'

She frowned. 'This isn't a game.'

'No, but that doesn't mean we can't enjoy it.'

She felt a little tingle in her bones, not of foreboding but of illicit excitement. 'You said something before about neutralising any scandal…'

She turned to watch him carry the dishes to the dishwasher and caught sight of the kitchen clock high on the wall. She checked it disbelievingly against her watch, appalled to see that the whole afternoon had slipped effortlessly away. She leapt to her feet, determined to assert herself, only to find her erstwhile kidnapper effusively helpful.

Quite how Matthew had persuaded her to allow him to drive her home in her own car she couldn't afterwards remember, but she knew it was a mistake as soon as he introduced himself to Robyn on the doorstep and insinuated himself inside to accept an offer of a cup of tea and endure a sisterly interrogation.

Looking perfectly at ease in the modest drawing room, he sipped his tea and listened to Robyn chatter about her last day at work, and proved so charming that when Rachel reminded him for the fourth time about the taxi he had supposedly come inside to call it was Robyn who leapt up and rushed away to do it.

'I suppose using your cellphone was out of the question,' Rachel said, knowing that he probably never went anywhere without a lifeline to the financial markets.

'I think the battery's flat,' he lied blatantly, as the front door slammed open and shut again, and feet pounded up the hall just ahead of an excited voice.

'Hey, guess what—my class threw a farewell party for me at school today!' Bethany skidded to a stop in the door, her hazel eyes and pink mouth rounding in recognition at the sight of the man rising politely to his feet. 'Wow, it's the babe!'

'I beg your pardon?' Matthew held out his hand, looking amused. 'I'm Matt Riordan.'

Bethany laughed as she shook it. 'You're the man from the photo—the one who was kissing Rachel's hand at that party.'

Only Rachel noticed the tip of his ears go pink. 'You *saw* those photos?'

'I opened them at the breakfast table,' Rachel said cruelly.

'I only looked at one—Rachel hid all the others. Were they horribly obscene or something?' asked Bethany.

'Utterly,' he grinned, slanting Rachel a sly look.

Bethany was sharp-eyed. She tilted up her chin. 'Are you and Rachel going out on a date?' There was mingled curiosity and disappointment in her voice.

He shook his head. 'I know this is your last night here, and you probably want to spend it together. Actually, I'm here to ask *you* for one.'

'Me?'

'I know Rachel is planning to see you and your mother off to Bangkok tomorrow evening, and I thought that you might allow me to take all three of you out to lunch and then run you over to the airport in my father's limousine.'

'Matt—'

'You mean a proper black limo with a chauffeur—a stretch?' The young girl cut eagerly across Rachel's faint protest.

'With a TV, video and computer in the back,' Matthew confirmed. 'You can e-mail your friends goodbye on the way to the airport.'

Bethany's eyes gleamed. 'We've got *hu-mung-ous* amounts of luggage!' she warned. 'We're taking *every*thing.'

'Then I guess we'll make that two limos—one for us and one for your luggage.'

Bethany giggled and flushed shyly. 'Are you serious?' He nodded, and she instantly beamed again. 'That would be fabulous, wouldn't it, Rachel? Some of the gang are coming to see me off—imagine their faces when I swan up in a *limo*! Does Mum know? Let me tell her!'

She bounced out of the room, only to pop her head back

around the door and say mischievously, 'I guess this means you've changed your mind about him being a slimy, scum-sucking slug, huh, Rachel?'

He stroked his lean jaw, studying her discomfiture. 'A *slug*?'

'It seemed apposite at the time,' said Rachel stoutly. 'About tomorrow—I don't think—'

'Come off it, Rachel, you know you aren't going to disappoint her. This way you all get to have a good time instead of moping around here prolonging your goodbyes. And Robyn won't have to worry about you being left on your own.' He glanced towards the door. 'Bethany's a very pretty girl.'

Rachel just stopped herself from saying thank you. 'Yes, yes, she is.'

'She's the spitting image of you—same eyes, same shape of face, same challenging heft of the chin when she takes on a dare... She's probably going to be as tall as you are, too,' he said in idle speculation.

'Yes...'

'In fact she looks far more like you than she does Robyn—' He stopped as he saw her face, and she hurriedly bent to put the empty teacups back onto the wooden tray.

'Rachel?'

She didn't answer him, and when she looked again he was standing by the window, looking at the little clutch of photographs on the side table, seeing the progression of Rachel from freckle-faced child stiffly posed between dour-faced parents to the laughing woman at David's side. And looking at the photos of Robyn, Bethany and Simon.

'Rachel?' He looked across at her, the knowledge dawning in his brown eyes, his expression deeply shaken. 'Bethany is *your* child, isn't she, not Robyn's?'

She nodded jerkily and he crossed the room, his voice low as he checked towards the door. 'Does she know?'

'Of course she does,' said Rachel fiercely. 'Robyn and Simon have always been honest with her about her adoption. She knows they can't conceive a baby themselves and that I—I couldn't look after the one that *I'd* conceived...'

His eyes darkened with turbulent emotion. 'But, my God, you must have been only—'

'Fifteen,' she said, to save him the calculation. 'The same age that Bethany is now...'

A freckle-faced half-child, half-woman, as delicate and fresh as a half-unfurled bud, thought Matthew.

To Rachel's shock he didn't ask about Bethany's father, or the circumstances of her birth. Instead he touched a gentle finger to her pale lips in a gentle salute.

'Congratulations on your wonderful daughter...and on the courage and strength it must have taken you to bring her into the world...'

Her eyes stung as he replaced his finger with a gossamer-light touch of his lips and an admiring whisper.

'Until tomorrow, my brave lioness...'

CHAPTER SEVEN

'WHAT IN THE hell is going on?'

'Frank!' Rachel was startled to see her partner on her front doorstep, a folded newspaper clutched in his fist. After David died their social contact had dwindled sharply, and since she had been working full-time at WSS they rarely met outside the office. She knew Frank usually spent his Saturdays catching up with paperwork, on call for any problems with the weekend roster.

'Uh, come in,' she invited belatedly as he brushed past her. 'Robyn and Bethany have just gone out to say goodbye to Simon's mother—' she began, wondering if he had come to make his farewells.

Frank swung around just inside the door, his fair skin flushed with anger. 'Since when have you been seeing Matthew Riordan?' he interrupted harshly. 'I thought we were supposed to be on the same side? You let me run off my mouth about him—you even agreed that he was a stiff-necked bastard who had it in for us—and now I find out that you two are secretly an item! Do you know what a bloody fool this makes me look?'

He didn't wait for an answer, bulldozing on in a fury. 'I can't believe you let things go this far without telling me. Instead I had to read it in the morning paper along with everybody else!' he spat, thrusting the newspaper under her nose.

Rachel's heart plunged as she took it with shaking fingers. 'What're you talking about? I don't get the weekend papers—'

'I'm talking about that!' Frank's thick finger stabbed forcefully at the article folded uppermost—a few paragraphs under a small photograph of Matt wearing a faint social smile that made him look flatteringly enigmatic. 'It says a lot of crap about your engagement being the result of a "whirlwind romance"— it must have been one hell of a whirlwind since you only met couple of months ago and you always acted like you couldn't stand him. I thought Riordan was supposed to be getting married to some snotty society woman!'

Jolted by his angry crudity, Rachel blinked with eyes that refused to focus, her brain scrambling to sort out the black and white print.

'I—I don't know where they got this—' she faltered.

'I do. I rang the paper as soon as I saw it,' Frank rapped. 'That was a press release from Riordan's publicist. The whole *world* knows you're engaged to the man—didn't you think you owed me even a *hint*?'

His words hit Rachel between the eyes.

The whole world knows you're engaged... What scandal was there in a man playing sex games with his fiancée in the privacy of their own bedroom?

This was how Matt planned to 'neutralise' any blackmail threat? Without even *warning* her?

'But I—this isn't right...'

His blue eyes were pebble-hard. 'You're telling me it's not true?' he snapped. 'That you didn't leap at the chance to investigate him so you could spend more time with your *lover*?'

'I—'

'Where were you yesterday afternoon, anyway? I couldn't get you on your cellphone.'

She remembered the posters in the coronary ward, warning that portable phones could interfere with monitoring equipment. 'I'm sorry. I turned it off and forgot to switch it back on.'

He was quick to pounce on the hint of guilt. 'You were with *him*, weren't you?' And as her flush deepened he swore. 'So it *is* true!'

'I'm sorry, Frank.' She indicated the paper. 'But I didn't know he was going to do this—'

'So that makes it all right? Is there anything *else* you should have told me?'

She had said she wasn't frightened of him, but she hesitated to add further fuel to his blazing fury. She shook her head helplessly and that seemed to uncork the full force of his rage.

'You really think you can have it all, don't you, Rachel? You're living here in Dave's house, on the back of his business, and you're sneaking around with a guy who's threatening everything that Dave and I built up! You didn't utter a peep when I told you about Riordan taking over at KR. Maybe you already knew! I guess sleeping with the enemy means that your loyalty counts for nothing anymore.'

Rachel was winded by his punches. 'This has nothing to do with David. And I haven't slept with Matthew—'

'Oh, been holding out for marriage, have you?' he sneered. 'And now you've had a taste of the high life with Mr Moneybags, I suppose you'd like to conveniently forget Dave ever existed. He always said you were hard-headed and practical—I call it having an eye out for the main chance. But just remember there's no profit in being dead! Ask yourself why, if he was such a crash-hot husband, the first Mrs Riordan topped herself!'

There was more, bitter, personal invective that left Rachel pale and shaken.

'I think you'll find that getting engaged to Riordan and getting him to marry you are two entirely different things. He's

just amusing himself with you. You haven't got the right connections. He may be loaded, but he comes from trash and he
knows it. Men like him always marry up, not down!'

Robyn and Bethany arrived back just as he was delivering
his parting shot, almost bumped off the garden path by his
headlong rush.

'What's his problem?' Robyn watched him roar off in his car
and frowned at Rachel's pale cheeks. 'What's he been saying?'

Rachel managed to summon a thin smile. 'Nothing he hasn't
been thinking for a long time, I suppose. Maybe it was just temper talking,' she said generously, trying to put the ugly accusations into perspective. 'I always knew he didn't think I was
good enough for David; I just didn't expect him to throw it up
at me again after all this time. I thought we'd at least learned
to respect each other.'

'I never did like Frank very much,' said Robyn flatly. 'I don't
think he's capable of trusting anyone—he never even trusted
David to decide what was best for himself, did he? It never
occurred to him that his precious brother was *lucky* to find a
woman who loved him as much as you did! What put him in
such a temper, anyway?'

'Uh...' Rachel hid the crumpled newspaper behind her back,
surreptitiously trying to stuff it down the back of the telephone
table.

Fortunately Bethany came up beside her mother and distracted her beautifully by asking Rachel when she was planning to get ready for their promised lunch.

'But I am ready,' protested Rachel, looking down at her white
overshirt, blue boat-necked top and cropped narrow trousers.

Robyn and Bethany looked at each other and rolled their
eyes. 'Oh, no, you're not!' they chorused.

Rachel's strenuous protests fell on deaf ears as they bore her
off to plunder the contents of her wardrobe.

'Hey, I remember this!' said Robyn, discovering the purple

linen halterneck dress with its gauzy see-through jacket pushed to the back of the closet. 'David bought this for you, didn't he?'

'No one wears halternecks anymore,' objected Rachel, eyeing the deep neckline.

'Are you kidding? The retro look is hot. I saw a designer dress like this in last month's *Vogue*,' said Bethany, sealing her fate.

'I probably won't get into it—it always was rather snug...'

If anything she seemed to have lost weight since she had last worn it.

'This is ridiculous. I'm way overdressed,' she grumbled, turning away from the sight of the three of them in the mirror, realising with a pang that it might be a very long time before she had her sister and daughter to chivvy her over feminine fripperies.

'Then we'll all look ridiculous together—we're dressed up too,' pointed out Robyn. 'But I bet Matthew won't think so...' she added smugly.

By the time he arrived Bethany was in a fever of expectation, dashing out to the gate to greet him, coltishly graceful in her multi-coloured slip-dress and white lace cardigan.

'I thought you said there'd be two of them!' she pouted as the chauffeur began to marshal their bags.

'Kale assures me that this thing has a boot like the hold of a 747,' grinned Matt, following her up the path to help with the luggage.

'Ladies...' His eyes politely admired Robyn's classic mint-green ensemble, but lingered on the purple dress with a smouldering pleasure that he made no effort to disguise. This morning his spectacles were narrow rectangles rimmed in silver. He saw her looking at them and adjusted them unnecessarily on his aquiline nose.

'They're not new—I have a whole wardrobe of them,' he said, with a tinge of defensiveness that caused Rachel to hide a smile.

'Vanity, thy name is man,' she said, amused by the chink in his armour. 'Can't you wear contacts?'

He looked even more self-conscious. 'Lenses aren't as convenient when you're not a full-time wearer, and my short-sightedness is only marginal. I simply prefer glasses.'

'Because they make you appear like a mild-mannered intellectual rather than the ruthless competitor you really are?' Something in his expression prompted a leap of intuition. 'Are they part of that cool image you like to project? Do you use them to help fend off some of those society she-wolves, on the principal that girls don't make passes at guys who wear glasses...?'

'Well, the superficial types do tend not to look beyond the face furniture.' His bland reply neither confirmed nor denied the allegation.

'Then they must be dim-witted as well as superficial, because—' She hurriedly cut herself off, but too late for the spark of laughter that lit his eyes.

'What? You find them sexy?' He lowered them on his nose to peer at her over the top of them. 'Do we share a secret fantasy about you seducing a certain seemingly mild-mannered intellectual? Stripping off his spectacles along with his—*oof!*' He doubled over the suitcase that Rachel thrust into his stomach.

'Here, how about flexing a muscle *other* than your tongue!'

'Oh, believe me, I am,' he murmured wickedly, laughing as she flounced away in a flutter of purple.

He managed the heavy suitcase with surprising ease, and Rachel found herself surreptitiously watching the flex of his body as he hefted it over the raised lip of the boot. In cream trousers and a pale jacket over a white shirt with a yellow tie he managed to look both elegant and summery, and she was suddenly glad she had let herself be bullied into wearing something bold. She would need all the help she could get to hold her own against him for the next few hours.

In the bustle of loading there was no chance of taxing him about his press release, but, after making a final check of the empty spare bedrooms and locking up, she managed a brief exchange as they walked back to the limo.

'I need to talk to you,' she threatened under her breath.

He had the audacity to look innocent. 'About?'

'About a certain *engagement*,' she ground out.

'Can you think of any better way to take the heat off us?' he asked in an equally low tone.

The problem was that she couldn't. 'Promise you won't say anything to Robyn?' she hissed, balking as he tried to hand her in to the back of the car.

'Trust me,' he said, with a sweet smile that made her insides do a strange flip. 'I won't say anything to worry your sister.' He slid along the bench seat with her, settling to face Robyn and Bethany and draping his arm along the back of the seat behind her silky head.

Bethany made the most of their luxurious ride, and when they arrived at the restaurant Robyn smirked across at her sister.

'Aren't you glad you dressed up? I told you he'd be taking us somewhere posh!'

The restaurant was an elegant old house set in park-like grounds, and in between the prearranged courses they strolled the gardens, feeding the goldfish in the numerous ponds and admiring the peacocks parading their pride on the jewel-green lawns. Once again, Matthew proved himself capable of disconcerting charm, gently teasing Bethany into feeling comfortable with the formal service and ensnaring Robyn's professional interest and personal sympathy with talk of his father's imminent by-pass surgery, managing to casually drop into the conversation the fact that Rachel had met both his parents. Robyn's attention was also kept busy monitoring the small courtesies Matthew constantly paid to Rachel.

'You know, you should wear clothes like that more often,' he told her, his warm brown eyes enjoying the visual feast she presented. 'You have such a superbly majestic figure it's a shame to swamp it in layers of fabric. And that particular shade is perfect for your colouring; it gives your skin a kind of lustrous glow...'

'David chose this dress for me,' she informed him with a hint of belligerence.

'Then he obviously had excellent taste—in both clothes and women,' he said quietly, with an exquisite diplomacy that made Robyn sigh gustily.

As they progressed through the leisurely meal Rachel was forced to admire his ability to appear to be frank and open while cleverly avoiding contentious issues and retaining firm control of the conversation. She remembered that he had cut his financial teeth in the maverick world of foreign exchange dealing, and now she saw the qualities that had enabled him to excel in those pressure-cooker conditions, to make lightning decisions involving millions of dollars based on calculated risks that sane men would reject as reckless. Since he had assumed the mantle at Ayr Holdings he had relinquished his maverick status to become the epitome of solid conservatism, but now she realised that under that respectable façade the volatile taker of extreme risks still existed, albeit constrained by maturity and experience.

Rachel ate the delicious food and drank the champagne, refusing to dwell on the implications of her sudden insight.

Later, en route to the airport, as she was beginning to tense at the thought of the coming ordeal, Matthew took her hand in his and pressed it against his taut thigh.

'I know Rachel hasn't told you much about us, but perhaps I'd better warn you...'

Rachel's arm jerked, but the strong masculine fingers were too determined to allow her to pull free.

'About what?' asked Robyn, her eyes darting expectantly between them.

'Just that you might be hearing some news from us soon.'

'What news?'

Matthew gave her a limpid smile. 'It would be premature to say. Your sister is a very independent and stubborn female.'

Robyn chuckled back, relaxing again in her seat. 'She is that. She's always been a fighter.'

Matthew's hand tested his jaw. 'I can certainly attest to that,' he said drily. 'I just thought you'd like to know she has someone else on her side.'

'Good—she needs someone. Since Mum and Dad retired to the Gold Coast there's no help from that quarter...not that they were ever much of a support—too busy living their own lives and protecting their precious respectability. And Frank is a dead loss. You should have seen the way he stormed out of our place this morning.'

'Frank Weston came to see you?' Matthew looked sharply at Rachel, taking a shrewd guess as to the reason for his visit, but it was Robyn who answered, telling him about the angry visit that had left Rachel so upset.

'I don't know what he was so furious about, but he had no right to pitch into Rachel about David. He always was a hard-nosed cynic, but you'd think he'd have got over his jealousy by now.'

'Of David?'

Rachel simmered at Matthew's swift curiosity. Did he think she was the type of woman to play one brother off against another?

Robyn burbled on. 'No—of *Rachel* and David—because they were so great together. It's all water under the bridge now, anyway. I told her that he might ease up if she appealed to his sense of justice—told him about all this other stuff she's spooked about at the moment—but of course she won't.'

'All what other stuff?'

'Robyn, no—'

But her sister was in full throttle now as she enlarged on the harassments that Rachel had endured over the past few months and her recently expressed theory that they were part of a deliberate campaign.

Sensing the pressure of his interest, Rachel uttered an inner sigh of relief as the international terminal came into view and

Bethany bobbed up out of the sunroof and began shrieking and waving to her friends as they pulled up in the drop-off zone.

The tedium of the check-in was considerably relieved when Robyn and Bethany were drawn aside from the queue by a uniformed representative from the airline to be told that they had been upgraded to First Class, and given access cards to the hospitality lounge where they could relax in luxury before their flight.

Robyn was the first to twig. 'Matt, did you have anything to do with this?'

'We do a considerable amount of corporate business with this airline,' he admitted with a self-deprecating smile. 'What's the use of having influence if you can't use it on behalf of your friends?'

'First Class!' Robyn hugged her ticket blissfully. 'Now I'm *really* glad we didn't wear jeans and T-shirts!'

Robyn and Bethany were so elated that they were eager to go through to the departure lounge, and after they had browsed through the duty-free shops Matthew sensitively excused himself to give the three females sufficient time for their private farewells.

Rachel bore up well until they reached the departure gate and exchanged final hugs.

Robyn held her snugly close and whispered teasingly in her ear, 'He's a gentleman, Rach, definitely a keeper—don't let him slip through your fingers!'

Bethany exchanged last, tearful words with her excited school friends, and managed a wobbly smile with her hug.

'Be happy,' said Rachel simply, smoothing the blonde hair back from her daughter's clear forehead. 'And don't let your mother drink too much free champagne on the flight.'

'I won't.' Bethany sniffed and looked shyly at Matthew. 'Thanks for the limo and—and...everything!' She went on tip-toe and gave him a quick kiss on the jaw, which he returned with a continental salute on both her tear-stained cheeks that made her blush.

'It was my pleasure,' he said gravely. 'You're a delightful young woman, Beth...and a credit to all your family.'

His subtle phrasing caused her to give him a sudden look of mature comprehension. 'I guess I'll see you again some time, then...' she said.

'I guess you will.'

She glanced again at the woman at his side. 'See you, Rachel...'

'See you...'

'You're allowed to cry, you know,' murmured Matthew, as Rachel turned her back on her last glimpse of the pair and walked stiffly away, shoulders squared and jaw clenched, her long legs eating up the broad expanse of terminal carpet. 'It's considered *de rigueur* at airports.'

'I'm not going to cry,' she denied.

She got into the back of the limo and slid across to the far window, leaving a wide expanse of leather seat between them. As the limo purred back into the flow of traffic she kept her head turned to stare with fierce concentration out of the tinted window. After a few kilometres of thick silence she heard a soft rustle, and a white handkerchief appeared on the edge of her blurry vision.

'Thank you, but I have some tissues somewhere...' Her sight almost totally obscured by her silent stream of tears, she wrestled with the catch on her bag until suddenly it was wrenched out of her hands and thrown onto the opposite seat.

'Dammit, Rachel, just take it!' He forced his handkerchief into her hand, and she startled them both by suddenly twisting her body around and throwing herself against his shoulder in a paroxysm of noisy sobs.

He had unclicked his seat belt to draw near, and now he undid hers so that he could wrap his arms around her trembling torso

and hold her more tightly against his warm chest, uttering soothing reassurances as she wept into his jacket.

'It's OK, it's OK,' he murmured, patting her back, his chin
resting on top of her ruffled head. 'You have a right to cry...'

'I'm always saying goodbye. Everyone always leaves...'

'I'm not leaving. I'm right here. And your daughter is moving on to a new phase of her life, but she'll still be your daughter wherever she is...' She was shaken by a renewed storm of
sobs. 'That's right, let it all out...'

She did, in a series of disjointed little rushes, punctuated
with fresh tears.

'It isn't as if I haven't already let go... I did that when she
was born...before that, even. I—my parents didn't want to know
about the baby—they even tried to stop Robyn adopting her.
But she knew I hated the idea of losing touch completely, and
she so badly wanted a child herself...it seemed like fate. And
then, just after Beth was born, Simon was posted to Hong Kong
for six years.'

'Oh, darling...'

She hastened to dismiss his shocked pity. 'No, no—it was
better that way; it was the exactly right thing to happen.' She
hiccuped between sobs. 'It would have been too confusing otherwise. The clean break gave Robyn and Beth a chance to really bond as mother and child, and it gave me a chance to grow
up. So by the time they came back to New Zealand to live Beth
was just like a real niece to me—someone I loved, but more as
an indivisible part of Simon and Robyn than as a part of me...
you know what I mean...?' She was aware of Matt nodding
against the curve of her scalp. 'It all seemed so natural, and Beth
was so secure that she never had any problem knowing that I
was the one who gave birth to her. I've *never* regretted it...not
really—' She choked. 'Robyn is such a terrific mum.'

He cupped her chin and tilted her face up to his so that she
couldn't hide her expression. 'And I bet *you* will be too,' he
told her quietly.

His soft words dropped into the hollow of her heart.

'I'm nearly thirty-one!' she pointed out, her hazel eyes brimming.

'Oh, dear—then you'd better make sure you take a younger lover, with plenty of lusty enthusiasm and stamina,' he murmured, looking down into the deep V of her dress, where her ripe breasts nestled in mouth-watering splendour. 'What a coincidence there's someone on hand who happens to meet the specifications.'

His mouth came down on hers, smothering her squeak of outrage that he should make such a mockery of her pain, but she was swiftly appeased by the steamy pleasure of his soul-deep kisses. His arm tightened around the back of her waist and she angled her mouth against his to give him even greater access, crushing the lapels of his jacket in her eager hands. Her tears dried up completely, her aching awareness of loss replaced by a sense of straining fullness, the temperature in the air-conditioned back seat steadily rising as the limo wound its way back across town.

When Rachel resurfaced, conscious of the sudden cessation of engine vibration, she was aghast to find herself plastered astride Matthew's lap; his hands were burrowed inside her halter, his head thrown back against the headrest, his parted mouth wet with her kisses, his eyes behind his fogged spectacles shut tight and his face drawn into a rictus of agonised restraint.

'Just—don't move for a moment,' he instructed in a stifled voice.

Glancing out of the window, Rachel saw she was back home, and felt a traitorous stab of disappointment as she ignored his plea, pushing away his hands and scrambling frantically off his lap, lunging for the door.

She nearly fell out of the car in her eagerness to alight, and dashed up the path, only to pull up short at the front door when she realised she didn't have her keys.

She turned and found Matthew, walking with preternatural

care, bringing her her bag and the gauzy jacket she had shed some time on the feverish return journey.

He had smoothed down his wildly disordered hair but his eyes still had a hectic glitter behind the silver frames.

Rachel had intended to shut the door in his face, but he was on her heels as she stepped inside, and instead of taking him to task she froze, a prickle running down her spine, her senses swiftly changing focus.

CHAPTER EIGHT

RACHEL FROWNED, and began a swift prowl of the rooms.

Matthew, alert to every nuance of her expression, stuck close. 'What's the matter?'

It took her a little while to figure out why she was getting a feeling of wrongness. 'Someone's been here in the house while we've been gone.'

'Are you sure?'

Rachel adjusted a file on the desk in the corner of the lounge. 'Things have been moved, doors left in a different position…'

'Maybe Robyn or Beth—'

'No. I rechecked the whole house before we left and I have an excellent visual memory.' She pushed in a drawer of the desk that wasn't quite closed and shivered. 'Nothing too overt, but someone's definitely been in here, going through my things. I know it. I can *feel* it.'

He didn't deride her intuition, as Frank would have done. Instead he insisted she go through the house with him again, pointing out the subtle evidence, discovering the slight rearrangement of clothing in her drawers. 'Whoever it was has

done a very neat job,' he commented. 'Can you tell if anything
is missing?

'There doesn't seem to be,' she said, nibbling her lower lip
and finding it embarrassingly tender. 'There's no sign of a
forced entry-point, either, so it's not a run-of-the-mill B&E; it
has to have been a skeleton-key job...'

'You don't have an alarm?' He frowned.

She shrugged. 'We don't get much crime in this area—it's
a friendly neighbourhood—and, anyway, I don't have a great
deal of stuff worth stealing—the computer, the microwave and
video are usually first to go in a burglary, but it looks as though
they haven't even been touched.'

'Probably not a burglary, then. Someone looking for something else? Do you keep any of Westons' security-sensitive
stuff here?'

'Certainly not—Frank's very strict about that kind of thing.'

'What about this mysterious harasser Robyn was talking
about? Could he or she have turned to stalking?'

'It simply doesn't fit the pattern—all the other things have
been impersonal ways of getting at me from afar, without running any risk of a face-to-face confrontation.'

'Then what *is* worth someone running that sort of risk for?'

The thought struck them both at the same time, and Rachel
rolled away her computer chair and hauled out her briefcase,
which she had shoved to the back of the tunnel under her desk.

'The photographs—' she said in dismay when she knelt down
and unsnapped the case. She sat back on her haunches. 'They're
gone!'

Matthew swore. 'So it could very well have been our blackmailer.'

'But no one knew I had them! Except *you*...'

His eyes kindled. 'Are you accusing me of paying someone
to toss over your house while we were making out on the back
seat of my Dad's car?'

His phrasing was deliberately designed to make her blush,

but she refused to give him the satisfaction. 'No, of course not,' she said weakly, rising back to her feet.

'I know you don't really trust me yet, but at least credit me with *some* sense of morality,' he scolded her, before turning back to the immediate problem. 'Since our engagement was announced maybe whoever it is needs to urgently find out what's *really* going on between us. And, since my residences are pretty well impregnable, the logical place to troll for stray information on our relationship would be here. The fact part of the evidence has been retrieved might indicate our blackmailer is getting cold feet. Thank God you keep that unfortunate note I wrote to you close to your heart—'

'It's in my *wallet*,' she corrected him sharply.

He grinned. 'I was speaking figuratively,' he soothed.

'Well, there was nothing else to be found, so I doubt whoever it is will come back,' murmured Rachel, wrapping her arms around her waist. The late afternoon was edging into evening, and soon she would have to start thinking about her solitary meal. She lifted her chin. She probably wouldn't feel like anything much after their superb four-course lunch. Maybe just a boiled egg in front of the TV...

Matthew was observing her contradictory body language. 'Not that it matters, because, friendly neighbourhood or not— you're not staying here,' he announced. 'Not tonight, anyway. And preferably not until we arrange to have the locks changed and a decent alarm installed.'

Rachel tossed her head, her eyes flaring with pride. 'I'm not scared!'

'Maybe not, my dear lioness, but *I* am,' he said with rueful truth. 'If anything happened to you I'd feel responsible, and I have enough on my conscience. I'm not prepared to leave you here alone, Rachel, and that's that! And if you're honest you'll admit you don't really want to be by yourself tonight, either. You're staying with me.'

Honesty hadn't had a hell of a lot to do with allowing herself to be persuaded into his unnecessarily protective custody, Rachel thought to herself later, as she lay in a huge bath of bubbles in one of the upstairs bedrooms of his country fortress. The real truth was that she had craved more of those mind-blowing kisses, and in that she had been severely disappointed for Matthew had suddenly become as virtuous as a priest.

After entertaining her with a detailed tour both inside and outside his house that would have done credit to the impersonality of a real estate salesman, Matt had urged Rachel to have a swim while he prepared another of his delicious light salads, this time with shrimp, for their evening meal. He had served it with a crisp white wine and kept the conversation innocuous, and then, leaving the dishes in the sink for the housekeeper to deal with the next morning, had pleaded pressure of work and gone through a stack of papers while Rachel had curled up on the other end of the couch and tried to concentrate on a borrowed book, sipping her way through another glass and a half of wine.

She had felt all her senses humming by the time he had closed the last folder, only to find herself confronted by a masculine yawn and a polite goodnight that had shunted her off to her room...alone. There her thoughts had grown oppressively melancholy, until she had banished them by mentally weaving a series of passionate fantasies which she now had an urgent desire to turn into reality.

Stepping out of her bubble bath and patting herself dry on the huge dark green bath-sheet, Rachel reached for the sexy knee-length white satin chemise that Robyn had given her as a thank-you present that morning. It had looked quite modest in the box, but, looking at herself in the mirror, she realised that the slinky fabric concealed yet cleverly revealed the peaks and valleys of her body, sliding against her skin with every breath, the tips of her breasts showing as sharp points against the pearly satin.

She smoothed down the sides with trembling hands, a little tingle shooting through her as her fingers encountered her silky thighs through the daring slits that reached almost to her hip. She had had just enough wine to free her from nervous inhibition, and more than enough to dispel any niggling fear of rejection. She ached with a deep-seated need that Matt was destined to appease.

He hadn't told her where his own room was—a glaring omission which Rachel refused to consider a deterrent. Her feet bare, she embarked on her quest through the maze of quiet, carpeted hallways on the upper floor, her figure shimmering like a ghost in the pale rays of the silver moon which shone down through the strips of patterned glass in the ceiling.

When she finally saw the mellow glow of an electric light spilling out through a half-open door, Rachel ventured in without knocking.

'You said I wouldn't want to be by myself tonight, and you were right...'

Matt, clad only in his cream trousers, his belt unbuckled, whirled around from the low mirrored bureau, his unshielded eyes flaring with shock. He threw the towel he was holding onto the dark-covered bed and strode towards her.

'Dammit, Rachel, what are you doing here?' His voice was hoarse as his gaze slid over the waterfall of satin to focus briefly on the rippling V where her thighs met before racing back up to her face. Even without his glasses he could still recognise trouble when he saw it. 'If I'd already turned on the motion sensors the security board would be lit up like a Christmas tree right now!'

'But you hadn't. You knew I might be lonely,' she said huskily, and reached out to walk her fingers up his naked chest. 'You told me I shouldn't be alone tonight...'

He caught her wrist. 'Don't do that,' he ordered roughly.

'Why not?' With her other hand she touched his flat nipple. It was hot, dry and beaded instantly under her touch. She felt a surge of reckless pleasure. 'Isn't this what you expected when you brought me here?'

'For God's sake.' His fingers manacled both her wrists, holding them out to her sides. 'Not now, not like this…'

'Like what?' she asked, moving forward so that the front of her thighs brushed his and her satin-tipped breasts settled against his skin. She bent her knee, excited by her own daring, allowing it to nudge between his muscle-locked legs. She lifted her face and touched her tongue to the ridge of his jaw, tasting his tangy male flavour.

'When?' she murmured seductively. 'When will you make love to me, Matt?' The lighting was sensuously low, and the simple functionality of the room spurred her imagination. 'I want you to love me here, now…on the bed, on the bureau, on the floor—I don't care,' she purred. 'I just know we can make each other feel good…'

'Rachel—' He groaned as she tasted him again, sipping and nibbling at the dark stubble on his chin, pushing closer and rubbing herself wantonly against his stiff body. 'Dammit, I promised myself I wasn't going to let this happen,' he gritted. 'I should never have let you drink the rest of that wine, but I thought it might help you relax…'

'I'm relaxed,' she whispered against his mouth, insinuating her leg further between his. 'I'm not drunk, I know what I'm doing…'

'It's night, your biorhythms are low, your emotional defences are down…and you're missing the people you love,' he said raggedly, pulling his reluctant mouth away from her kiss. 'The feel-good bit is just an illusion—it won't last the dawn. You don't really want sex, you want love, and you don't really want *me* to love you; you just want to be close to someone—*any*one—who can fill the emptiness for a while. Don't think I'm not tempted,' he grunted, jerking his hardening body away from her sinuously stroking hips. 'But I won't be used as an emotional substitute—not ever again. I've been used like that once before, and it was sheer hell…'

He shuddered, drawing her hands together, binding them in

an attitude of prayer as he pressed them to his lips. 'I want you to trust me, not resent me for taking advantage of your vulnerability.'

Rachel shook her head fiercely. 'You wouldn't be taking advantage. Do you think I don't know the difference between seduction and force? I know what it's like to be *truly* forced.' She spoke feverishly in her effort to convince. 'That's how Bethany was conceived. I was raped by a drunk—the father of a boy I'd started dating. At first I was too scared and too ashamed to tell anyone, and then I found I was pregnant.

'It turned out that he'd raped other girls, too, even younger than me, and there was a court case during which he died. I was glad! I hated him for what he did, and it took me a long time to learn to trust men again. It also made me very selective about with whom I chose to be sexual.' She swayed against him. 'So if you're my choice then I *must* trust you...'

'Oh, no—oh, God, Rachel...' Matt's eyes were smouldering coals in a face which was suddenly ash-grey. 'I never imagined—I'm so *sorry*...' His voice was racked with a deep torment that seemed to go beyond empathy.

'I had Bethany,' she said, as if it explained her survival, and in many ways it did. 'What goes wrong in our lives doesn't always turn out to be all for the worst.' Desire made her impatient. 'Anyway, what does it matter *why* we want each other tonight?'

'It matters.' He looked painfully shaken, the barrier of his will breached by her honesty, but not broken. 'I can't do this casually. I—Leigh was the first woman I ever loved.'

'I know that—'

'No, you *don't* know. No one really knows how it was with Leigh!' He turned away to pace the room, punching his words out in jagged phrases. 'I had—I was extremely...introverted and awkward around girls as a teenager, but she lived just up the road from us and was kind to me whenever our paths crossed. From the age of seventeen I was wildly in love with her. At least, I thought it was in the cause of love I was keeping myself chaste and true, but now I wonder whether it was just infatuation, intensified by the fact that she encouraged my emotional attachment but kept me physically at arm's length. Then I introduced her to my cousin, and she fell for him like a ton of bricks.'

'Neville?' The spiky relationship between the two men was suddenly explained.

His head jerked in assent. 'Even when I knew they were sleeping together I was still tied up in knots about her. I stayed faithful to her on the strength of our friendship, in the hope that one day she'd realise that it was me she actually loved. Neville didn't have a good track record with women. Whenever they had a row she'd run to cry on my shoulder, and I'd beg her to give him up and marry me——'

'And one day she said yes,' supplied Rachel tentatively, wondering where these raw revelations were leading.

'Oh, yes, she married me—in a fit of despair and pregnant with Neville's baby.' He ran a hand through his hair, his voice sounding unutterably weary. 'Leigh was a nurse—she'd tested positive for HIV after a needle-stick accident, and when Neville found out he couldn't handle it and dumped her. He was terrified of the idea of being infected, or being stuck with a partner with full-blown AIDS, and when she told him she was pregnant he told her to have an abortion. So Leigh finally took me up on my offer. I was young and arrogant enough to think myself her gallant saviour, but she never stopped loving Neville long enough to try and build any sort of real life with me. She was so traumatised by the way she'd lost him she took on his attitude as a kind of self-punishing obsession.'

The long muscles of his arms rippled as he bunched his fists at the memory. 'She went ahead with an abortion without telling me and then decided that I was far too good for her and that she had no right to my love. She'd always been emotionally delicate, but she became an obsessive-ecompulsive, constantly cleaning the house and herself, afraid that she was going to accidentally contaminate somebody else. Her HIV status never changed, but she was convinced she was tainted, unworthy of being happy. She was a nurse, and intellectually she knew that HIV isn't the sentence of doom it once was, but she still couldn't exercise any control over her fears without the help of tranquillisers. Do you know what she wrote in her suicide note? That sometimes just to live is an act of courage, and that hers had all dwindled away...'

'Oh, Matt...' Rachel's throat ached to find the words to ease his pain. When she had researched his background she had read the initial news report of Leigh Riordan's death, which had included a reference to Leigh being Matt's 'childhood sweetheart' and a wedding photo of a slender and fine-boned bride, wearing a gamine smile and looking ethereally young in her fairytale gown. At her side twenty-year-old Matt had appeared touchingly grave in comparison.

'I was only ever a substitute to Leigh, and obviously a poor one at that,' he continued choppily. 'She certainly found no solace in my arms, because she wouldn't let me touch her for most of our marriage, let alone ever make love to her—no matter what precautions I offered to take...'

She had been bracing herself for him to admit that he was also HIV positive, and now Rachel sucked in a sharp breath. 'You mean...?'

He stopped his pacing and stared directly into her stunned eyes. 'I mean that our marriage was never consummated.'

'I—I see...'

'I don't think you do. One way or another—through love, loyalty, or guilt over her death—Leigh has kept me celibate since the tender age of seventeen.' He paused as her hazel eyes widened even more, her lips parting in disbelief. 'The very, *very* tender age...' he drawled significantly.

Rachel felt hot and cold and dizzy, all at the same time. 'I—what exactly are you saying?'

He rubbed his bare chest with slow, distracting strokes. 'Exactly? That far from being the accomplished lover my behaviour so far may have encouraged you to believe, my practical sexual experience is virtually nil. I've never been anyone's lover.'

Rachel tore her attention away from his chest and took an involuntary step back, crossing her arms across her breasts to hug herself in thunderstruck confusion. 'But I...you—'

'Don't worry.' He interrupted her babble with a wry smile that made her even more flustered. 'Virginity isn't catching.'

Virginity? His? This lean, sexy, hard-bodied man she had been fantasising so lustily about was still a *virgin*? Colour poured into Rachel's face as she felt her body react helplessly to the notion, her nipples peaking against her shielding arms and darting thrills radiating through her lower extremities.

'Shouldn't *I* be the one blushing?' he asked, and indeed there was high colour streaking along his cheekbones as he watched her struggle with the arousing concept of his innocence.

'I had no idea...' she murmured inanely.

'I do try and keep that kind of information out of the public domain,' was his dry reply. 'Virginity is not something for which a mature man is traditionally admired. My enemies would have a field-day with their jokes.'

He put his hands on her bare shoulders, toying with the shoe-string straps of the chemise. 'Seeing you in this erotic piece of confection excites me,' he admitted huskily. 'I very much want to make love with you. But I wanted you to know why it's so important to me that there not be any mistake about what you're really feeling. You need to know what you're taking on when you invite me to be your lover. I don't want my first time with a woman to be a one-night stand or a casual fling. For once in my life I want the woman of my desiring to come to me freely— from joy, not from sorrow...'

She bit her lip, torn between fear of the tumultuous emotions his words had aroused and the wild passion urging her to throw caution to the winds and take what she wanted—and worry about having to pay for it later.

Instead of disappointing him, her gnawing teeth, softly furrowed brow and slightly resentful gold stare brought a sultry amusement to his gaze. He smoothed his hands over her elbows and down to the wide swell of her hips, applying enough firm pressure to turn her around to face the way she had come.

'Of course, I expect the sex to be utterly spectacular when we *do* get together,' he murmured in her ear as he gently propelled her to the door, his warm hand curving on her rounded bottom for a final farewell pat. 'So remind me to make sure those motion sensors are switched off; otherwise, when the earth moves for us, we'll have a squad of policemen thundering into our bedroom!'

CHAPTER NINE

RACHEL WAS GIVEN no chance to suffer any morning-after awkwardness from the night before.

Surprisingly, considering the state in which she had finally gone to bed, she had slept dreamlessly and well, to be woken next morning by the kiss of dark-roasted coffee on her nostrils. Opening her eyes, she saw Matt, breakfast tray in hand, sitting himself down on the side of her bed. As she struggled upright against the luxurious stack of fluffy pillows behind her he leaned over to place the light silver tray across her lap.

'Good morning!' he said with shattering cheerfulness.

Still dazed with sleep, Rachel looked down at the crisp strips of curling bacon and a sunny egg, surrounded by triangles of whole-meal toast and garnished with a yellow rosebud. A glass of orange juice stood beside the gently steaming coffee cup. She couldn't remember when she had last been offered the luxury of breakfast in bed.

'I can't eat all this,' she protested automatically, tucking the silk sheet modestly across her breasts.

'I'll help.' Matt casually hitched up the drooping left shoulder-strap on her chemise, and, smiling into her slumberous eyes, filched a piece of bacon, crunching into it with his strong white teeth.

'Did you cook this?' she asked, picking up her fork, trying not to notice how sexy he looked in pale blue jeans and a crisp, white cotton shirt open at the throat. She was in danger of getting sex on the brain!

'Sara did—my housekeeper,' he said. 'I had something earlier—but I've worked up a whole new appetite waiting for you to wake up.' Her fork clattered against her plate as his not-so-innocent smile invited her to speculate on which particular new appetite he had in mind. 'Eat up. We have a busy day ahead of us.'

'We do?' Had he guessed she might wake up with cold feet, appalled by the way she had thrown herself at him?

'Well, a single announcement doesn't an engagement make, you know. If we want to persuade people we're a genuine couple we have to *act* like a proper couple. Fortunately, I've never been flamboyant enough to be of interest to the popular press. My PR man had to offer a serious bribe to get that little titbit about us in yesterday's paper. So if the photos *do* surface I don't think even the tabloids will work up any enthusiasm about some boring businessman's faked-up cavortings with his fiancée...'

Rachel knew when she was being distracted. 'What do you mean, *act* like a couple...?' she asked dubiously.

She found out over the next few days, as all her spare time was reassigned to support the notion of their 'whirlwind courtship'.

First was their Sunday visit to the hospital, where Rachel had to suffer the embarrassment of being fussed over by Dorothy Riordan, who chided her son for having been in too much of a rush to even buy a ring for his new fiancée.

'She couldn't decide which one she wanted,' he lied with a grin. 'She's a hard woman to please.'

'That's not true, Mrs Riordan,' Rachel defended herself vigorously. 'Matt didn't even bother to *ask* me to marry him. He simply *announced* it to the world!'

There—that had wiped the smirk off his face!

Instead of looking properly disapproving, the other woman was amused by her son's sudden chagrin.

'Did he really? What a coincidence—his father did much the same thing when he met me. I must say, it did make for a very exhilarating courtship,' she added reminiscently, observing the crackling tension between the pair. 'As I told you the other day, my dear... Matt can be annoyingly *managing...*'

'I call it being masterful,' he said, to which Rachel answered with an inelegant snort.

'I haven't mentioned it to your dad yet, darling...you know what he's like,' the sprightly lady warned Matt as he prepared to look in on his father. 'I think we'd better leave it until safely after his operation tomorrow, don't you? He's bound to get excited. He still has that crazy bee in his bonnet about...' She nudged Matt aside and lowered her voice to a stage whisper which was clearly audible to Rachel's burning ears. 'About you and *you know who...*'

Matt patted his mother's shoulder with a chuckle. 'It's OK, Mum, Rachel knows all about Cheryl-Ann. And she's more than capable of standing up to Dad if he tries to cut up rough. She might not have the social pedigree he's been touting for, but she has far more enduring qualities. She has the heart of a lion, the strength of an Amazon, the compassion of an angel... all wrapped up in the most gorgeous body I've ever seen!'

'You didn't have to lay it on so thick,' muttered Rachel afterwards. 'You made me sound like a cross between Joan of Arc, Wonder Woman and a Playboy bunny! I hate deceiving your mother like this; she's going to be so hurt when she finds out this is all a pack of lies.'

'Why should she? If our engagement doesn't end up at the altar she'll be disappointed for me, but I know she'd prefer to see us break up than for me to go through another wretched marriage.'

If...? Not *when*? Rachel wondered whether to challenge him on his use of words as he continued.

'I don't want to add to her burden of worry about Dad by telling her my troubles. At least I've been able to find out that Dad never looked at his private mail the day of his heart attack—thank God! With luck our engagement will be all the disincentive our malicious ill-wisher needs to persuade him he's flogging a dead horse...'

To that end, their next visit was to a jeweller's, where Matt told the obsequious salesman that his main requirement was that his fiancée's ring be 'big and bold'.

'Now he thinks you're crass,' murmured Rachel as she left the store with what felt like a huge weight dragging on her finger.

'Nonsense, darling. He only has to look at you to realise what beauty there is in opulence.' To the amusement of passers-by he smothered her huff with a kiss to which she recklessly responded, quieting her conscience by telling herself that she was just playing a part.

'I thought something dainty and small would be all wrong for your hands,' he said, taking her hand as they walked to the Porsche. 'I like this one because it's so unashamedly different. That beaten gold gives it a lovely, barbaric look, don't you think? Like something an Amazon queen might have worn...'

She remembered the strikingly eccentric pieces of art in his house and looked again at the flash of fire on her ring-finger, seeing it not only with her eyes but with her heart. He could have chosen something bland and generic to go with the pretence, but instead he had gone for something that he thought would specifically suit *her*, something eye-catching yet also resonant with a deeper symbolism, a ring that was as sensuous as it was striking.

'I suppose so...' she admitted reluctantly. It wouldn't do

for her to fall in love with something that she knew was only on loan.

Like the man himself...

The ring was a big hit with everyone who saw it, and even prompted a generous apology from Frank.

'I'm sorry I blew my top at you the way I did on Saturday,' he told her after their Monday staff meeting, and Rachel waited for him to add the usual rider which would award her partial responsibility for incurring his wrath. Instead he had rambled on about the pressures he was operating under, saying that he hoped he hadn't damaged their working relationship to the extent that she felt unable to confide in him.

Wary of the tension underlying his affability, Rachel stuck to the cover story which she and Matt had agreed upon. To distract Frank from any inconsistencies she told him about the mysterious intruder at the house, stressing that nothing had been taken.

Frank instantly snapped back into professional mode, demanding to know whether she'd called the police.

'I didn't see much point, since nothing was taken.' She shrugged. Seeking to divert him further, she told him about the string of problems she had been having with the council, the post and the tax department. 'But I don't think they're connected with this latest thing...'

'Hmm...why don't I look into it for you?' he offered, with surprising alacrity and none of the stinging criticism she had been prepared to resent. 'It's the least I can do after the way I carried on. Could be that it's related to some case that's gone through here.' He turned to leave her office before swinging back to add as an afterthought, 'Oh, by the way, I've had to let Max Armstrong go.'

'The new man?' Although Frank usually handled dismissals, he normally discussed them with her first. 'You fired him? But I thought you said he was working out quite well.'

'He had a bit of an attitude problem—you know how stroppy those ex-undercover guys can be. With things as financially uncertain as they are right now we have to make extra sure that everyone's pulling their weight. I didn't fire him; I just explained it was a policy of last on, first off...'

Rachel watched him go, vaguely uneasy. Frank never apologised and rarely explained himself, and just now he had done both!

She remembered Matt saying that a doubtful friend was worse than a certain enemy. She had never felt secure in Frank's friendship, and, thinking back to all the times he had played on her sense of inferiority to get his own way, to how he had only incrementally allowed her access to the business and never encouraged personal confidences, her unease deepened. What had suddenly made him so anxious to stand in her trust? Did he think that she might be persuaded to use her new 'influence' with Matt for the benefit of WSS?

Her distaste for the idea made her sharp when Matt rang to make plans for the evening, but she still found herself coaxed into having dinner with his mother and spending another night under his roof, this time in his city apartment.

'But I'm not sleeping with you,' she stated bluntly, not sure who she was punishing most. Since Matt was the cause of her painfully conflicted feelings, she hoped it was him!

Her attempt to reduce his powerful impact on her to its most basic physical—and therefore manageable—level had backfired. Instead she found herself even more deeply ensnared by the attraction, forced to deal with the real man rather than the fantasy, aware that to fulfil his demand for trust would mean surrendering to the frightening emotions he aroused.

As well as a fear of opening herself up to more hurt, Rachel felt intimated by the awesome responsibility he had handed to her: the knowledge that when they made love she would be initiating him into one of the great pleasures of life.

Of course, I expect the sex to be utterly spectacular...

He had only been teasing, but what if she disappointed him? She had enjoyed a good sex life with David, but it had been nothing spectacular, and he had usually been the one to take the lead.

But even when she was back in her house she no longer found it the peaceful haven it had once been. In a startlingly short time Matt had become all-pervasive in her life. At least she had little time to miss Robyn and Bethany, she thought, as she shuttled between the office, the gym and dates with Matt that she was careful to keep confined to public places—although she made no attempt to avoid the passionate kisses on the doorstep which left them both aching and dissatisfied.

His father had come through his by-pass surgery with flying colours, and Rachel was grateful when his doctor restricted visitors to immediate family only for a further few days. She had a feeling that Kevin Riordan was too shrewd to be taken in by the kind of charade which had convinced his wife, and if he asked Rachel flat-out in front of Matt whether she was in love with his son, she feared she didn't know whether the lie she was supposed to admit would also be the truth she was trying to deny.

On the third evening after the operation, Rachel was waiting on the ward for Matt to finish his visit so that they could go to dinner when she was surprised by a familiar voice.

'I understand that congratulations are in order...'

She whirled around to face the tall, handsome man in a pinstriped suit. 'Neville! I didn't know you were back...'

'Not before time, it seems.' Neville's cool grey eyes were checking out her ring. 'So it's true. I didn't believe that Matthew would risk throwing his hat into the ring again, not when he's still carrying a torch for poor Leigh...'

Rachel didn't think her expression had changed, but the cordial politeness on Neville's flat face congealed.

'Ah, I see he's told you his wife's tragic story. I don't suppose he happened to mention that my mother died of Parkinson's disease? A long, slow degeneration that turned my father into a bitter old man who drank himself to death. I went through hell until I tested free of the Parkinson's gene. I loved Leigh, but I know my own limitations. Sickness disgusts me.' His nostrils flared as he looked around him in distaste. 'I would have been no good to her if she'd got ill. Matt was far better equipped to play the white knight. It was what he'd wanted all along, after all. He still blames me, but how was I supposed to know that Leigh would turn out to be so emotionally unstable?'

Rachel's pity warred with her discomfort. 'I don't think we should be talking about it—'

'Aren't you in the least bit curious to hear the other side of the story?'

'I'm sure Matt will tell me anything I want to know.'

'Are you sure? Oh, he'll tell you everything you could find out from other sources—after all, he knows you run a detective agency—but what about the *really* damning secrets? The ones that *aren't* on any public records...?'

His knowing smile sent a trickle of ice down her spine. 'I really don't think this is the time or place—'

He flicked a glance over her shoulder and picked up her hand. 'Quite right. How about a cosy chat over dinner some time?'

She couldn't believe his audacity. 'No—I—Matt—'

His mouth twisted cynically. 'Lunch, then? Surely he can't object to that?'

'Object to what?' asked Matt, coming up beside them.

Rachel pulled her hand away, flustered when Neville didn't easily let it go.

'Rachel and I were just talking about having lunch. Hope you got my faxes, old boy...thanks for keeping the seat warm for me. How's Uncle Kevin?'

'He's resting,' Matt clipped.

Neville bristled with challenge. 'Are you telling me I can't even see him?'

The two men squared off at each other, then Matt shrugged with impatience. 'Of course not, go ahead—just be aware that he doesn't know about Rachel and I yet...'

'Really? How interesting? *More* family secrets?' Neville's

smile was redolent with meaning as he tilted his head towards Rachel and strolled off down the corridor.

Matt turned to Rachel, his eyes stormy. 'He asked you to lunch? Did you accept?'

Rachel was casually dressed in trousers and a cotton sweater, for they were dining at a waterfront café, but she was wearing high-heeled sandals, and now she was glad of the opportunity to coolly look down her nose at him.

'What do *you* think?'

For a moment his narrow face remained tight with fury, then his bunched jaw relaxed. 'I think I'm being unreasonably jealous.'

'Of me, or of Leigh?' she dared.

His darkened eyes moved over her proud face. 'Oh, definitely of you,' he said softly. 'In spite of that stupid, kneejerk reaction I know you're nothing like Leigh.'

And yet it was Leigh with whom he had fallen so helplessly in love...

She looked in the direction that his cousin had gone. 'Admiration and envy can be quite a poisonous mix. It strikes me that Neville would quite happily cause you trouble if he could. Have you considered that *he* might be behind any attempt at a smear...?'

She found Matt already one step ahead of her. 'I haven't discounted him, though it's not really his style. If the pictures fell into his hands I suppose he wouldn't let the opportunity go to waste, but he'd consider it beneath him to stoop to such methods himself. Nor would he like the idea of being anyone else's tool. His ambitious schemes tend to be more lofty. And I don't see him continuing to target Dad after his heart attack. Apart from the fact he's genuinely fond of my parents, he wouldn't want his spite to reflect back on himself and jeopardise his position in the family. And don't forget he's been in Japan for the past two and a half weeks.'

So...maybe this wasn't a solo effort, she mused. Maybe

he had an accomplice. It was an idea worth following up, she thought to herself as they left the hospital.

The next day she had told Matt she was working late at the gym, but to her dismay he turned up far too early to collect her, looking vastly out of place in his dark suit and tie as he propped himself against an exercise bike and watched her chivvy one of her regulars into adding an extra set of reps to her weights programme. The sight of Rachel in stretch shorts and a cropped T-shirt under her cutaway leotard seemed to afford him endless fascination.

'I exhausted myself just watching you,' he murmured, handing over her towel and water bottle at the end of the session, licking his dry lips as he watched her blot the perspiration from her face and throat. 'You stood over that poor woman like a drill sergeant...'

'That "poor woman" is one of the country's leading aerobics competitors. She *pays* me to make sure she doesn't slack off!'

He looked around the gym. 'You work a full day and then come and do this? And sometimes work in the mornings as well...also at a very physical job? No wonder you nearly fall asleep over dinner some nights.'

He was checking up on her? 'Well, you can't say I'm not fit enough to handle it,' she said, not knowing whether to be flattered or insulted. She flipped the towel over her shoulder, hoping he hadn't noticed her nipples beginning to show through her exercise bra and damp T-shirt. 'Excuse me, I'm going to have a shower.' She made the mistake of looking over her shoulder as she left, and found his eyes fixed on the rolling flex of her bottom in the thin Lycra shorts.

Later, as she devoured a chocolate mousse to replace some of the calories she had worked off, he returned to the topic. 'Tell me, Rachel, when do you get any spare time for yourself? I notice Frank Weston doesn't have to moonlight to make ends meet. You shouldn't have to hold down more than one job to survive.'

'And I wouldn't have to if you gave Westons the KR contract,' she said facetiously. She noticed *he* had no problem appropriating her precious spare time! 'How about it?'

'Only if you agree to sleep with me first,' he responded with equal sarcasm.

He was so confident that she was joking! On the one hand it was infuriating; on the other it indicated a complete faith in her integrity.

'Fine! Let's do it!'

She had the pleasure of seeing him winded. 'Fine? What do you mean—*fine*?'

'I accept your offer. It's a deal!'

He recovered quickly. 'You know damned well I don't have the power to do any such deal,' he growled. 'Nor do I want it. Neville's back, thank God—it's his decision. I want nothing to do with it.'

She looked at him through her lashes. 'What if I agree to sleep with you anyway?'

He stilled, staring across the table. 'Do you mean that?'

She hesitated, and nodded.

He let out a rough sigh of pent-up frustration. 'Hold that thought! You do choose your moments, lioness... I'm flying to Sydney on the red-eye tomorrow morning.'

Rachel's reckless heart felt as if it had been plunged into ice.

'Only for a few days,' he added swiftly, and her heart shuddered back into life. 'I've already postponed this meeting twice over the last couple of weeks, and now that Dad is out of the woods I can't put it off any longer. But I'll be back for your birthday.' He leaned forward, placing his hand over hers on the table and gripping it hard. 'I look forward to resuming this discussion when I get back...'

Discussion? What was there left to talk about? A panicked sense of urgency made Rachel wish that he would simply whisk her straight back to his bedroom for a quick consummation, but the knowledge that he would be walking out of the door before dawn put the brakes on her impatient desire. No more than he did she want this first time to be a snatched interlude that would set the scene for future brief encounters. When she made love to him she wanted to do so at leisure, with no distractions, anxieties or interruptions...

The next three days were merely a confirmation of what she had already suspected. They were flat and colourless and she missed Matt more than she would have believed possible. She tried to fill some of the emptiness by putting in overtime at Westons, checking up on Neville, who proved disappointingly clean, and digging into some of the back files that yielded some unexpected and unsettling results.

Matt rang each night for long, lazy chats, but the conversations were inherently unsatisfying as Rachel struggled not to blurt out her newly discovered feelings. It was too late to worry about being hurt, but she wanted to see him, touch him, look into his eyes before she surrendered her wary heart completely into his keeping.

Typically there was only a briefly inscribed card from her parents on her birthday, but there were e-mails, cards and a gorgeous Thai-silk suit from Robyn and Bethany, and at the office she was given a cake and a group-signed card ribbing her about wrinkles.

Having no appointments at the gym, she'd expected the evening to lag as she waited for Matt's flight to get in, secretly hurt by the fact that he had refused her offer to greet his plane. But as she was preparing to leave work Lannie came dashing breathlessly into her office to tell her that a limo driver was asking for her.

Thinking it was one of their security chauffeurs, Rachel was disarmed when she was handed an armful of red roses and a sealed note in memorable green ink.

Go with Kale. He knows what to do. Happy Birthday.

Kevin Riordan's chauffeur professed ignorance as he led her out to the car and placed a glass of champagne in her hand for the mystery ride, but Rachel soon discovered to her amusement and delight that their destination was Auckland's most exclusive beauty clinic. There she was treated to a sinfully sybaritic experience—bathed in mud, wrapped in towels, soaked in a spa, plucked, waxed, massaged in oils, given a facial, a hairdo, a manicure, a pedicure—and generally wallowed in the sensuous luxury of top-to-toe pampering. Like a harem girl being prepared for her master, she thought with a giggle.

She emerged tingling with vitality and filled with a glorious sense of physical well-being that increased when Kale informed her that his instructions were to take her home to change and then on to Matt's country house for dinner.

Matt's face, as he opened the door and saw her standing there in her new peacock-blue silk suit, her glowing cheeks flushed with excitement and her hazel eyes alight with warm pleasure, reassured her that she was making the right decision. This man was not one she wanted to let get away!

'Happy Birthday. You look even more gorgeous than I remember,' were his first words, his glittering gaze taking in the short, narrow skirt and fitting, short-sleeved jacket with its stand-up collar and an array of tiny silk toggles marching down her front.

'Thanks to Robyn—she sent me this,' husked Rachel, fiddling nervously with a toggle under his wildly flattering gaze. In blue-black trousers and shirt, his hair still damp from a shower, he made her knees weak. 'And thanks to you. It was a wonderful present. I've never been to a beauty spa before; it was a totally new experience...'

The flames leapt in his eyes at her gratifying admission. His arm snaked around her waist and he pulled her inside, kicking the door shut on the world as his mouth came down on hers. 'I'm glad. I want to give you lots of wonderful new experiences,' he murmured, rediscovering the silky contrast of textures inside her mouth.

As she followed him through to the room where he had first entertained her she noticed him discreetly rotating his left shoulder and wincing.

'What's the matter with your arm?'

'The taxi was involved in a slight accident on the way to Sydney airport.'

'My God, were you hurt?' asked Rachel anxiously.

'I just jolted my shoulder against the seat belt. Actually, I think the stiffness is more a build-up of tension from having to use my laptop exclusively for the last few days...'

All the blood rushed to Rachel's head. 'Why don't you let me help you with that?' she heard herself say.

'Help me how?' he said, crossing to the cabinet on which an ice-bucket now reposed.

'Give you a massage...for your shoulder,' she said steadily.

He halted and turned. His chest rose and fell under the dark shirt. 'Are you offering to take my pain away?'

She moved closer, deliberately taking his words at face value. 'If you're over-tense it's the perfect way to ease your muscles into relaxing—I should know; I've just had one myself. Of course it means putting yourself in my hands—'

'I rather think I've done that already.'

'But I *am* fully trained.'

His nostrils flared, the skin on his face tightening as his eyes fell from her lustrous eyes to her smudged lips and her silk-sheathed breasts. I—dinner is almost ready,' he said reluctantly.

She had never felt less hungry in her life. 'Is it anything that can't wait?'

'You mean like a soufflé?' His sultry smile was crooked. 'No, nothing that can't wait...all night long, if necessary.'

Her smoke-coloured eyelids drooped. 'It might well take all night...if you're especially stiff...'

His face flushed. 'I'm sure I'm going to be a very difficult and demanding case...' he murmured thickly. He looked around the room. 'Where do you want to do it? The couch?'

She shook her head as she tried to tamp down her excitement. 'Too soft—not enough support.' She pretended to consider the other furniture in the room before turning her golden gaze to his. 'The bed in your room looked fairly firm...'

She saw his hard throat move as he swallowed. 'Yes, it is.'

'Well, then...' She held out her hand with a glittering smile. 'Shall we go?'

'Just a moment.' He snagged the ice-bucket containing a bottle of champagne and two glasses. 'In case we get thirsty,' he told her as he took her hand, and fairly raced her up the stairs.

'The way you're jostling it, that champagne is going to fizz over when you try to open it,' she warned as they arrived breathless in his bedroom.

'That makes two of us,' he muttered under his breath as he set the ice-bucket down beside the bed and switched on the lamps. He removed his spectacles and swung eagerly towards her. 'Now what?'

She moistened her lips. 'Now you take off your shirt. Have you got any lotion I can use?'

'I'll have a look.' He walked towards the bathroom, dragging open his buttons as he went.

'In fact, take all of your clothes off,' ordered Rachel daringly as he clicked on the light. 'It'll be more comfortable for you that way.'

There was no sound from the bathroom for long moments, and she was about to investigate when he stepped out.

She sucked in a shaky breath. He was wearing nothing but a small white towel wrapped low on his lean hips, pulling tightly across his strong thighs and exposing a vertical strip of bare skin where the two ends only just overlapped. He stood for a moment, letting her look her fill, revelling in her smoky-eyed approval. Then his muscles meshed smoothly into motion, his skin gleaming like dull satin in the lamplight, as he prowled towards her and handed her a slim bottle of skin moisturiser, and something else.

'You might find some use for this, too,' he said, wrapping her fingers around the small foil packet.

She blushed when she opened her hand and saw what it was. 'I—yes, I probably will,' she stammered.

'You started this game, honey,' he purred. 'Maybe you're not quite as brazen as you want me to think you are.'

She tossed her head and strode to the bedside, placing the condom down beside the bottle of champagne. With a flourish she ripped back the navy covers and threw them to the bottom of the bed. 'Face down on the bed, please.'

He paused with one knee on the edge of the mattress, putting the towel to indecent strain and revealing a flash of dark hair against the pale skin of his groin. 'As I recall, the last time you invited me to have a massage I ended up tied to the bed.'

'Lie down, please,' she said sternly, sliding a pillow under his shoulders as he settled on his stomach, his face turned towards her on the white sheet.

Her hands went to the zip at the back of her waist and she watched the ripple of tension invade his entire body. 'What are you doing?'

'I don't want to get any lotion on my new skirt.' She took it off and placed it—neatly folded—on the bureau.

He gave a tortured groan when she strolled back to stand by the head of the bed. 'You wicked *tease*...'

She smoothed a finger down the white lace suspender that secured her gauzy stocking, and back up to the high-cut side of her white silk thong. 'Not at all. It's a matter of practicality,' she lied. 'Stockings are much cooler than pantyhose in the summer.'

'What about your top?' he said slyly. 'You don't want to get lotion on that, either.'

'I think I'll leave that on...for now.' She poured lotion on her hands and stroked them together in front of his fascinated gaze, hoping he would not notice that they were trembling.

Instructing him to fold his arms out to his sides, she leaned over and placed her hands against the nape of his neck, just below the occipital bone. It didn't take her long to identify the congested bands of muscle, and she began to use long strokes to create a deep friction that made him moan with pleasurable pain. Progressing slowly over his back with a gradually increasing pressure, she bent into her work, enjoying the sensuous slide of her thumbs as they dug into the pressure points and worked out the tightness on either side of his spine.

'Oh, God, that feels good!' he muttered.

'I haven't even *begun*,' she promised throatily, her hand going to his towel.

He tensed as she dragged it off, and uttered a hiss of shock as she climbed onto the bed, straddling his naked thighs and beginning to knead his clenched buttocks, hooking her strong fingers deeply into the gluteal muscles. He buried his face in the sheet, uttering another groan, his arms contracting around the pillow under his chest.

She admired him with her hands as well as her eyes, free to gloat over her enticing prize. He was so wonderfully, indisputably *male*, his skin so fine-grained as it curved over the flexing muscle, and lightly dusted with a mist of dark hair that vanished into the intriguing crease between his buttocks. She traced it lightly with one very unprofessional finger.

Sweat broke out on his back. 'Oh, God, Rachel, what are you doing to me...?'

'Shh,' she murmured, as she pushed the heel of her hand against the swell of his buttock and began to rock against his hip with her full weight. 'I think you have some serious chronic tension here...let me see what I can do to relieve it...'

'I can tell you, you're making it ten times worse!' he groaned as she continued to stroke him, compressing his hips rhythmically into the bed. 'Much more of this and I'm in danger of exploding like that champagne bottle!'

He reared up when he felt the warm press of lips in the hollow at the base of his spine and the moist flick of a tongue. 'I bet that's not in any damned massage manual,' he gasped.

'It's in *my* manual,' murmured Rachel, propping herself over him on her hands and knees as she kissed her way slowly up his long spine. 'My love manual,' she teased. 'Turn over,' she whispered in his ear, before easing aside to let him make the move.

'I hope you're prepared to take the consequences,' he said, rolling boldly onto his back. His colour was high, his eyes challenging as he watched her assess the bold thrust of his manhood, jutting from the dark fur in his loins.

'Oh, yes...' Rachel felt a gush of heat between her legs. With a rough sound Matt grabbed her by the arms and pulled her down against his chest.

'Aren't you going to finish what you started?' he demanded, dragging her thighs on either side of his and wedging her tight against the thrusting boldness. He slid his hand up into her hair and tugged, guiding her mouth down to his, biting kisses against her soft lips as he said harshly, 'I love the feel of your hands on me...your mouth...your body...everything about you. I want everything you have to give...'

She struggled upright, feeling the thick heaviness of him butting against the fragile silk thong, aware of the musky scent of his arousal mingling with the sharp fragrance of the lotion she had massaged into his back. She squirmed against him, frantic with excitement, driving herself closer to the very edge of sensual endurance. Her head tipped back, her eyes closing as she stroked his chest, overflowing with love and longing, not caring that she was no longer playing her part. She wanted him, she loved him, she didn't want to wait any longer to make herself irrevocably part of him...

'Isn't it time for you take off your jacket?' he wondered, and she drew his hand to the lowest toggle.

'Here, you do it...'

He was clumsy, too eager. 'These are too little...my hands are shaking like crazy...'

'So are mine.' She showed him, laughing down at him as he fumbled at his task.

He laughed exultantly back. 'You can't be more nervous than I am.' He pulled apart her jacket at last and uttered a choked sound. 'I think I've died and gone to heaven—what *is* this piece of confectionery?' He explored the boning that shaped her body, up to the glory of her breasts, spilling over the top of the frothy lace, the blue veins prominent against the translucence of her skin.

'A basque. It laces down the front, see…'

'Oh, God, more fastenings…' Their fingers tangled together as she impatiently assisted, and as the delicate structure slid away in a tangle of ribbons and lace they both sighed in mutual delight.

'Glorious…all the woman I could ever want…' he murmured, gathering her up in his cupped hands and burying his face in her abundance.

Her hands clasped his head and she cried out as his seeking mouth found her straining nipple and drew on it with hungry fervour, drinking in the richly feminine flavour of her velvety-soft skin.

'Such a delicious mouthful…' He grazed to her other breast, and suckled there, too, drawing out her nipple with his teeth until it throbbed with delicious agony.

She sobbed. 'Matt—'

'What—am I hurting you?'

'No, oh, no—'

'Good…' his mouth surrounded her nipple again, lashing it with his tongue '…because I don't think I can stop…'

His hands reached down to touch the pouting plumpness between her legs. 'Oh, God, you're so wet here…and swollen…' He insinuated his fingers under her thong to torture her with his passionate curiosity, and she twisted frantically so that she could free herself from the last impediment to their lovemaking. As she kicked away the scrap of fabric he shuddered at the settling of her scalding heat against his pulsing erection.

He rolled over on top of her with a hoarse cry, crushing her breasts against his chest as he positioned himself heavily between her thighs, his hair-roughened skin rasping against her smooth stockings. He snatched the small packet from the bedside and cursed as he failed to get it open. In the end Rachel had to do it, but he wouldn't let her help him put the condom on. In a thick voice he told her bluntly that if she touched him like that it would be all over.

The waiting intensified the desire, and soon she was dipping into his mouth again with her tongue, her nails digging into his scalp as she felt his explorative touch parting her intimate folds and his hips jerk as he tested himself against her tight sheath.

'Am I hurting you?'

She felt a delicious stretching, but no pain, and she shook her head on the pillow. Matt raised himself up on one arm, gazing triumphantly down into her passion-blurred face. 'Now...' Looking deep into her eyes, he took her hand and pushed it down between their steamy bodies to cup his virility. 'Show me...take me...' He used her fingers to guide him inside her. 'I want to feel everything you feel. I want it to be you and me, together, every step of the way...' He eased slowly forward, gritting his teeth and shaking with the effort of restraining himself, until she wound her legs around him and deliberately unleashed his most primitive urges, the violent series of penetrating thrusts that shattered their separate selves and fused them into a single, sensual being.

And, true to his naive expectations, the resulting mutual pleasure was utterly spectacular!

CHAPTER TEN

WAKING UP NEXT to the man you loved was, Rachel discovered next morning, one of life's most joyous delights. She'd thought Matt had sated himself on his exhaustive exploration of new-found pleasures and would be bound to wake sluggish and heavy-eyed after a long night of vigorous physical activity.

She was wrong.

When her eyes fluttered open he was already lying on his side, propped up on one elbow on the sunlit bed, his gaze bright with curiosity as he watched her lazily shift her shoulder-blades against the firm mattress and wake herself with a low, slow stretch that ended in a soft groan at the pleasant pull of aching muscles. Either he or their nocturnal stirrings had pushed the sheet that was their only covering somewhere down around their hips, and he was clearly enjoying the voluptuous visual extravaganza.

'You're insatiable,' she groaned, correctly interpreting the gleam in his eye.

'You're the one who made me that way,' he said with a grin, noticing that she made no effort to draw up the sheets. 'It's rude to watch people while they're sleeping,' she murmured, basking in his admiration.

'I haven't got my glasses on; I can't see a thing,' he lied boldly. He stroked her bare arm where it lay against her side, his knuckles brushing against the relaxed swell of her breast, burnished by a shaft of early-morning sunlight. 'You're very still when you sleep—no shifting, no twitching or sighing... just pure, unadulterated peace.'

'Which you've been longing to disturb,' she teased.

'Fair's fair. You've been disturbing *me* just by lying there!' He bent to brush his lips over hers. 'I woke up wanting you.' He deepened the kiss and broke it off slowly, in juicy little bites. 'I woke up imagining that we were still making love, that your gorgeous wet mouth was doing those wicked things to me that made me scream myself hoarse—'

She was suffused by a wave of delicious embarrassment. 'Matt!'

'What? Don't you like to talk about it? You had plenty to say last night. 'Not there, Matt!' 'Do it like this, Matt'.'

Her giggles burst like sweet honey on his tongue. 'I didn't! You didn't seem to need much instruction.'

'Mmm, I was responding to a very basic instinct.' He nibbled down the side of her throat and over the top of her breastbone. 'I obviously have a natural talent for pleasing you.'

'And yourself,' she pointed out, shifting so that her breasts moved enticingly within his area of interest.

'Oh, no, that's entirely your doing.' He blew experimentally on her soft pink nipples, a warm, moist zephyr that caused them to pucker and rise eagerly from the surrounding creamy flesh. He rewarded their jaunty salute to his authority with a soft rain of kisses around the dusky areolae. 'You make love the way you do everything else—with courageous strength and a fiery spirit.'

His ardent praise ignited the passionate sizzle of her senses into a blazing conflagration. 'You mean like this?' she said, kicking away the sheet and rolling over to mash herself against his length.

He growled, and they wrestled across the bed, Rachel somehow ending up easily overpowered and pinned facedown beneath him. He grunted as she arched her spine, pushing her wriggling bottom into his groin.

'Why, you *let* me win, didn't you? You little cheat,' he panted in realisation as she pushed up on her knees, his voice thickening with excitement as he recognised the erotic potential of her submissive position. 'Do you want me to take you like this? Is that it?' he murmured, stroking her bottom and the curvature of her spine with a possessive hand.

He sank his teeth into her shoulder, gently holding her captive as he reached for the replenished supply of protection beside the bed. His chest braced her back, his hands slipping underneath her, one to fondle her swaying breasts, the other to splay across her taut belly, adjusting her to his thrust as he discovered a new and intensely pleasurable thrill to add to his expanding repertoire.

Afterwards he took her in his arms and kissed her damp forehead. 'I thought you might not like the feeling of being sexually dominated like that,' he said, explaining the constraint that he had shown through the dark hours of the night, when he had proved eagerly experimental in most other ways.

She tilted her head back and looked at him with clear eyes. 'You mean because of the rape?'

A painful tautness entered his body, his irises darkening with a haunting uncertainty. 'I know it's not a trauma you'll ever be able to forget or forgive.'

'No, but time is a great healer. I learned that to keep yourself safe doesn't mean to bury yourself out of the way of life.'

Responding to his tender concern, she lay in the safety of his embrace and told him all about the ugliness of the rape, the bitterness it had created with her parents, the pain and joy of bearing an illegitimate child.

She sensed his silent search for words and wondered if she had misinterpreted his compassion. She tried to ease herself out of his embrace. 'But I suppose some people might think I'm tarnished for life—death before dishonour and all that...'

He was swift to disabuse her. 'Oh, no! God, Rachel, no—you can't believe I'd think that of you. Still affected by it, yes—tarnished, *never*!' His hands tightened around her back as he said grimly, 'In fact, if either of us is tainted by the past, it's me—'

Her hand over his lips stopped the words in his mouth. 'Don't. It doesn't worry me that you had a wife with HIV,' she said, assuming he was talking about Leigh. 'You've always been honest with me, and I know you wouldn't put me in danger. I've worked around health professionals—I'm not susceptible to scare mongering.'

'Rachel—'

'The past is the past. It's what we are *now* that matters.' She didn't want to mention the future—that seemed, as yet, too fragile.

'And what *are* we?' He smiled wryly, accepting her philosophy with a mixture of reluctance and bitter relief.

One step at a time, she told herself. 'Why, lovers of course!' she purred.

A ping sounded from the bedside table and she peeped over his shoulder at his electronic watch and sighed. 'I think it's time we got up.'

'I've been up all night,' he said, grinning.

He looked so splendidly cocky he made her laugh. 'I hope you're not going to be this insufferably self-satisfied all day!'

'Of course I'm not; now I have *you* to satisfy me, I don't have to rely on myself,' he said with a leer.

When she swatted him a stinging reproach on his bare chest he chased her into the shower, which delayed them another half-hour.

Over a rather rushed breakfast, he said, 'You know, watching you at the gym, it occurred to me that we could do with some sort of corporate fitness programme at Ayr Holdings. We have a fully-equipped executive gym, and someone to oversee the equipment, but no one providing expert help or supervised workouts. How about it? Would you be interested in submitting a proposal?'

Rachel stared at him over her coffee. 'Me? But I already have too many jobs, remember?'

'In fact I know quite a few companies that might be interested in sponsoring employee fitness programmes,' he went on. 'It could be the basis of a whole new career for you.'

'I *have* a career: at Westons,' she stressed. 'Why else have I been struggling to learn the trade, working for virtually nothing in an effort to help salvage David's dream—'

'*David's* dream,' he picked up. 'Not yours?'

'Not at first, but now—well, it's opened new doors for me. The work is always challenging, always different.'

'As long as you're sure.'

She drank her coffee. 'You're as bad as Frank. He worries I'm not serious about it, either. Whenever we hit the doldrums he offers to let me bail out if I want to, so I won't be tied to a losing proposition—even though it would be a hardship for him to scrape up the money to purchase my share.'

He studied her thoughtfully. 'That's very generous of him. Ever been tempted to take him up on it?'

'No. I guess he's figured out by now that I'm not a quitter. You wouldn't be making this offer to me because you think it's too down-market for a tycoon like you to have a girlfriend—'

'Fiancée.'

'—who's a security chick, would you?'

'A *security chick*?' He grinned. 'Is that what they call you on the streets? Is that an updated version of a red-hot mama?'

She turned her nose up at him. 'If you're ashamed of what I do—'

He got up from the breakfast bar and kissed her mouth. 'Of

course I'm not. Don't be silly, darling. It was just an idea, that's all. I just want you to be happy.'

'You'll be telling me not to worry my fluffy little head about it next,' she muttered sarcastically, and they both suddenly creased with laughter at the absurdity of the image.

But the disruptive thought returned to trouble her in the heady days that followed, as she fell ever more profoundly in love with the complex man who had brought such unexpected drama and passion into her life.

The emotional intensity of their affair was such that, at times, she believed that Matt's feelings ran as deeply as hers, that even though their love remained undeclared he was as desirous as she to move forward to the next level of intimacy. They talked for hours about almost every aspect of their lives, and made love with impassioned ardour, but at other times Rachel's heightened sensitivity to his moods made her aware of an element of reserve in Matt, a waiting quality that erected an invisible barrier which she was afraid to broach for fear of what lay behind it.

She thought it might be because of his father, who had thrown the expected tantrum when he had been told that his fully-grown son had got himself unofficially engaged to someone who was not on his list of approved political assets. Rachel had weathered her first encounter with the post-operative Kevin Riordan with a gutsy good humour that had gained his grudging respect, but when she taxed Matt afterwards about whether she should stay out of his family's orbit, in order not to create a further rift between father and son, he was adamant in his refusal.

'My love-life is none of his business. Dad never had a hope in hell of breeding me to some dippy debutante and he knows it. He never wanted me to marry Leigh, either...'

Rachel forbore to point out that his father's negative attitude had been fully justified. Even though no one else had been told about Leigh's HIV status, the Riordans couldn't have escaped knowing that her turbulent affair with their nephew had scarcely come to an end before she'd rushed to the altar with Matt.

'He thinks I'm too old for you, as well.' "Not enough child-bearing years left" was the delicate way Kevin Riordan had actually put it!

'It's a wonder Mum didn't brain him with his bedpan—seeing she's three years older than him herself!' Matt said wryly. 'He's just blowing smoke in your eyes, Rachel, like he was with all that rot about my shining political future. He knows I have no interest in public office, but it pleases him to pretend to his pals that he's a potential king-maker.'

He took her in his arms and kissed her. 'Stop worrying so much about what other people are thinking. We both know that life is too precious to waste storing up grief for ourselves—let's just enjoy what we have while we have it...'

That sounded ominously like a warning against building castles in the air, and a few days later Rachel's nebulous doubts and fears were given a devastating credibility.

She had arranged to meet Matt after work at his apartment, for which he had given her a key, and, having brought some paperwork to work on until he arrived, she absently answered the phone when it rang instead of leaving the answer-machine to pick up.

It was Neville Stiller, returning a prior call from Matt letting him know that Kevin Riordan was now convalescing at home.

'I didn't know you two had moved in together,' he probed, when Rachel told him that Matt wasn't home.

'We haven't,' she told him coolly.

'We never did get around to having that lunch...' 'No.'

She didn't say anything else, but he had no difficulty in reading her silence. 'And never will, either, huh? Not even as a thank-you to me for giving you that contract you and your partner have been busting your buttons for?'

She didn't like the implication. 'That was a purely business decision on your part, not a personal favour. You should be thanking us for all the money we're going to save KR Industries over the next two years.'

'Does that mean our lunch is on, after all?'

She rolled her eyes. 'Give it up, Neville, you're just trying to use me to get at Matt.'

'Maybe I'm concerned for you? After all, you haven't known him as long as I have—you probably haven't seen the dark side of his personality yet. Anyone who spent time in prison for rape and then had a wife who killed herself is bound to have psychological problems, wouldn't you think?'

Rachel collapsed in the chair by the telephone. 'What did you say?' she whispered in agonised disbelief. 'About his having been in prison?'

'Oops. I suppose that's something that never came up in your conversations. Of course, since he was charged as a minor the information is sealed by the records—so he would have no incentive to tell you, would he? I guess no man likes to admit to a new girlfriend that he served time for raping a fifteen-year-old...'

Rachel hardly heard the rest. Her hand was shaking so badly she dropped the receiver into the cradle and then staggered into the bathroom to be violently sick in the basin.

It couldn't be true; it just *couldn't*, she told her ghastly white face in the bathroom mirror. That would make everything he had told her—everything he was—everything that she loved—a lie!

She looked down at the ring on her finger and shuddered, pulling it off and letting it clatter onto the bathroom cabinet.

The sound of the key in the door of the apartment gave her no time to reorder her splintered thoughts. Nor did she give Matt any time to take her in his arms for their usual greeting.

'Neville called. He said—I—Please, just tell me it's not true?' she pleaded, the instant he walked in the door.

'What isn't true?' Matt asked warily, his eyes on her distraught face as she backed away from his embrace.

'That when you were young you were arrested for raping a

girl—a *fifteen-year-old* girl. That you went to *prison* for it?'
She put a hand over her mouth to hold in the choked sobs.

To her sick horror Matt didn't leap in with an instant denial.
His face was suddenly as white as hers. 'Rachel, it's not what
it seems—'

'What it *seems*? Don't tell me how it *seems*—I just want to
know if it's true!' she demanded hysterically.

'Rachel, I was going to tell you—'

'*Is it true?*' She screamed. 'It's a simple enough question:
were you or were you not charged with rape?'

'Yes, but—'

'And you went to prison?'

'Yes, I was remanded in custody, but—'

'My God...' Tears of shock and misery spurted out of her
eyes. She felt as if she had been violated all over again. 'My
God, it's all true...'

'No! For God's sake, Rachel, listen to me—*I didn't do it*!'

He reached for her and she backed away, shaking her pounding head. 'I believed you. Like a fool I believed all that stuff
about you being a virgin,' she said hysterically, 'a man of honour. I fell in love with you and actually *believed* you...'

Blood darkened his face as he confronted her bewildered
horror. 'Then believe me *now*,' he pleaded hoarsely. 'You know
I wouldn't lie to you.'

She pressed her hands against her temples. What ghastly
irony. Had she fallen in love with a man who had done to another young girl what had been done to her? 'I don't know—I
can't think. Why didn't you *tell* me?'

'Because I was afraid. I wanted you to get to know me first,
so you wouldn't have any doubts when I told you—so I took
the coward's way out...' His desperation turned to a kind of tortured anger. 'For God's sake—I'm in love with you, Rachel, I
would never do anything to hurt you! I know I made a mistake
not telling you, but is your faith in me really so fragile? You really think I just *pretended* to be sexually inexperienced as part

of some sick charade? Believe me—as God is my witness—*I never committed any rape...*'

'I don't know what to believe anymore,' she choked, snatching up her purse. Nausea churned in her belly as she plunged for the door. *Now* he talked about being in love with her? Not in a moment of passion or tenderness, but hitting her with it while she was weak and wounded? And only after she had betrayed her own wretched vulnerability...

'Rachel—'

'No, I have to go. Don't try to follow me—I have to be alone!'

She knew it was dangerous to drive her car in the state she was in, but she didn't care—the homing instinct was paramount: the need to find a place of safety in which to lick her wounds.

Yet before she'd turned thankfully into her own driveway her shocked brain had begun to function again, feeding her the questions that she should have stayed to ask, separating fact from assumption, logical thought from unreasoning emotion.

Think! she urged herself. *Follow the chain of evidence.*

What had Neville actually *said* amongst all that sick innuendo about Matt's 'dark side'?

That Matt had been charged with rape, her memory dredged up. Being charged was very different from being convicted, and surely Neville would have used the stronger word in his accusation if that was the case.

Matt admitted he had been in prison, but he had said he was *remanded*. Remand meant pre-trial.

Matt claimed he had never committed rape.

Given the choice, who would she pick as the more self-serving individual: Neville or Matt?

Which man did she most trust to tell her the truth?

She knew which one she *wanted* to trust, and it was because she had wanted it so very much that she had been afraid to trust her own instincts. That was the crux of her dilemma.

Trust.

All this time she had thought it was Matt holding back on

their relationship, but maybe it was really herself who had been waiting for the other shoe to drop. Now it had, and instead of picking it up and inspecting the clue, like a good detective, she had run away.

She had condemned the man she loved without a hearing.

Turning off the engine, she rested her weary forehead on the steering wheel and closed her eyes.

He had been a minor himself at the time. A boy. And he had grown into a man whom she liked and respected...and loved...

A tapping on her window made her jerk her head up, her heart soaring with relief, but it wasn't Matt's face looking in at her.

'Miss Blair? I wonder if I could have a word with you?' Rachel scrubbed at her salt-encrusted cheeks and fussed around with her bag, waiting for her heartbeat to settle before she got out of the car to face the thin, wiry figure of Max Armstrong.

'What about?' she asked warily, wondering if he was going to berate her for the loss of his job, or plead with her to intercede in getting it back.

After one curious look at her blotched complexion Armstrong said dourly, 'Don't worry, I have no grudge against you—that's why I'm here. I'm off to Aussie, where the pay's better. I just thought I'd better warn you that you might get some aggro down the line from that partner of yours.'

'Frank?'

'Yeah. Remember that high-society party gig we did a few weeks ago...the one with the silver cabinets?'

Merrilyn's! How could she forget? Max Armstrong had been one of two guards dressed as a waiters.

Rachel stiffened against the impending blow. 'Maybe you'd better come inside—'

He wagged his head, his thinning ponytail catching on the collar of his denim jacket. 'No, thanks. As far as I'm concerned I'm not even here. I just wanted to tell you that Weston asked me to keep you under surveillance that night, to see how you handled things...said he wasn't sure you were up to it and he wanted evidence if anything chancy happened—any sort of stuff-up that could be put down to you. He gave me a camera, one of those new, ultra-lowlight, long-lens jobs, and, well…after that guy fell in the pool, I followed you and him to the guest-house…' He tailed off and Rachel tersely picked up the thread.

'You took photos of us?' She didn't need to ask, but she was still struggling to accept that her recent suspicions had yielded bitter fruit.

'Look, it was no big deal as far as I was concerned—but a job is a job. I reeled off a few shots. I don't know how the photos came out, or even if they did, I just handed the camera over to Weston the next day. I told him that there was nothing to it—that you'd had a falling-down drunk on your hands—and he said OK.

'But you were always pretty decent to me, and after Weston suddenly decided I was surplus to his requirements I had a hunch that maybe he was blowing me off because he was afraid I'd let on about his secret agenda. I always play my hunches, so there you are—that's all I have to say.' He shrugged, thrusting his hands in the pockets of his jacket.

'Thanks for the information,' Rachel roused herself to croak as he turned away.

He gave her a sour grin. 'Yeah, well—consider it my fare-well gift. With partners like him, who needs enemies, huh? I'd watch my back, if I were you.'

'Oh, I intend to…'

Rachel watched him walk away into the gathering dusk. She didn't even bother to go into the house. She got back into her car and called Frank on her cellphone, hanging up as soon as he answered. Then she drove over to his place and parked out-side, trying to dredge up the courage from her battered soul to take charge of the part of her life that she *did* have the power to control.

As she sat there, staring at the lighted windows in Frank's

downstairs flat, the passenger door of the car snicked open and a shadowy figure slid into the seat beside her.

The breath stuttered in Rachel's chest. 'What are you doing here? Did you *follow* me?' She tried to summon some outrage, but all she could achieve was a faint echo of reproach.

Matt's silver-rimmed spectacles glinted in the gloom as he turned his face to hers, his expression sober.

'Lucky for you that I don't take orders well. Were you planning to confront a blackmailer without any back-up?'

She raised her hand to her tight throat. 'You *know*?'

'It's no real big surprise. I've had feelers out with a few contacts—and found out that Frank's the one who's been causing all your petty problems with bureaucracy. It seems that he's been trying to make your private life more stressful on top of loading you up with unnecessary business worries—'

'I went through some back files—found that he'd padded out the quotes on some of the jobs we missed out on in the past couple of years, deliberately pricing us out of contention,' Rachel interrupted numbly. 'But I had no idea that he was behind all that other stuff...' No wonder Frank had been so keen to investigate her mysterious harasser—he never would have tracked down himself!

Matt continued implacably, 'After you left me I called Neville—I threatened to tell Mum and Dad about the real reason Leigh married me if he didn't lay off. He knows that would seriously damage his image with Dad, so he threw me the bone about Frank—said Weston had told him he had compromising photos of you and me but he'd considered it too risky to get involved other than to make an under-the-table agreement that he would hold off granting the security contract he intended to give to WSS until Frank had stirred up sufficient trouble to ease you out of the company. Neville didn't care about Frank's motive—all he was interested in was the by-product: me being humiliated in front of my father, and anyone else he could leak the juicy details to...'

Rachel hunched her shoulders, shivering in the light summer shirt-dress she had donned with such joyous anticipation that morning. 'But...it always seemed so *generous* of Frank to be willing to buy me out if things went wrong...'

'What appears to be generosity is sometimes only ambition disguised. He obviously didn't want to alienate you into a costly open fight over ownership of the business. Instead he kept the value of it carefully depressed. You'd probably have found that after you'd sold out business suddenly picked up again...'

Rachel looked straight ahead, her hands clenched in her lap. She wanted nothing more than to bury her face in Matt's shoulder and bawl out her compound misery. 'I can't put this off. I have to have it out with him.'

'I know. But you're not going in there alone.'

Matt was offering her the kind of bedrock support that she had denied him. She was stricken with shame. 'Thanks, but I don't need you—'

'Oh, yes, you do, Rachel,' he said, with a quiet certainty that skewered her heart. 'You just don't want to admit it yet...'

She turned her head jerkily. He had been brave enough to seek her out after her betrayal of faith; she owed him a similar courage in return. 'I'm sorry,' she choked. 'I shouldn't have reacted the way I did. I know you didn't rape that girl.'

The gravity of his smile was challenging. '*Know?* You've discovered some fresh evidence in the last half-hour?'

Yes, the irrefutable evidence of her love. 'Believe, then...'

She searched for the words to convince him. 'Matt, I don't have to know the details, I—'

He stopped her with a slight gesture of his hand. 'Wait. Let's tackle one problem at a time. First, let's tidy away this business with Frank...'

Her partner took one look at the two of them standing shoulder-to-shoulder on the doorstep and grimaced.

'So you were the hang-up,' he said to Rachel, his blue eyes cynical. 'Checking I was home?'

'Can we come in?' she asked, ignoring his redundant remark. 'We'd like to talk to you about a communication problem you and I seem to be having.'

Frank looked as if he was debating refusing, but he eventually stood back and let them in, following them through to the cramped lounge.

Rachel indicated the computer, scanner and printer in one corner. 'I suppose that would be the gear you used to alter the photos Armstrong gave you. I noticed you purchased some pretty sophisticated image-handling software through the company a few months ago...'

To make sure there was no misunderstanding, she angrily challenged him with the discoveries that she and Matt had made.

To her shock Frank produced no belligerent bluster to dispute the facts. If anything he looked relieved to have it out in the open.

'I guess you're a better detective than either of us ever thought, then, huh?' he said.

'You're not even going to *try* to deny it?' Rachel asked painfully, aware of Matt's solid warmth at her back.

'What's the point? To tell you the truth, I'm sick of the whole mess,' he said, running his hand through his sun-streaked blond hair. 'I never expected to go this far...things just seemed to escalate when you wouldn't bloody well give up the notion of being a full partner...'

Rachel groped for Matt's hand behind her back and held it tightly as Frank continued his self-derisive monologue.

'I was stupid. I don't even know why I did it.' He pulled himself up with a jerk. 'Yes, yes, I do...of course I do.' He mocked himself with an angry laugh. 'It was because I worked damned hard to get where I am today. Dave and I started Westons—the two of us—and we agreed that it would *always* be just the two of us... And then Dave went and got himself killed and pulled the rug out from under me. He knew I'd left him *my* share of Westons in *my* will!'

'You weren't married,' Rachel pointed out.

'Neither was David! He could have waited, couldn't he?' he said, with a logic that didn't bear examination. 'He should at least have *asked* me about it first! So, I thought, OK, a silent partner, I can handle that...but then you started insisting on "helping". So I figured to let the business slide just enough that it wouldn't cost me too much when you decided it was all too hard—but, no, instead you announced that you were going try stepping completely into Dave's shoes. I couldn't stop you while you had the deciding share, but I figured if I kept the pressure on I might eventually be able to persuade you it was a bad idea—especially if you were also having hassles with people like the council and the IRS.

'And then Armstrong lucked out with those snaps. It seemed like the hand of fate. I wasn't looking to do anything illegal, just create enough embarrassment to give me an excuse to demand you resign. And when Stiller agreed to play along, keeping our future prospects looking rocky, that seemed like the icing on the cake...'

'And you couldn't resist decorating the frosting,' Matt crunched out. 'The nudity wasn't enough; you had to add the whip?'

'Yeah, that was purely stupid. I guess I got carried away with my own cleverness. And sending out that second set of photos was even dumber. I mean, I woke up afterwards and thought, What am I *doing*?' He rubbed a hand across his unshaven face. 'I was jeopardising everything I'd worked for—and for what? So I destroyed the negs and prints and hoped the hell it would all go away if I ignored it.

'I even went to see the psychologist I used to work with when I was in the police. I've spent the past week working out that *I'm* the one who's the problem. Hell...the fact is that Dave is dead and I *do* need another partner to share the load. I've just been resenting it so long I couldn't see the wood for the trees... And the stupidest part of it is—Rachel's proved to have far more guts and go than some of the competitors I let get the jump on us...'

'The question is, what happens now?' said Matt, when Frank's well of remorse had run dry. 'Or rather what does Rachel want to happen?—since I think it's her call.'

She struggled with conflicting feelings. 'Maybe I haven't been at it as long, but I've worked hard for Westons, tooI don't want to throw all that away. But after what you've done, I don't know if I could ever trust working with you again,' she told Frank slowly.

'In that case we either dissolve the partnership or I buy you out, I suppose,' he said tiredly, showing no elation at either prospect. 'I guess if you're going to be a rich man's wife you won't even *have* to work...'

Rachel ignored the dig. 'But that would mean you win,' she instantly objected. 'I don't see why you should get away scot-free.'

'I won't—seeing that we have the KR contract in our pockets, the value of your shares has just shot up.'

'What's the matter with Rachel buying *you* out?' suggested Matt, causing both their jaws to drop. 'I think she's proved capable, don't you? And I'd be happy to help her put up the capital. There's no reason why she couldn't run the business herself...'

'Westons without a Weston?' Frank came back to furious life. 'Look, Rachel, don't rush into anything—think things over for a few days. I'm sure we can work something out... OK, I did some bad things, but nothing I can't make up for, and nothing illegal except maybe when I used Dave's old key to get into your place and pinch those photos back...and maybe that redirection thing with your mail...'

'I don't believe the gall of that man!' stormed Rachel as she and Matt walked out onto the footpath a few minutes later. 'Saying that maybe we should be *thanking* him!'

'He's right, though, isn't he? But for him we wouldn't have gone public with an engagement. And unbeknownst to him, by mailing those photos he *did* bring us together. So I guess we could regard him as our unlikely cupid.'

Cupid. As in the god of love.

Rachel halted under a street-lamp, placing a staying hand on his arm. 'Matt,' she said earnestly, as he turned towards her. 'I—I want you to know I admire you more than any man I've ever known!'

This reckless accolade brought an indulgent smile to his lips. 'That sounds extremely promising. Would you care to take that statement one step further...?'

The overhead light threw his eyes under the shadow of his brow, but she knew they were fixed on her flushed face. She didn't blame him for mocking her. 'I know you probably won't believe I love you—'

'Any more than you dare believe that I love you?'

'After the way I failed my first test of faith.' She faltered under his tenderly caressing tone. 'Everything was so right and then I let it all go wrong.'

'Some very wise and wonderful woman once told me that what goes wrong in one's life doesn't always turn out to be all for the worst.' He reminded her of her own words as he picked up both her hands and carried them separately to his warm lips. 'In fact, sometimes it can force us to be at our best. You were right to be angry with me. I *should* have been as open with you as you were with me. I don't want to have any more secrets from you.'

Her hands tightened on his, her eyes shining with tears. 'I told you, I don't need you to explain.'

'But I need to say the things I should have said before. I need you to know that your faith in me is justified.' His voice became rougher, more choppy, as he told her about the alleged rape that had ended his boyhood and blunted his burgeoning sexual curiosity.

'It was nothing dramatic—just a silly girl lying to cover up the fact she'd been having sex. Her boyfriend got rough one night after a dance, and when her parents caught her sneaking home she panicked and claimed she'd been attacked. When her parents called the police she didn't want to get her boyfriend into trouble so she pointed the finger at me, because I'd been at the dance and she'd seen me leaving on my own about the time she and her boyfriend took off on his motorcycle. She swore black and blue that she'd been a virgin and I'd threatened to kill her if she told anyone what I'd done.'

Now it was Matt clinging to Rachel's strong fingers as he sketched out the rest of the ugly story. 'I didn't have an alibi and I was remanded to prison because there were no beds available in the juvenile facilities.' His eyes briefly reflected a glimpse of the shattered boy he had been. 'I was in there for three days.

'I was pinning my hopes on getting out when the forensic testing came through, but—' here he offered her an ironic smile '—all the charges were dropped when a private detective hired by Dad caught the girl and her the boyfriend together, and she confessed. Thank God Mum and Dad stood by me, but it was rough being treated like a sex-fiend when I was only just getting interested in sex. It certainly curbed any urge to experiment. For a while I was scared that any girl who showed she liked me was going to accuse me of rape. Maybe that's partly why I fell so hard for Leigh…her apparent unattainability made her seem safe…

'I had to wait for you to come along to discover the full potential of love between a man and a woman…'

There, in the warmth of the summer night, Rachel fell in love with him all over again. She drew their joined hands against her breast, letting him feel the beat of her steady heart. 'I can't take away the hurt you've already suffered, but I'm glad to be the woman you waited for. I'm just sorry to have given you such a bad time.'

'But with you, even the bad times are good,' he said, not entirely teasing. 'My life has certainly been a lot more exciting since you entered into it.'

'I don't know if I can supply quite this level of excitement on a permanent basis,' she said shakily, and then realised she was being presumptuous.

'So…where do we go from here?' she asked, freeing her hands and looking from her car to his. But he knew she wasn't talking about mere transport.

'Where do you want us to go?'

'I don't care,' she said recklessly, 'as long as we're together. I'd happily spend the rest of my life proving my love to you.'

'Then you'll probably be needing this,' he said, reaching into the inside pocket of his jacket and producing the brazen engagement ring which she had left behind.

'I didn't throw your roses away, you know,' she blurted. 'The yellow ones you sent after the party. I kept changing the water and they lasted for a week…'

'And you kept that prissy note they came with,' he said huskily. 'That gave me the courage to hope. Courage is like love. It has to have hope for nourishment. I couldn't stop thinking of you after that party. I kept hoping that we would run into one another again soon, wondering if I could invent some excuse for calling you…'

He held out the ring. 'Take it. It's yours.'

'But… I don't want to pretend any more…' she whispered.

'Nor do I.' He slid the ring onto her finger. 'So let's do it all over again, this time for real…'

EPILOGUE

WAKING UP NEXT to the man you loved was, Rachel decided, one of life's most joyous delights.

'Good morning, husband,' she murmured to the darkhaired man gazing at her with clearly lecherous intent.

'Happy anniversary, wife,' he purred.

Feeling deliciously wicked, she eased on top of him, enjoying the feel of skin on skin…his naked body adjusting to her flagrantly voluptuous contours.

'Six years and you're still as insatiable as ever,' she accused him laughingly.

'Who's on top of whom?' he pointed out, wrapping his arms around her and luxuriating in her eager kisses.

A blinding flash from the doorway had them both freezing in shock. With a squeak Rachel squirmed off her husband, pulling up the sheets.

'A pitcha, a pitcha—, Kevin taked a pitcha!' the darkheaded four-year-old shrieked excitedly, dancing on chubby legs across the bedroom carpet, the expensive instant camera waving precariously in his stubby fist.

He flung himself against the side of the mattress, giggling as a strong, masculine arm reached down to hook him up onto the bed to join his parents.

He bounced up and down in glee as his mother detached the camera from his dimpled fingers and peeled off the film.

'Oh, God!' Rachel blushed as she watched it develop in full, eye-catching colour. 'My son,' she moaned, 'the budding blackmailer!'

'Let me see.' Matt plucked it from her hands and studied it in amusement. 'Mmm, this brings back some very interesting memories. I'll have to add it to my private collection,' he leered.

'Matt, you don't still have those wretched photos?' she gasped laughingly.

'Of course. They have great sentimental value to me,' he said with a pious look, and then spoiled it by adding slyly, 'I used to sleep with them under my pillow whenever you were away.'

'Well, you won't need them from now on!'

Rachel and Frank had made their difficult peace, going on to build a new, more equal relationship out of the ruins of the old one. Weston Security Services had gone from strength to strength in the past few years, but since Kevin had been born Rachel had cut back her office hours and done an increasing amount of her work from home. Now WSS had merged with another company and acquired two new partners, and she intended to take a complete break for a while, eager to spend more time with her family.

'Mr Mischief,' she scolded Kevin lovingly, as he crawled between them for a hug and a tickle on his pyjama-clad stomach. 'Stick to your own toys from now on!'

'Tickle Mummy's tummy. Mummy's fat!' Kevin chortled at his rude joke as he clumsily patted her swollen abdomen.

'That's not fat, that's your little baby sister,' Matt corrected him, gentling his hand.

'*Sister?*' Rachel's eyebrows rose. 'Do you know something I don't?'

'Well, you've always given me everything I wanted.' He grinned. 'Why stop now? Besides, isn't that what Dad's ordered this time round? 'Got to keep the dynasty balanced!' He mimicked his father's bark.

'It could be twins,' she teased.

His eyes met hers in blissful unconcern. 'Double the love? I should be so lucky...'

And, much to Rachel's delighted consternation—he was!

* * * * *

Gold Ring Of Betrayal

Michelle Reid

MICHELLE REID grew up on the southern edges of Manchester, England, the youngest in a family of five lively children. But now she lives in the beautiful county of Cheshire with her busy executive husband and two grown-up daughters. She loves reading, the ballet and playing tennis when she gets the chance. She hates cooking, cleaning, and despises ironing! Sleep she can do without, and she produces some of her best written work during the early hours of the morning.

CHAPTER ONE

LONDON. BIG HOUSE. Big address close to Hyde Park. The time: 17.45 p.m. Six hours since it happened.

And the tension in the formal drawing room was so fraught it picked at the flesh. People were standing about in small clusters, some talking in low, worried voices, some breaking into soft bouts of weeping now and then, others comforting, others holding themselves apart from it all, standing or sitting with a fierce self-control about them which held them silent and still. Waiting.

Sara was of the latter group, sitting alone on one of the soft-cushioned sofas. She appeared calm, outwardly composed now as she stared down at the pale carpet beneath her feet, seemingly oblivious to everyone else.

But she was far from oblivious. Far from composed. Every movement, each sound was reverberating shrilly inside her head. And she was sitting there like that, straight-backed and very still, because she knew that if she did so much as move a muscle all her severely reined in self-control would gush screaming out of her.

It had already happened once. When the dreadful news had been brought to her, her initial reaction had been one of almost uncontrollable horror. They had tried to put her to bed then. Tried to force tranquillizers down her throat to put her out of her torment. Tried to render her oblivious to it all.

She'd refused. Of course she'd refused! How could any woman—any mother take refuge in sleep at a time like this?

But because they had been alarmed by her reaction, because they'd needed something tangible to worry about and she'd seemed the most obvious candidate, and because she'd found she did not have it in her to fight them as well as fight the multitude of terrors rattling around inside her head she had made herself calm down, pretend to get a hold on herself, and had taken up her silent vigil here, on this sofa, where she had been sitting for hours now. Hours...

Waiting.

Like the rest of them. Waiting for the man who was at the centre of all this trauma to come and take control of the situation.

He was on his way, they'd told her, as though expecting that piece of information to make her feel better. It didn't. Nothing did. Nothing would.

So she sat very still, blue eyes lowered so no one could see what was happening inside her head, and concentrated all her attention on remaining calm while they, in their own anxiety, did not seem to notice the way the stark blackness of her long-sleeved T-shirt and tight leggings accentuated the whitened strain in her face. Nor did they seem to realise that she was sitting so straight because shock was holding her spine like a rigid rod of iron, or that her hands, clasped quietly on her lap, were in actual fact clenched and cold and so stiff that she didn't think she could unclasp them again even if she tried to.

But at least they didn't approach. At least they weren't trying to comfort her by murmuring useless platitudes no mother wanted to hear at a time like this. At least they were leaving her alone.

The sudden sound of crunching tires on the gravel driveway outside the house had everyone else jumping to attention. Sara did not move. She did not so much as lift her head in response.

There was the sound of voices in the hallway, one deep, sharp and authoritative, standing out from the rest as special. And the air in the room began to fizz.

Then footsteps, firm, precise, came towards the closed drawing-room door. Everyone inside the room turned towards it as it shot open, their eyes fixing expectantly on the man who appeared in its aperture.

But Sara kept her gaze fixed on the small square of carpet she'd had it fixed on for ages now, carefully counting the tiny rosebuds which made up part of the pale blue and peach design.

Tall, lean-featured, black hair, tight body. White shirt, dark tie, grey suit that sat on him as expensive silk should. Tanned skin—natural, not worked on. Long, thin nose, ruthlessly drawn, resolute sensual mouth. And the sharp and shrewd eyes of a hunter. Gold, like a tiger. Cold, like the features. A man hewn from rock.

He stood poised like that in the doorway for some long, immeasurable seconds, emitting a leashed power into the room that had everyone else holding their breath. His strange eyes flicked from one anxious face to another, surveying the scene as a whole without so much as acknowledging a single person. The young girl sitting in a chair by the window let out a muffled sob when his gaze touched her; her cheeks blotchy, eyes red and swollen, she stared up at him as if she were begging for her very life. Coldly, dismissively he moved on—and on. Until his eyes found Sara, sitting there in her isolated splendour, face lowered and seemingly unaware.

Then something happened to the eyes. What was difficult to determine but it sent an icy chill down the spines of those who saw it. He began to move, loose-limbed and graceful. Without so

much as affording anyone else a second glance he walked across
the patterned carpet and came to a stop directly in front of her.

'Sara,' he prompted quietly.

She did not move. Her eyes did focus dimly on the pair of
handmade leather shoes which were now obscuring the patch
of carpet she had been concentrating on. But other than that she
showed no sign that she was aware of his presence.

'Sara.' There was more command threaded into the tone
this time.

It had the required effect, making her dusky lashes quiver
before her eyes began the slow, sluggish journey upwards, skimming his long, silk-clad legs, powerful thighs, his lean, tight
torso made of solid muscle and covered by a white shirt that
did not quite manage to hide the abundance of crisp black hair
shadowing satin-smooth, stretched-leather skin beneath.

She reached the throat, taut and tanned. Then the chin, rigidly chiselled. Then the shadow of a line that was his grimly
held, perfectly sculptured mouth. His nose thin, straight and
uncompromisingly masculine. Cheeks, lean and sheened with
the silken lustre of well cared for skin. Then at last the eyes.
Her blank blue gaze lifted to clash with the hunter's gold eyes
belonging to the one man in this world whom she had most
wished never to see again.

What was it? she found herself thinking dully. Two years
since she'd seen him—coming closer to three? He had changed
little.

Yet why should he have changed? He was Nicolas Santino.
Big man. Powerful man. A wealthy man who could afford
houses with big addresses in every important capital of the
world. He was a slick, smooth, beautifully cared for human
being. Born to power, raised to power and used to power. When
he frowned people cowered.

The man with everything. Good looks, great body. Why
should three small years change any of that? He possessed the
godlike features of a man of fable. The hair, so black it gleamed

navy blue in the light. The nose, that arrogant appendage he made no apologies for. The mouth, firm, set, a perfectly drawn shadow on a golden bone structure hewn from the same privileged rock those fabled men had come from. And finally the eyes. The eyes of a lion, a tiger, a sleek black panther.

The eyes of a hard, cold, ruthless predator. Cruel and unforgiving.

Unforgiving.

If her mouth had been up to it, it would have smiled, albeit bitterly.

He the unforgiving one. She the sinner.

It was a shame she viewed the whole situation the other way around. It meant that neither was prepared to give an inch. Or hate the other less.

Three years, she was thinking. Three years of cold, silent festering. And it was all still there—lying hidden beneath the surface right now, but there all the same. Three years since he had last allowed himself to share the same space as her. And now he had the gall to appear before her and say her name as though it were the most natural thing in the world for him to do.

But it wasn't. And they both knew it wasn't. And Sara was in no fit state to play stupid, pride-saving games to the opposite. Not with him. Not with this man, whom she had once loved and now hated with the same intensity.

She looked away, eyes lowering back down his length, dismissing his handsome face, dismissing his superb body, dismissing his long legs encased in expensive silk. Dismissing the man in his entirety.

The message was loud and clear. The room gasped.

'Get out.'

It was quietly spoken, almost conversationally so, yet there was not a person in the room who did not understand the command or whom it was aimed directly at. Indifferent to them all, unmoving, he remained directly in front of Sara's bowed head while he waited in silence for his instruction to be carried out.

And they jolted into action, responding like mechanical toys, heads, bodies, limbs jerking with a complete lack of coordination that shifted them *en masse* towards the door. Two policemen, both in plain clothes. One uniformed chauffeur, hat gone, hair mussed, face white. One weepy young nanny with her face buried in a handkerchief. A harried-looking housekeeper and her grim-faced man-of-all-trades husband. And the doctor who had been called out to treat the young nanny and had ended up staying because he had been seriously concerned that Sara was ready to collapse.

Or maybe because he had been ordered to stay by this man.

Who knew—who cared? Sara didn't. He might be able to make other people quail in their shoes. He might be able to command mute obedience from anyone who came within his despotic reach. But not her. Never her! And she found it amazing if not pathetic that one man could walk in somewhere and command that kind of sheep-like obedience without even having to give his name.

But then, this one man was not just any man. This was a man who wielded such power that he could walk into any room anywhere in the world and command immediate attention. The same man who had had this house and its beautiful grounds locked up like a fortress within an hour of the incident happening.

It was a shame he had not had the foresight to do it before it had happened. Then this unwelcome meeting between them would not have needed to take place.

The last one out drew the door shut behind them. Sara heard it close with a gentle click, and felt the new silence settle around her like a shroud.

He moved away, coming back moments later to sit down beside her. The next thing, a glass was being pressed to her bloodless mouth.

'Drink,' he commanded.

The distinctive smell of brandy invading her nostrils almost made her gag and she shook her head, her waist-length, fine-spun, straight golden hair shimmering against her black-clad shoulders and arms.

He ignored the gesture. 'Drink,' he repeated. 'You look like death,' he added bluntly. 'Drink or I shall make you.'

No idle threat. That became clear when his hand came up, his long, strong, blunt-ended fingers taking a grip on her chin so he could force her mouth open.

She drank—then gasped as the liquid slid like fire down her paper-dry throat, the air sucking frantically into her lungs as though it had been trying to do that for hours now without any success.

'That's better,' he murmured, believing it was the brandy that had made her gasp like that when in actual fact it had been his touch—his touch acting like an electric charge to her system, shooting stinging shocks of recognition into every corner of her frozen flesh. 'Now drink some more.'

She drank, if only to hide the new horror that was attacking her. Him. This man. The bitter fact that she could still respond so violently to physical contact with this—person who had caused her so much pain and disillusionment and grief.

He made her take several sips at the brandy before deciding she'd had enough. His fingers let go. The glass was removed. By then the brandy had put some colour back into her cheeks—and his touch a glint of bitter condemnation into the blue eyes she managed to lift to his.

'Is this your doing?' she demanded, the words barely distinguishable as they scraped across her tense throat.

But he heard—and understood. The hardening of the eyes told her so. Eyes that continued to view her with a cold but steady scrutiny which quite efficiently gave her a reply.

He was denying it, using his eyes to demand how she dared suspect him of such a terrible thing.

But she did suspect him. 'I hate you,' she said. 'I despise the very ground you occupy. If anything happens to my baby then watch your back, Nicolas,' she warned him. 'Because I'll be there with a knife long enough to slice right through that piece of cold rock you may call a heart.'

He didn't respond, didn't react, which came as a surprise because his overgrown sense of self did not take kindly to threats. And she'd meant it—every single huskily spoken, virulent word.

'Tell me what happened,' he instructed quietly instead.

Her mind went hot at the bright, burning flashback to the young nanny stumbling through the door. 'Lia has been kidnapped!' she had screamed in outright hysteria. 'They just ran up and snatched her while we were playing in the park!'

The memory launched her with a bone-crunching jerk to her feet, turning her from a wax-like dummy into a shivering, shaking mass of anguish. '*You know* what happened, you evil monster!' she seared at him. Blue eyes sparked down on him with hatred, with fear, with a bitter, filthy contempt. 'She was your one humiliation so you've had her removed, haven't you—*haven't you?*'

By contrast the golden eyes remained calm, unaffected. He sat back, crossed one neat ankle over a beautifully clad knee, stretched a silk-clad arm across the back of the sofa and studied her quivering frame quite detachedly.

'I did not take your child,' he stated.

Not *his* child, she noted. Not even *our* child. Her shaking mouth compressed into a line of disgust. 'Yes, you did.' She said it without a hint of uncertainty. 'It bears all the hallmarks of one of your lot.' Not said nicely and not meant to be. 'Vendetta is your middle name. Or should be. The only thing I don't understand is why I wasn't taken out at the same time.'

'Work on it,' he suggested. 'You may, with a bit of luck, come up with a half-intelligent answer.'

She turned away, hating to look at him, hating that look of cruel indifference on his arrogant face. This was their daughter's life they were discussing here! And he could sit there looking like—that!

'God, you make me sick,' she breathed, moving away, arms wrapping around her tense body as she went to stand by the window, gazing out on the veritable wall of security now cordoning off the property: men with mobile telephones fastened to their ears, some with big, ugly-looking dogs on strong-looking leashes. A laugh broke from her, thick with scorn. 'Putting on a show for the punters,' she derided. 'Do you honestly think anyone will be fooled by it?'

'Not you, obviously!' He didn't even try to misunderstand what she was talking about, his mockery as dry as her derision. 'They are there to keep the media at bay,' he then flatly explained. 'That foolish nanny was supposed to be trained on how to respond to this kind of contingency. Instead she stood in the park screaming so loud that she brought half of London out to find out what was the matter.' His sigh showed the first hint of anger. 'Now the whole world knows that the child has been taken. Which is going to really make it simple to get her back with the minimum of fuss!'

'Oh, God.' Sara's hand went up to cover her mouth, panic suddenly clawing at her again. 'Why, Nicolas?' she cried in wretched despair. 'She's only two years old! She was no threat to you! Why did you take my baby away?'

She didn't see him move, yet he was at her side in an instant, his fingers burning that damned electrical charge into her flesh as he spun her around to face him. 'I won't repeat this again,' he clipped. 'So listen well. I did not take your child.'

'S-someone did,' she choked, blue eyes luminous with bulging tears. 'Who else do you know who hated her enough to do that?'

He sighed again, not answering that one—not answering because he couldn't deny her accusation. 'Come and sit down again before you drop,' he suggested. 'And we will—'

'I don't want to sit down!' she angrily refused. 'And I don't want you touching me!' Violently, she wrenched free of his grasp.

His mouth tightened, a sign that at last her manner towards him was beginning to get through his thick skin. 'Who else, Nicolas?' she repeated starkly. 'Who else would want to take my baby from me?'

'Not from you,' he said quietly, turning away. 'They have taken her from *me.*'

'You?' Sara stared at the rigid wall of his back in blank incredulity. 'But why should they want to do that? You disowned her!' she cried.

'But the world does not know that.'

Sara went cold. Stone-still, icy cold as realisation slapped her full in the face. 'You mean—?' She swallowed, having to battle to rise above a new kind of fear suddenly clutching at her breast. She had banked on this being his doing. Banked on it so much that it came as a desperate blow to have him place an alternative in her mind.

'I am a powerful man.' He stated the unarguable. 'Power brings its own enemies—'

But—'No.' She was shaking her head in denial even before he'd finished speaking. 'No,' she repeated. 'This is family stuff. I know it is. I spoke to them on the—'

'You spoke to them?' He turned, those predator's eyes suddenly razor-like with surprise.

'On the phone.' She nodded, swallowing as the terrible sickness she had experienced during that dreadful call came back to torment her.

'When?' His voice had roughened, hardened. He didn't like it that she had been able to tell him something he had not been told already. It pricked his insufferable belief that he was omnipotent, the man who knew everything. 'When did this telephone conversation take place?'

'A-about an hour after they t-took her,' she whispered, then added bitterly, 'They said you would know what to do!' She stared at him in despair, her summer-blue eyes suddenly turned into dark, dark pools in an agonised face. 'Well, do it, Nicolas!' she cried. 'For God's sake do it!'

He muttered a violent curse, and was suddenly at her side again, hard fingers coiling around her slender arm, brooking no protest this time as he pushed her back into the sofa.

'Now listen...' he said, coming to sit down beside her. 'I need to know what they said to you, Sara. And I need to know how they said it. You understand?'

Understand? Of course she understood! 'You want to know if they were Sicilian,' she choked. 'Well, yes! They were Sicilian—like you!' she said accusingly. 'I recognised the accent, the same blinding contempt for anything and anyone who is not of the same breed!'

He ignored all of that. 'Male or female?' he persisted.

'M-male,' she breathed.

'Old—young—could you tell?'

She shook her head. 'M-muffled. The v-voice was m-muffled—by something held over the m-mouthpiece, I think.' Then she gagged, her hand whipping up to cover her quivering mouth.

Yet, ruthlessly, he reached up to catch the hand, removed it, held it trapped in his own in a firm command for attention.

'Did he speak in English?'

She nodded. 'But with a Sicilian accent. Let go of me...'

He ignored that. 'And what did he say? Exactly, Sara,' be insisted. 'What did he say?'

She began to shake all over—shake violently, eyes closing as she locked herself onto that terrible conversation that had confirmed her worst fears. "We h-have your ch-hild,' 'she quoted, word for mind-numbing word. Her fingers were icy cold and trembling so badly that he began gently chafing them with his own. "Sh-she is s-safe for now. Get S-Santino. He will know wh-what to do. We w-will contact you again at seventh-thirty..." Dazedly she glanced around the room. 'What time is it?' she asked jerkily.

'Shush. Not yet six,' he murmured calmingly. 'Concentrate,

Sara. Did he say anything else? Did you hear anything else? Any background sound, other voices, a plane, a car—anything?'

She shook her head. 'N-nothing.' No sound. Only the voice. Not even the sound of a child crying—'Oh, God.' She whipped her hand out from between his to cover her eyes. 'My baby,' she whispered. 'My poor baby... I want her here!' She turned on him, holding out her arms and looking lost and tormented and heart-rendingly pathetic. 'In my arms...' Her arms folded and closed around her slender body, hugging, hugging as if the small child were already there and safe. 'Oh, God,' she groaned. 'Oh, God, Nicolas, do something. Do something!'

'OK,' he muttered, but distractedly. 'OK. It will be done. But I want to know why the hell I was not informed of this telephone conversation. Was it taped?' He was frowning blackly. 'The police have a trace on this line. It must have been taped!'

'Afraid someone may recognise the voice?' she seared at him scathingly. His golden eyes withered her with a look, then he climbed grimly to his feet. Alarm shot through her. 'Where are you going?' she bit out shrilly.

Glancing down at her, he could have been hewn from stone again. 'To do something about this, as you requested,' he replied. 'In the meantime I suggest you go to your room and try to rest.' His gaze flicked dispassionately over her. 'I will keep you informed of any developments.'

'Leave it all to you, you mean,' she surmised from that.

His cool nod confirmed it. 'It is, after all, why I am here.'

The only reason why he was here. 'Where were you?' she asked him, curious suddenly. 'When they told you. Where were you?'

'New York.'

She frowned. 'New York? But it's been only six hours since—'

'Concorde,' he drawled—then added tauntingly, 'Still suspecting me of stealing your child?'

Her chin came up, bitterness turning her blue eyes as cold

as his tiger ones. 'We both know you're quite capable of it,' she said.

'But why should I want to?' he quite sensibly pointed out. 'She bears no threat to me.'

'No?' Sara questioned that statement. 'Until he rids himself of one wife and finds himself another, Lia is the legitimate heir of Nicolas Santino. Whether or not he was man enough to conceive her.'

As a provocation it was one step too far. She knew it even as his eyes flashed, and he was suddenly leaning over her, his white teeth glinting dangerously between tightened lips, the alluring scent of his aftershave completely overlaid by the stark scent of danger. 'Take care, *wife*,' he gritted, 'what you say to me!'

'And you take care,' she threw shakily back, 'that you hand my baby back to me in one whole and hearty piece. Or so help me, Nicolas,' she vowed, 'I will drag the Santino name through the gutters of every tabloid in the world!'

The eyes flashed again, black spiralling into gold as they burned into blue. 'To tell them—what?' he demanded thinly. 'What vile crime do you believe you can lay at my feet, eh? Have I not given you and your child everything you could wish for? My home,' he listed. 'My money. And, not least, my name!'

Every one of which Sara saw entirely as her due. 'And for whose sake?' she derided him scathingly. 'Your own sake, Nicolas.' She gave the answer for him. 'To protect your own Sicilian pride!'

'What pride?' Abruptly he straightened and turned away. 'You killed my pride when you took another man to your bed.'

Her heart squeezed in a moment's pained sympathy for this man who had lived with that belief for the last three years. And he was right; even if what he was saying was wrong, simply believing it to be true must have dealt a lethal blow to his monumental pride.

'Ah!' His hand flew out, long, sculptured fingers flicking

her a gesture of distaste. 'I will not discuss this with you any further. You disgust me. I disgust myself even bothering to talk to you.' He turned, striding angrily to the door.

'Nicolas!' Forcing her stiff and aching limbs to propel her to her feet again, she stopped him as he went to leave the room.

He paused with his hand on the doorknob, his long body lean and lithe and pulsing with contempt. He did not turn back to face her, and tears—weak tears which came from that deep, dark well where she now kept the love she'd once felt for him—burned suddenly in her eyes.

'Nicolas—please...' she pleaded. 'Whatever you believe about me, Lia has committed no crime!'

'I know that,' he answered stiltedly.

The wretched sound of her anxiety wrenched from her in a sob. 'Then please—please get her safely back for me!'

Her plea stiffened his spine, made the muscles in the side of his neck stand out in response as he turned slightly to face her. His eyes, those hard, cold, angry eyes, fixed on the way she was standing there with her waist-length, gossamer-fine hair pushed back from her small face by a padded velvet band. She wasn't tall, and the simple style of her clothes accentuated her fine-boned slenderness.

A delicate creature. Always appearing as though the slightest puff of wind might blow her over. That a harsh word would cast her into despair. Yet—

If it was possible, the eyes hardened even more. 'The child was taken because she bears my name,' he stated coldly. 'I shall therefore do my best to return her to you unharmed.'

The door closed, leaving Sara staring angrily at the point where his stiff body had last been.

'The child', she was thinking bitterly. He referred to Lia as 'the child' as if she were a doll without a soul! A mere inanimate object which had been stolen. And because he accepted some twisted sense of responsibility for the crime he was therefore also willing to accept that it was his duty to get *it* back!

How kind! she thought as her trembling legs forced her to drop into a nearby chair. How magnanimous of him! Would he be that detached if he truly believed Lia was his own daughter? Or would he be the one requiring the reviving brandy, the one people were dying to pump sleeping pills into because they could see he couldn't cope with the horror of it all—the horror of their baby being snatched and carried away by some ruthless, evil monster? A monster, moreover, who was prepared to stop at nothing to get what he wanted from them!

'Oh, God,' she choked, burying her face in her hands in an effort to block out her thoughts because they were so unbearable.

Her baby, in the hands of a madman. Her baby, frightened and bewildered as to what was happening to her. Her baby, wanting her mama and not understanding why she was not there when she had always been there for her before—always!

What kind of unfeeling monster would take a small child away from her mama? she wondered starkly. What made a person that bad inside? That cruel? That—?

She stopped, dragging her hands from her face as a sudden thought leapt into her head.

There really was only one person she knew who was capable of doing something like this.

Alfredo Santino. Father to the son. And ten times more ruthless than Nicolas could ever learn to be.

And he hated Sara. Hated her for daring to think herself good enough for his wonderful son. He was the man who had vowed retribution on her for luring his son away from the high-powered Sicilian marriage he'd had mapped out for him, which had then made the father look a fool in the eyes of his peers—if Alfredo Santino accepted anyone as his peer, that was. If Nicolas saw himself as omnipotent, then the father considered himself the same but more so.

But Alfredo had already exacted his retribution on her, surely? She frowned. So why—?

'No.' Suddenly she was on her feet again, still trembling—

not with weakness this time but with a stark, clamouring fear
that made it a struggle even to keep upright as she stumbled
across the drawing-room floor and out into the hall.

CHAPTER TWO

A BIG MAN in a grey suit and with a tough-looking face stood guard just outside the door. A stranger.

'Where is Nicolas?' she asked shakily. 'M-my husband, where is he?'

His gaze drifted towards the closed study door. 'Mr Santino wished not to be disturbed.'

Sicilian. His accent was as Sicilian as the voice that had spoken to her on the phone. She shuddered and stepped past him, ignoring the very unsubtle hint in his reply, to hurry across the hallway and push open the study door.

He was half sitting on the edge of the big solid oak desk and he wasn't alone. The two policemen were with him, and someone she instantly recognised as Nicolas's right-hand man. Toni Valetta. All of them were in a huddle around something on the desk with their heads tilted down. But they shot upright in surprise at her abrupt entrance.

She ignored them all, her anxious eyes homing in on the only one in this room who counted. 'Nicolas...' She took a couple of urgent steps towards him. 'I—'

His hand snaked out—not towards her but to something on the desk. And it was only as she heard an electronic click followed by a sudden deathly silence that it hit her just what had been going on here, and what her ears had picked up but her mind had refused to recognise until Nicolas had rendered the room silent.

God. She stopped, went white, closed her eyes, swayed. It had been her Lia's voice, her baby murmuring, 'Mama? Mama?' before it had been so severely cut off.

'Don't touch her!'

The command was barked from a raspingly threatening throat.

She didn't know who had tried to touch her, who had reached her first as she began to sink, as if in slow motion, to the thick carpet beneath her feet. But she recognised Nicolas's arms as they came around her, breaking her fall, catching her to his chest and holding her there as something solid hit the back of her knees, impelling her to sit down.

He didn't leave go, lowering his body with hers as he guided her into the chair, so that she could still lean weakly against him. Her heart had accelerated out of all control, her breathing fast and shallow, her mind—her mind blanked out by a horror that was more than she could bear.

And he was cursing softly, roundly, cursing in Italian, in English, cursing over her head at someone, cursing at her. Her fingers came up, ice-cold and numb, scrambling over his shirt-front and up his taut throat until they found his mouth, tight-lipped with fury.

She could have slapped him full in the face for the reaction she got. He froze, right there in front of all those watching faces; he froze into a statue of stunned silence with her trembling fingers pressed against his mouth.

'Nic,' she whispered fraily, not even knowing that she had shortened his name to that more intimate version she'd rarely used to call him, and only then when she'd been totally, utterly lost in him. 'My baby. That was my baby...'

Nicolas Santino, squatting there with her wonderful hair splayed across his big shoulders so that the sweet rose scent of it completely surrounded him, closed his hard eyes on a moment of stark, muscle-locking pain.

Then, 'Shush,' he murmured, and reached up to grasp the fingers covering his mouth, touching them briefly to his lips before clasping them gently in his hand. 'Sara, she is fine. She is asking for you but she is not distressed. You understand me, *cara?* She is—'

She passed out. At last—and perhaps it seemed fortunate to all those who had worriedly observed her all day—she finally caved in beneath the pressure of it all and went limp against the man holding her.

She came around to find herself in her own room, lying on her own bed, with the doctor leaning over her. He smiled warmly but briefly. 'I want you to take these, Mrs Santino,' he murmured, holding two small white pills and a glass of water out to her.

But she shook her head, closing her eyes again while she tried to remember what had happened. She remembered running across the hall, remembered opening the door to the study and racing inside, but what she couldn't remember was why she'd felt the dire need to go there. She remembered seeing Nicolas in the room, and Toni and the two policemen. She remembered them all jerking to attention at her rude entry and her taking several steps towards Nicolas. Then—

Oh, God. Full recall shuddered through her on a nauseous wave. 'Where's Nicolas?' she gasped.

'Here,' his grim voice replied.

Her eyes flickered open to find him looking down at her from the other side of the bed. He looked different somehow, as if some of his usual arrogance had been stripped away. 'You heard from them, didn't you?' she whispered faintly. 'They called before the deadline.' Tears pushed into her eyes. 'They let my baby talk to you.'

The corner of his tensely held mouth ticked. 'Take the two pills the doctor is offering you, Sara,' was all he said by way of a reply.

She shook her head in refusal again. 'I want to know what they said,' she insisted.

'When you take the two pills, I will tell you what they said.'

But still she refused. 'You just want to put me to sleep. And I won't be put to sleep!'

'They are not sleeping tablets, Mrs Santino,' the doctor asserted. 'You won't sleep if you don't want to, but they will help to relax you a little. I'm telling you the truth,' he tagged on gravely as her sceptical gaze drifted his way. 'I can understand your need to remain alert throughout this ordeal, but I doubt your ability to do so if you don't accept some help. Shock and stress should not be treated lightly. You're near a complete collapse,' he diagnosed. 'Another shock like the one you received downstairs may just have the effect you've been fighting so hard against and shut you down completely. Take the pills.' He offered them to her again. 'Trust me.'

Trust him. She looked into his gravely sympathetic eyes and wondered if she could trust him. She had not allowed herself to trust any man in almost three years. Not any man.

'Take the pills, Sara.' Nicolas placed his own weight behind the advice, voice grim, utterly unmoving. 'Or watch me hold you down while the doctor sticks a hypodermic syringe in your arm.'

She took the pills. Nicolas had not and never would make idle threats. And she wasn't a fool. She knew that if they did resort to a needle it would not be injecting a relaxing aid into her system.

Nobody spoke for several minutes after that, Sara lying there with her eyes closed, the doctor standing by the bed with her wrist gently clasped between his finger and thumb, and the silence was so profound that she fancied she could actually hear the light tick of someone's watch as it counted out the seconds.

She knew even before the doctor dropped her wrist and gave the back of her hand a pat that her pulse had lost that hectic flurry it had had for the last several hours and returned to a more normal rate. She sensed the two men exchanging glances then heard the soft tread of feet moving across the room. The bedroom door opened and closed, then once again she was alone with Nicolas.

'You can tell me what happened now,' she murmured, not bothering to open her eyes. 'I won't have hysterics.'

'You did not have hysterics before,' he pointed out. 'You just dropped like a stone to the floor.'

'Déjà vu, Nicolas?' she taunted wanly.

To her surprise, he admitted it. 'Yes,' he said.

It made her open her eyes. 'Only last time you left me there, as I remember it.'

He turned away, ostensibly simply to hunt out a chair, which he drew up beside the bed, then sat down. But really she knew that he was turning away from the memory she had just evoked—of him looking murderous, fit to actually reach out and hit her, and her responding to the threat of it by passing out.

Only that particular incident had taken place in another house, another country, in another world altogether. And that time he had walked out and left her lying there.

She had not set eyes on him again until today.

'When did they call?' she asked.

'Just after I left you.'

'What did they say?'

That well-defined shadow called a mouth flexed slightly. 'You really don't need to know what they said,' he advised her. 'Let us just leave it that they wished me to be aware that they mean business.'

'What kind of business?' It was amazing, Sara noted as an

absent aside, how two small pills could take all the emotion out of her. 'Money business?'

His mouth took on a cynical tilt. 'I would have thought it obvious that they want money, since it is the one commodity I have in abundance.'

She nodded in agreement, then totally threw him by saying flatly, 'It's a lie. They don't want your money.'

He frowned. 'And how do you come to that conclusion?'

'Because they are Sicilian,' she said, as if that made everything clear. But just in case it didn't she spelled it out for him. 'If you'd said they'd taken her as part of a vendetta because you'd spoiled some big business deal of theirs or something I might have believed you. But not simply for money.'

'Are you by any chance still suspecting me of this crime?' he enquired very coolly.

If she could have done, Sara would have smiled at his affronted manner. But, having gone from rigid-tight to liquid-slack, her muscles were allowing her to do nothing other than lie here heavily on this bed.

'Not you,' she said flatly, 'but your father.'

That hardened him, honed away every bit of softening she'd seen in his face as he struck her with a narrowed glare. 'Leave my father out of this,' he commanded grimly.

'I wish I could,' she said. 'But I can't. You crossed him when you married me,' she reminded him. 'He never forgave me for that. And you're still crossing him now, by refusing to finish our marriage and find yourself another wife. How long do you think a man of his calibre will let such a situation go on before he decides to do something about it himself?'

'By stealing your child?' His derision was spiked. 'How, with your logic, does that make me jump to my father's bidding?'

Her eyes, bruised and darkened by anxiety, suddenly flickered into a clear and cynical brilliance. 'It has brought you here, hasn't it?' she pointed out. 'Made you face a mistake you have been refusing to face for three whole years.'

To her surprise, he laughed—not nicely but scathingly. 'If those are my father's tactics then he has made a grave error of judgement. What's mine I keep.' His eyes narrowed coldly on her. 'And though I will never wish to lay a finger on you myself again in this lifetime I am equally determined that no other man will have the privilege.'

The words sent a chill through her. 'Your own personal vendetta, Nicolas?' she taunted softly.

'If you like.' He didn't deny it.

Sara lifted a limp hand to cover her aching eyes. 'Then perhaps you should inform your father of that,' she said wearily.

'I don't need to,' he drawled. 'He already knows it. And even if he does pine for the day his son rids himself of one wife to get himself another,' he went on grimly, 'he is in no fit state to do anything about it.'

He got up, shifting the chair back to where he'd got it from, then turned back towards her, his face suddenly carved from stone again. 'You see, six months ago my father suffered a heart attack.' He watched coldly the way her hand slid away from her shocked eyes. 'It has left him weak in health and wheelchair-bound, barely fit to function unaided, never mind plot anything as underhand as this.'

Suddenly he was leaning over her again, intimidating and serious with it. 'So keep your nasty insinuations about my father to yourself, Sara,' he warned her. 'It is one thing you daring to insult me with your twisted view of my family, but my father is off limits; do you understand?'

'Yes,' she whispered, stunned—stunned to her very depths at the piece of news he had given her. Alfredo sick? she was thinking dazedly. That big, bullying man confined to a wheelchair? 'I'm sorry,' she said, meaning it—not for Alfredo but for Nicolas, who worshipped his father.

'I do not need your sympathy,' he said as he straightened. 'Just a curb on your vile tongue where he is concerned.'

A knock at the door heralded Toni's urgent appearance in

the doorway. He glanced warily at Sara then at his employer. 'They're on the phone again.'

Nicolas moved—so did Sara, lurching off the bed with a mixture of stark urgency and dizzying exhaustion to land swaying on her feet.

'No,' Nicolas said. 'You stay here.' He was already striding towards the door.

Her blue eyes lifted in horror. 'Nic—please!' She went to stumble after him.

'No,' he repeated brutally. 'Make her,' he instructed Toni as he went by him.

The door closed. 'I hate him,' she whispered in angry frustration. 'I hate him!'

'He is merely thinking of you, Sara,' Toni Valetta put in gently. 'It would not be pleasant being witness to the kind of discussion he is about to embark on.'

She laughed, much as Nicolas had laughed minutes ago— bitterly, scathingly. 'You mean the one where he barters for my daughter's life?'

Toni studied her wretched face but said nothing; she was only stating the raw truth of it, after all.

'Oh, damn it,' she whispered, and wilted weakly back onto the edge of the bed. Whether it was the acceptance of that truth or the pills the doctor had administered that took the legs from her she didn't know, but suddenly she found she did not have the necessary strength to remain standing any longer.

There was an uncomfortable silence, in which the man remained hovering by the closed bedroom door and Sara sat slumped, fighting the waves of exhaustion flooding through her.

'Go away, Toni,' she muttered eventually. 'Don't worry. I won't get you in trouble with your boss by making a bolt for the study as soon as your back is turned.'

His sigh was almost sad, but he did not leave; instead he moved over to stand by the window. 'I may not be the perfect choice of companion just now,' he replied heavily, 'but we used to be friends, Sara.'

Friends, she repeated to herself. Was that what they once had been? She knew Toni Valetta from years ago. He was Nicolas's tall, dark, handsome assistant. Together they made an invincible team—Toni the smooth, smiling charmer, Nicolas the ice-cold operator. Anything Nicolas could not do himself he entrusted to Toni, and Toni's loyalty to Nicolas was unimpeachable; the two men's relationship was that close. Once, years ago, Sara had believed his loyalty to Nicolas had broadened to encompass her as well. And she had considered him her friend—her only friend in a world of enemies. She had felt so alone then, so cut off from reality, bewildered by the new, rich, high-society life that Nicolas had propelled her into, and afraid of those people who openly resented her presence in it.

Toni had been the only person she could turn to in times of need when Nicolas was not there.

But when the chips had been stacked against her even Toni had turned his back on her.

'I need no one,' she said now, making her backbone erect. 'Only my baby.'

He nodded once, slowly, his gaze fixed on the garden outside. 'Nic will get her back for you,' he said with a quiet confidence that actually managed to soothe a little of that gnawing ache she was living with inside. He turned then, his dark brown eyes levelling sombrely on her. 'But you have to trust him to do it his way, Sara.'

Trust. She grimaced. There was that word again. Trust. 'They rang,' she said jerkily. 'Before their specified time. Did they say why they'd done that?'

He shrugged, his broad shoulders encased, like Nicolas's, in expensive dark silk. 'They were having us followed,' he explained. 'Nic and I. They tracked our journey from New York to here. I think they must have miscalculated how long it would take us to get to England and decided we couldn't make it before

the time they offered you.' His grimace was almost a smile. 'It
must not have occurred to them that Nic would fly Concorde...'

As he was a man who flew everywhere in his private jet, Sara
could understand it. It must have been quite a culture shock for
Nicolas Santino to use public transport—even if it was the best
public transport in the world, she mused acidly.

'The news affected him badly, Sara,' Toni put in deeply. 'I
don't think I have ever seen him so upset. Not since...'

The words tailed off. Sara didn't blame him. He had been
about to say since Nic discovered her betrayal. Not quite the
most diplomatic thing to have brought up right now.

'Nicolas said his father had been—ill.' Grimly she changed
the subject, not wanting to hear how Nicolas had felt. She
wouldn't believe Toni's interpretation of Nicolas's feelings
anyway.

'A terrible business,' Toni confirmed. 'It was fortunate he
was in London and not at home in Taormina when it happened,
or he would not be alive today.'

London? She frowned. Alfredo had been in London six
months ago when he'd been taken ill? But he never came to
London. Had always professed to hate the place!

'He spent two months in hospital here before he was well
enough to travel home. Nic hardly left his bedside for two
weeks.'

Nicolas had been that close to this house for two weeks and
she hadn't known it. She shivered.

'It was all kept very quiet, of course,' Toni continued. 'Alfredo had too many delicate fingers in too many delicate pies
for it to be—safe for the news of his illness to get out. Since
then, Nic has been working himself into the ground, doing the
job of two.'

'Poor Nic,' she murmured without an ounce of sympathy,
adding drily, 'Now this.'

Toni's eyes flashed at that—just as Nicolas's would flash to
warn of the sparking of his Sicilian temper. 'Don't mock him,

Sara,' he said stiffly. 'You of all people have no right to mock him! He is here, is he not?' His beautiful English began to deteriorate at the expense of his anger. 'He come to your aid without a second thought about it when most other men would have turned their back and walked the other way!'

'As you would have done?' His anger didn't subdue her. Once upon a time it might have done, but not anymore. None of these people would intimidate her with their hot Sicilian temperaments and cold Sicilian pride ever again. 'Then it's no wonder Nicolas is who he is and you are only his sidekick,' she derided. 'For at least he sees people as human beings and not pawns to be used or turned away from depending on how important they are to you!'

The door flew open. Sara leapt to her feet, Toni forgotten, as Nicolas came back into the room. He paused, shooting both of them a sharp glance. The air had to be thick with their exchange. And, even if it wasn't, the way Toni was standing there, all stiff Sicilian offence, would have given the game away.

'Well?' she said anxiously. 'Have they...?'

The words dwindled away, his expression enough to wipe what bit of life her hot exchange with Toni had put into her face right away again.

'Be calm,' he soothed as her arms whipped around her body and she began to shiver. 'They are still negotiating. Try to keep in the front of your mind, Sara, that they want what I have the power to give them more than they want to keep your child.'

But she hardly heard him. 'Negotiating?' she choked. 'What is there to negotiate about? Pay them, Nicolas!' she cried. 'You've got money to burn! So give it to them and get my baby back!'

He grimaced—she supposed at her naivety. But seeing it gave her pause. 'How much?' she whispered threadily.

'That part is not up for discussion,' he dismissed.

Her eyes flickered to Toni's studiedly blank face then back to Nicolas. And a low throb took up residence in her chest.

'They're asking for too much, aren't they?' she breathed. 'They want more than you can lay your hands on at such short notice.'

He smiled, not with amusement but with a kind of wry self-mockery. 'At least you are not accusing me of being tight,' he drawled.

'No.' She wasn't quite the fluffy-headed fool she sometimes sounded. She knew that people with riches made their money work for them rather than just let it take up room in some bank vault. 'So, what happens now?' she asked tensely.

'We wait.' He turned a brief nod on Toni, which was an instruction for him to leave them. The other man did as he was told, walking out of the room without saying a word.

Wait. It was over seven hours since Lia had been taken, the longest Sara had ever been without her, and it hurt—hurt so badly she could hardly bear it.

'Then what?'

'We hope by the time they call back again they will have begun to see sense.' He put it to her bluntly, as, she supposed, there was no other way to put it. 'When did you last have something to eat?'

'Hmm?' Her bruised eyes were lost in confusion, the question meaning absolutely nothing to her.

'Food,' he prompted. 'When did you last eat?'

She shook her head, lifting a hand to slide the black velvet band from her hair so that she could run shaky fingers through the thick silken strands. 'I can't eat.'

'When?' he repeated stubbornly.

'Breakfast.' Tossing the band onto the bed, she returned to hugging herself—remembering, seeing herself as she had been that morning, happy, smiling at Lia as they'd shared breakfast, the little girl smiling back. 'Oh, God.' She folded up like a paper doll onto the edge of the bed, tears of agonised helplessness filling her eyes.

'What is it?' Nicolas said tensely.

'They won't know—will they?' she choked. 'What she likes

to eat or how she likes to eat it. She'll be confused and start fretting. And she'll wonder why I'm not there with her. She—'

'Stop it.' Grimly he came to squat down in front of her. 'Listen to me, Sara. You cannot allow your mind to drift like that. Children are by nature resilient creatures. She will cope—probably better than you are coping. But you must help yourself by trying not to torment yourself like this or you will not stay the course.'

He was right. She knew it, and made a mammoth effort to calm herself, nodding her agreement, blinking away the tears. 'Did—?' Carefully she moistened paper-dry lips. 'Did they let you hear her again?'

His eyes, usually so coldly tigerish, were darker than usual. Almost as if against his wishes, his hand came up to brush her long hair away from her pale cheek. 'She is fine,' he murmured. 'I could hear her in the background chatting happily.'

'Did you record it?' she asked eagerly. 'I want to hear it.'

'No.' Suddenly he was on his feet, the cold, remote stranger he had arrived here as.

'But why not?' she demanded bewilderedly. 'I need to hear her—can't you understand that?'

'I can understand it,' he conceded. 'But I will not give in to it. It will distress you too much, so don't bother asking again.'

Stiffly he moved back towards the door, the discussion obviously over. Then he stopped, his attention caught by something standing on the polished walnut bureau. Sara's gaze followed his—then went still, just as everything inside her went still, even her breathing, as slowly he reached out with a long-fingered hand and picked up the framed photograph.

'She is very like you,' he observed after a long, taut moment.

'Yes,' was all she could manage in reply, because the facts were all there in that picture. Golden hair, pure blue eyes, pale, delicate skin. Lia was Sara's double. She bore no resemblance whatsoever to her father.

'She is very beautiful,' he added gruffly. 'You must love her very much.'

'Oh, Nicolas,' she cried, her chest growing heavy—heavy with despair for both man and child who had been robbed of their right to know and love each other. 'As you should love her! She's—!'

Your daughter too! she had been about to say. But he stopped her. 'No!' he cut in harshly—making Sara wince as he rejected both her claim and Lia's picture by snapping it back onto the polished top. 'You will not begin spouting those—frankly insulting claims all over again.' He turned, his face as coldly closed as she had ever seen it, golden eyes slaying her as they flicked over her in a contemptuous act of dismissal. 'I am not here to listen to your lies. I am here to recover your child. Your child!' he emphasized bitterly. 'Whoever the father is, it certainly is not me!'

'Yours,' she repeated, defiant in the face of his contempt. 'Your child, your conception—your betrayal of a trust I had a right to expect from you! Do you think it isn't equally insulting for me to know you can suspect me of being unfaithful to you? When?' she demanded. 'When did I ever give you reason to believe I could be capable of such a despicable crime? Me?' she choked, 'Go with another man? I was shy! So shy I would blush and stammer like an idiot if one so much as spoke to me!'

'Until you learned to taste your own powers over my sex,' he asserted. 'The powers I taught you to recognize!' He gave a deriding flick of his hand. 'Then you no longer blushed or stammered. You smiled and flirted!'

'I never did!' she denied hotly. 'My shyness irritated you so I strove to suppress it. But I would have had to have undergone a complete personality change to manage to flirt with anyone!'

'Not while I was there, no,' he agreed.

'And not while you were away!' she insisted. 'I tried to be what I thought you wanted me to be!' She appealed to his intelligence for understanding. 'I tried to behave as the other women behaved. I tried to become the upstanding member of your social circle you kept on telling me I should be! I tried very hard for your sake!'

'Too hard, then,' he clipped out. 'For I do not recall encouraging you to take a lover for my sake.'

'I did not take a lover,' she sighed.

'So the man I saw you wrapped in the arms of was a figment of my imagination, was he?' he taunted jeeringly.

'No,' she conceded, her arms wrapping around her own body in shuddering memory of that scene. 'He was real.'

'And in five weeks I had not so much as touched you, yet you still managed to become pregnant—a miracle,' he added.

'Your mathematics are poor,' she said. 'It was four weeks. And we made love several times that night.'

'And the next day you got your period which therefore cancels out that night.'

Sara sighed at that one, heavily, defeatedly. She had lied to him that next day. Lied because he had just told her that he was going away and she'd wanted to punish him for leaving her again so soon. She had concocted the lie which would deprive him of her body—and had learned to regret the lie every single day of her life since.

All of which she had confessed to him before without it making an ounce of difference to what he believed, so she was not going to try repeating it again now.

'No ready reply to that one, I note,' he drawled when she offered nothing in return.

Sara shook her head. 'Believe what you want to believe,' she tossed at him wearily. 'It really makes little difference to me any more...' She meant it, too; her expression told him so as she lifted blue eyes dulled of any hint of life to his. 'I once loved you more than life itself. Now my love for Lia takes precedence over anything I ever felt for you.'

All emotion was honed out of his face at that. 'Tidy yourself,' he instructed, turning with cold dismissal back to the door. 'Then come downstairs. I will go and arrange for something to eat.'

CHAPTER THREE

THE HOUSE HAD returned to its usual smooth running. Mrs Hobbit, the housekeeper, bustled about. Mr Hobbit, Sara noticed when she glanced out of her bedroom window before going down, was busily working on the new play area he and Sara had been planning at the bottom of the garden. It wrenched at her heart to see him rhythmically spreading bark chippings over the specially prepared patch where, next week, a garden swing and slide were due to be fixed—yet, oddly, it comforted her. Mr Hobbit had not given up hope of Lia's return and neither would she.

When she eventually made herself go downstairs to the dining room she found Nicolas standing at the window watching the old man at his work. It was June and the sun set late in the evenings. You could work outside until ten o'clock if you were so inclined. This evening the garden was bathed in a rich coral glow that cast a warmth over everything, including Nicolas.

Something stirred inside her—something long, long suppressed. The ache of a woman for the man she loved.

And for a moment she couldn't move or speak, couldn't let

him know she was there because she was suddenly seeing another man from another time who used to stand by the window like that. A man whom she would have gone to join, slipping her arm through the crook of his and leaning against him while she described all the plans she had made for their garden. Their daughter.

How would Nicolas have responded if things had not been as they were between them and she had been able to go freely and tell him what Mr Hobbit was doing? Would he have been amused? Interested? Would he have wanted to join in the planning of their child's first play garden?

Her eyes glazed over, sudden tears blurring his silhouette as rain would against a sheet of glass.

The first time she had met Nicolas it had been raining, Sara recalled. Not the fine summer rain you tended to get at this time of year, but a sudden heavy cloudburst that had sent people running in an effort to get out of it as soon as they could.

She'd been a very ordinary assistant in a big garden centre on the outskirts of central London then. Twenty-one years old and so painfully shy that her cheeks flushed if a stranger so much as smiled at her, she had been more happy to spend her time amongst the shrubs and plants than to deal with customers. But the garden centre had run a plant service whereby they'd provided and cared for the plants the big office blocks in the city liked to decorate their foyers with. One aspect of her job had been to attend to a certain section of these 'rentals', as they called them. But it had taken every ounce of courage she possessed to walk into some of the palatial foyers on her list.

The shyness had been left over from the quiet, lonely childhood spent with her widowed, ageing father who had taken early retirement from teaching when his wife had died leaving him solely responsible for their only child. They'd moved away from the quiet London suburb to the wild, lonely fells of Yorkshire, where he'd decided to teach his daughter himself rather than send her the five miles to the nearest school.

She was thirteen years old when he died, quite suddenly, of a heart attack while walking on his beloved fells. The first thing Sara knew of it was when his dog, Sammie, came back without him, whimpering at the cottage door.

After that she was sent to a boarding-school to finish her education, paid for out of her father's estate. But by then the shyness was already an inherent part of her and she found it difficult if not painful to interact with any of the other girls. She coped, though—barely, but she coped—learned to deal with other people on a quiet, timid level. But she did not manage to make any real friends, and spent most of her free time wandering around the school's private grounds, which was probably how she developed such an interest in plants—that and the fact that the school's resident gardener was a quiet little man who reminded her of her father, which meant she could at least relax with him.

It was with his quiet encouragement that she discovered she had a flair for gardening. Green-fingered, he called it—an ability to make anything grow—and she would have gone on to horticultural college after leaving the school, but then another disaster struck when she contracted glandular fever just before her final exams, which stopped her taking them. The virus lingered with her for over a year. By the time it had gone, so had her funds. And rather than take her exams a year late then try for college she had to get herself a job instead.

Which was why she was in that particular street in London the day she bumped into Nicolas—literally bumped into him, she on her way back from attending to her customer list, he as he climbed out of a black cab.

It was lunchtime. A heavy downpour of rain had just opened up. People were running, as was Sara herself—hurrying with her head down as a black cab drew up at the curb just in front of her. The door flew open and a man got out, almost knocking her off her feet when they collided.

'Apologies,' he clipped. That was all; she didn't think he even glanced at her then, just strode off across the flow of rushing pedestrians and into the nearest building.

That should have been the end of it. And sometimes when she looked back she found herself wishing that it had been the end of it. Her life would have been so different if Nicolas had not come barging into it as he had. But then at other times she could only count her blessings, because without knowing him she would not have learned that she could love another person as deeply as she had learned to love him—she had been too shy to experiment with feelings at all, until she'd met him. She would not have learned about her own simmering passions or how they could overpower any shyness when coaxed to do so by a man whose own passions ran hot and dynamic through his blood.

And she would not have known the greatest loves of all. The love of a child for its mother. And the love a mother could feel for her child.

So no, no matter what had happened to them since, she was not sorry now that her first encounter with Nicolas had not been the last encounter. But coming into contact with a man of Nicolas Santino's dynamic personality had been a bit like being a dove devoured by an eagle.

He'd dropped his wallet. Right at her feet and in the pouring rain. He had stalked off without knowing he had dropped it, having absently tried to shove the wallet back into his jacket pocket.

Standing there with the rain pouring down on her head and still feeling a bit winded by the way he had bumped into her, she had taken a moment to realise what it was that had fallen onto her feet. She'd bent, picked it up, glanced a bit dazedly around her for a sign of what to do next. He had already disappeared into the building by then, and logic had told her that she really had no choice but to follow him.

The rest, she supposed, was history—her following him into the building, luckily seeing him standing by the reception desk with a bevy of dark-suited men around him all shaking hands, her approaching shyly.

'Excuse me...' Tentatively she touched his arm.

He turned, looked down at her, and she could still remember the way his golden eyes made her quiver oddly inside as they lanced into her.

The soft green sweatshirt she was wearing, with the logo of the garden centre she worked for emblazoned on the front, was wet through. Her hair, braided in a single thick plait, dripped water down her back. Her face was wet, not to mention her jean-clad legs and trainers. He took it all in seemingly without needing to remove his gaze from her blushing face.

'Yes?' he prompted.

'I th-think you dropped th-this when you bumped into me just n-now...' Nervously she held out the wallet towards him. 'Could y-you please check if it's y-yours?'

It was sheer reaction that sent his hands up to pat his pockets. But he did not take his eyes off her face. A small silence developed while she held out the wallet and he ignored it. A couple of the entourage gathered around him shuffled their feet when they picked up on the sudden tension flowing through the air.

He was tall and she wasn't, the top of her head barely reaching his chin, so she had to tilt her head to look into his face. The rain had caught him too, but only briefly, so the drops sat on the expensive silk of his jacket in small crystal globules that could easily be brushed away. His hair was so black that it reminded her of midnight, gleaming damply but not dripping wet like hers.

She didn't know then that the great Nicolas Santino stood there like that in silence because he was completely and utterly love-struck. He admitted that to her later—weeks later when his single-minded campaign to break through her shy reserve was successful—on a night when she lay in his arms on a bed of fine linen, their bodies damp, limbs tangled, his hand gently stroking her long hair across the pillow. And she was shy—still shy even though he had just guided her through the most intimate journey a man and woman could share with each other.

A week after that, they married in a registry office in London. That was the first time she met Toni—when he stood witness for Nicolas. She remembered how strangely he looked at her—as if he couldn't believe the kind of woman his employer had decided to marry. And the hushed conversation they'd shared before they'd gone in to the ceremony had confirmed his disbelief.

'What the hell are you playing at, Nic?' he'd muttered urgently. 'She doesn't look strong enough to manage you, never mind a hostile father-in-law!'

Hostile? She had begun to get very nervous at that point, frightened even. But then Nicolas had smiled. She could still conjure up that smile now and feel the warmth of it fill her.

'She manages me fine,' he had murmured softly. 'She is my opposite in every way that matters and with her I am complete. She will manage my father as well; you will see,' he'd ordained.

He had been wrong. She had not managed his father. In fact, she had been terrified of him from their first meeting. He was a sly, selfish, power-hungry and nasty old man who'd seen her as the single obstacle spoiling the glorious plans he had made for his only child. But he was also clever—clever enough never to let Nicolas see how much he hated Sara for getting in the way of those plans.

Oh, he voiced his initial disappointment in his son's choice of bride, showed anger, a bitter scepticism of the English in general and of Sara's ability to cope with the kind of lifestyle they led. Then when he met the brick wall of his son's own determination to run his life his own way he stepped back to the sidelines and watched and plotted and waited for his moment to pounce.

He picked up on her shyness and timidity straight away and used it ruthlessly against her, forcing her into situations where she would feel totally out of her depth. He knew the great Santino wealth and power intimidated her. He knew she only felt comfortable when Nicolas was at her side, so he arranged it so that Nicolas was hardly ever there.

And Alfredo put himself up as her escort, cloaking his hostility towards her in the presence of his son, displaying a willingness to be Sara's mentor while she got used to the kind of socialising expected of a Santino woman—while Nicolas got on with more important things, like running the Santino empire.

Consequently, she spent the first year of her marriage in a bewildering world of fine clothes and expensive cars and brittle, bright, sophisticated people who were quite happy to follow the great Alfredo Santino's lead and mock his very unsophisticated daughter-in-law whenever the chance arose. The fact that on the few occasions she tried to tell Nicolas this he got angry and actually took offence on his father's behalf only made her feel more helplessly out of her depth, more isolated, more miserable.

It began to put a strain on their marriage. When Nicholas was home, his father would be all charm, which made Sara tense up with a wariness her husband could not understand. When they went out together, the same people who followed Alfredo's lead would now follow Nicolas's lead and treat his wife with a warmth she was, quite naturally, suspicious of and Nicolas saw as her being standoffish and cold.

Then a man—an Englishman, Jason Castell—began showing her a lot of attention. Whenever she was out with Alfredo, he would appear at her side, sit with her, dance with her, forever trying to monopolise her attention. If she was out with Nicolas, Jason would be conspicuous in his absence.

Yet Nicolas still heard about him. 'Who is this Englishman I hear you've befriended?' he asked her one evening as they were getting ready for bed.

'Who, Jason?' she asked. 'He's a friend of your father's, not mine.'

'That is not how I hear it,' he said coolly. 'I would prefer it if my wife did not have her name connected with another man. Break the friendship, Sara,' he warned. 'Or watch me break it for you.'

For some time her desire to fight back, if only with Nicolas, had been growing stronger the more pressure Alfredo applied to her nerves. And this once she retaliated, hard and tight. 'If you can rarely be bothered to be here with me yourself, then I don't see what right you have to tell me who I can and cannot spend my time with.'

'I have the right of a husband,' he arrogantly replied.

'Is that what you call yourself? I call you the man who occasionally visits my bed! How long have you been away this time, Nicolas?' she demanded as his eyes flashed a warning. 'Two, nearly three weeks? What am I supposed to do with myself when you're not here—hide away in purdah?' In her mind this was not an argument about Jason Castell, but about their lifestyle in general. 'If you want to know what I'm doing every single minute of the day then stay around and find out!'

'I have a business to run!' he threw back harshly. 'The same business which pays for all your fine clothes and the luxury surroundings for you to wear them in!'

'And did I ask for the clothes?' she challenged. 'Did I ask for the luxury accommodation? When I fell in love with you I fell in love with the man, not his money! But I rarely see the man, do I?'

'You're seeing him now,' he murmured huskily.

And she was, seeing him in all his golden-skinned, sensually sinewed, naked glory.

But for the first time ever she turned away from the invitation his husky words had offered. 'We've been married for almost a year,' she said. 'And I can count on the fingers of one hand how many weeks we've actually spent together. This isn't even my home, it's your father's!' she sighed. 'And on the rare occasions you do find time to come here your father takes priority.'

'I refuse to pander to your unnatural jealousy of my relationship with my father,' he clipped.

'And I hate living here,' she told him bluntly. 'And if you can't be here more than you are then I want to go home, to London. I want to get a job and work to fill my days. I want a life, Nicolas,' she appealed to his steadily closing face, 'that doesn't revolve around couture shops and beauty parlours and feeling the outsider with all these tight-knit, clannish Sicilians!'

'A life with an Englishman, perhaps.'

She sighed again, irritably this time. 'This has nothing to do with Jason.'

'No?'

'No!' she denied. 'It is to do with you and me and a marriage that isn't a marriage because you aren't here enough! It's to do with me being unhappy here!' Tears, honest tears, filled her eyes at that point; she could see him blur out of focus as she appealed to him to understand. 'I can't go on like this—can't you see? They—your father, your friends—overwhelm me! I'm frightened when you're not here!'

An appeal from the heart. It should have cut into him, reminded him of the soft, gentle creature he had originally fallen in love with. The one who had been so timid that she used to cling to him when he'd introduced her to someone he knew, or had reached for his hand if they'd crossed the road, or could be tongue-tied by a painful shyness when teased.

But he was Sicilian. And a Sicilian man was by nature territorial and possessive. And if Sara dismissed Jason Castell from her mind as unimportant Nicolas didn't. Because she hadn't voiced all of these complaints before the Englishman's name had begun cropping up in conversations around the island. She hadn't dared to argue with him like this before the man had come on the scene.

And she had never turned away from the blatant invitation of his body before the Englishman's appearance.

'Get into bed,' he gritted.

'No.' She began to quiver at the expression on his face. 'I w-want to talk this through...'

He began striding around the bed towards her. She backed away, her hands outstretched to ward him off, long, delicately boned fingers trembling. 'Please don't,' she whispered unsteadily. 'You're frightening me. I don't want to be frightened of you too...'

But he wasn't listening, or maybe didn't care at that moment that he was about to murder the one firm bit of faith she had—that he, this hard-headed, ruthless hunter she had married, would not, could not hurt her.

He hurt her. Oh, not in the physical sense, but with a hard, ruthless sensuality that left her feeling ravaged to the point of shock. 'Go near the Englishman and I shall kill you both,' he then vowed tautly. 'What's mine I keep, and you are most definitely mine!'

'What's mine I keep...'

He never retracted that vow. Not throughout the following month when she never saw him, never heard from him, never left the villa. She didn't even hear Alfredo's mocking little jibes about her failing marriage and his son's preference for being anywhere but with his pathetic little wife.

She didn't so much as suspect the neat little trap that Alfredo was setting for her when he delivered a message from Nicolas one evening telling her to meet him in Catania in a hotel they had sometimes stayed in when attending some function in the city.

She arrived at the appointed suite, nervous, a little frightened, praying that he had asked her to come here because he was at last beginning to accept that she was unhappy and they needed to be alone to talk without fear of interruption. She let herself in with the provided key, took the overnight bag Nicolas had told her to bring with her through to the bedroom, then went back into the sitting room to wait.

He didn't come. By ten o'clock she was feeling let down and angry. By eleven she'd grimly got ready for bed. By twelve she was trying hard to fall asleep when she heard another key in the door. Elation sent her scrambling in her lovely cream silk nightdress out of the bed and towards the bedroom door just as it opened inwards.

Then came the shock, the horror, the confusion, because it wasn't Nicolas who came through the door but Jason. Jason, who paused in the open doorway, smiled, and murmured, 'Sara, darling, you look exquisite—as always.'

Blank incomprehension held her stunned and silent. He stepped closer, pulling her into his arms and she let him do it, utterly incapable of working out how to deal with the situation.

A mistake, she was thinking stupidly. Jason had somehow made a terrible, terrible mistake!

A hand landing hard against its wood sent the door flying open. And then Nicolas stood there. Nicolas, with his face turned to rock. Nicolas, who stared at her with his hunter's gold eyes turned yellow with shock while she stared helplessly back, the frissons of confusion, alarm, horror and shock wild inside her.

'So my father was right. You bitch,' he said. That was all.

Guilty as charged. Her silence damned her. Her blushing cheeks damned her. The way Jason made a lurching dive for the balcony doors and disappeared through them to go she neither knew nor cared where damned her. And the sheer silk nightdress bought especially for this meeting and which showed every contour of her slender body beneath damned her.

He still didn't move and neither could she. Her mind was rocketing through all the reasons why Jason could have come here believing that she was waiting for him. Then it hit her, and she went white—not with shame but with fury.

Alfredo. Alfredo had set her up—set this up! Alfredo.

'Nic-please!' Her blue eyes were slightly wild and begging. 'This isn't what you—'

He took a step towards her, his face turning from rock to murderous threat. His hand came up, the back of it aimed to lash out at her.

'No!' she cried, instinctively cowering away, long hair flying in a wild arc as her arms came up to protect her face.

It stopped him; seeing her cower like that did manage to stop him. 'For God's sake!' she pleaded, wretchedly from behind her protecting hands. 'You must listen to me!'

'Never,' he said through gritted teeth. 'You no longer exist.'

He meant it. She could see in the glacial gold of his eyes that he meant it. It was too much. She fainted at his feet. When she came round she was alone, lying where he had left her.

She hadn't so much as spoken to him again until today. She had not been allowed back in the villa. And that same hotel suite had become her prison for the next few terrible days until Toni, cold-eyed and uncommunicative, had come to personally escort her off the island and back to London.

Wretched with despair and weak with nervous reaction, she'd done as she was told, come here to this house, sat here in this house for weeks—weeks waiting for him to calm down, see sense, realise that she, of all people, could never do such a wicked thing as to take another lover.

Then she'd discovered she was pregnant, and everything had changed. She'd tried phoning him; he'd refused to take her calls. She'd tried writing to him; he hadn't acknowledged her letters. In the end she'd turned to Toni for help, called him on the phone and begged him—begged him to persuade Nicolas to see her, listen to what she had to say! 'I'm going to have his baby, Toni!' Even now, three years on, she could still hear the anguish in her voice. 'Surely that must mean something to him!'

It hadn't. The next day the phone had rung. It was Toni.

'He says you lie,' he informed her coldly. 'The child you carry cannot be his. You may have the use of the house you are in at present.' He went on in that same icy vein. 'Everything you and the child may need will be provided so long as you remain there and say nothing of your betrayal.'

'If he feels like that, then why doesn't he just throw me out on the street and divorce me?' she sliced back bitterly, hurt and angered by the injustice of it all.

'You have humiliated him enough without the added scandal of a divorce,' he clipped. 'But hear this,' he then warned icily.

'Let another man near you and he will kill you both; make no mistake about that.'

Did that mean Jason already lay dead somewhere in Sicily? she wondered, and found she couldn't care less. Jason had to have been in cahoots with Alfredo. It had not taken her long to work that one out. And for that he deserved anything Nicolas might have decided to deal out to him. It was only a shame that Alfredo would not be getting his due for his part in it all.

But maybe Alfredo had got what was due to him, she now thought as she slowly returned to the present. Because in his determination to get rid of the woman he saw as an unfit wife for his son he had lost the right to love one of the most wonderful creatures ever placed on this earth: Lia. Was he ever curious? she wondered. Did he ever just sit and wonder about his son's child who was also his grandchild? Did he ever suffer from pangs of regret?

She hoped he did. She really hoped that, sick man or not now, he suffered daily from bitter, bitter regrets.

And that, she acknowledged grimly, was her own desire for vengeance rearing its ugly head.

A movement just behind her in the doorway made her turn to find herself captured by Toni's narrowed, watchful eyes. And for a moment—a brief but stinging moment—she had a feeling he knew exactly what she had been thinking.

Then the connection was broken because Nicolas heard them and turned around. But all through dinner she felt Toni's eyes on her, and stung with the uncomfortable feeling that he had sensed her thirst for revenge.

He was Sicilian. And Sicilians claimed exclusive rights on vendettas. He would not take kindly to the idea of a mere English woman encroaching on those rights. Especially against a fellow Sicilian.

The meal was an ordeal. Sara forced down a couple of small bites of the braised chicken placed in front of her but other than that could swallow nothing. Nicolas and Toni ate with her, their occasional bursts of conversation to do with some business deal they were presently involved in. But these exchanges were brief, and largely they respected her desire to keep silent.

'Excuse me.' At last she stood up from the table, bringing both dark heads up sharply. 'I've had enough. I think I'll go and take a shower...'

'Try to rest,' Nicolas quietly advised. 'I promise I will come and tell you the moment I have any news.'

She nodded, wearied—too weary to want to argue. She wouldn't rest—she knew she wouldn't—but it was easier to let him think that she might than to battle.

She didn't think she would sleep again until she had her baby back in her arms.

CHAPTER FOUR

IT WAS A long night. Sara dozed fitfully and came down to breakfast the next morning hollow-eyed and wan-faced, to find Nicolas sitting alone at the breakfast table, a newspaper spread out in front of him.

He folded it away when he saw her, though, making a narrow-eyed study of the obvious evidence of strain in her face.

She gave an inward grimace, entirely aware of exactly how terrible she looked.

She was wearing no make-up, and the peaches-and-cream bloom that her skin usually wore was missing. She had brushed her hair, but only so she could tie it at the back to keep the long, heavy mass out of the way. And she was wearing a simple, sprigged muslin skirt teamed with a long, loose silk knit jumper in a delicate shade of blue. Under normal circumstances the pastel colour would have suited her, but today it just enhanced the washed-out look—not that she cared. She didn't care about anything to do with herself right now.

He didn't look too hot either, she noted. His lean face had a drawn quality about it that suggested he hadn't slept much himself last night. But at least the slick silk business suit had gone, his casual beige linen trousers and long-sleeved polo shirt in mint-green softening the harder edges of his tycoon persona. And the shirt was big enough not to mold his impressive torso but soft enough to make her aware of the muscled breast flexing beneath it as he moved.

'What has happened to the nanny?' she asked, pulling out a chair and sitting down. 'I went to see how she was this morning, but she wasn't there, and her room has been cleared out.'

'She was taken home to her parents last night,' he informed her. 'She was too distressed to be any use here so...' His concluding shrug said the rest.

No use, so remove her. Sara found a small smile. 'I never wanted a nanny in the first place,' she remarked.

'You were ill,' he reminded her, getting up to go over to the internal telephone. 'Tea for my wife,' he ordered curtly to whoever it was who answered. 'And whatever she usually eats for breakfast.

'You needed help with the child,' he continued as he returned to his seat.

That filled her eyes with a rueful wryness that rid them of a little bit of strain. 'Have I managed to make a single move during the last three years that you don't know about?' she mocked, not expecting an answer—and not getting one.

She knew how Nicolas worked. 'What's mine I keep,' et cetera. And that was exactly what he had done over the last three years—kept his wife and her child in the kind of comfort that would be expected of a man of his stature.

So when Sara had gone down with a severe bout of flu several months ago Julie, the nanny, had appeared to take over caring for Lia. Since then, she'd stayed, not by Sara's request but probably because this man had ordained it so. Now the nanny had been banished again. For being of no use. For falling into a fit of hysterics in the park instead of responding as she should have responded when her charge was snatched from right beneath her nose and coming straight home to inform Lucas, the chauffeur, who would have then immediately informed Nicolas, his boss—probably before he would have informed Sara. Because Lucas the chauffeur was not just a chauffeur. He was Sara's guard, and she chose the word selectively. Lucas was paid to guard one of Nicolas Santino's possessions, namely his wife—not the child, who he did not believe was his child and therefore did not warrant her own guard to watch her every move. Which was why someone had managed to take her.

The breakfast-room door opened and Mrs Hobbit came in carrying a tray loaded with tea things and some lightly toasted whole-meal bread. She smiled nervously at Nicolas and warmly at Sara.

'Now, you eat this toast,' she commanded sternly, her busy hands emptying the tray onto the table in front of Sara. 'Or I shall just follow you around with it until you do.'

'I will,' Sara whispered, her eyes filling with a sudden burst of weak tears at the older woman's rough kind of affection. 'Thank you.'

'Oh!' the housekeeper exclaimed in dismay when she saw the tears. And suddenly Sara was being engulfed by a big, homely bosom. 'Now, there, there,' Mrs Hobbit murmured soothingly. 'You need a good cry, and don't we all?' Her soft bosom quivered on a sigh. 'But the little princess will be back here before you know it, all safe and sound; you wait and see.'

'Yes. Of course.' With a mammoth drag on her energy, Sara pulled herself together, straightening out of the older woman's arms. 'I'm sorry. It was just...' Her words trailed off, lost in the helplessness she was feeling inside.

'I know exactly what it was,' Mrs Hobbit said grimly. 'You don't have to explain anything to me, madam. Not a thing...'

With that she patted Sara's arm and walked out, leaving Sara alone with a very still Nicolas who had observed the whole exchange without uttering a single word.

Sara didn't look at him—couldn't. She had an idea that he had been rather shocked by Mrs Hobbit's affectionate display.

'They all—care for you a great deal, don't they?' he commented at last. 'I've already had Lucas in this morning enquiring about how you are coping. And Mr Hobbit stopped me in the garden earlier to do the same.'

Was he making a comparison with the cold, stiff way his Sicilian servants had treated her? He should do. The difference was palpable. 'Surprised, are you?' she countered drily, reaching out with an unsteady hand for the teapot. 'That anyone could care for the likes of me?'

To her surprise he got up and stepped tensely over to the window. 'No,' he replied, the single negative raking over a throat that sounded usually dry for him.

A silence fell, and Sara poured herself a cup of tea then cupped it in her fingers, bringing it to her lips to sip lightly at the steaming hot drink. He didn't turn back to the table, and they remained like that for long, taut minutes, she sipping at her drink, he lost inside some tense part of himself.

'Is she?' he asked suddenly. 'A little princess?' Sara stared at his long, straight back and felt the bitter burn of a bloody anger begin to swell inside her. Today he had the damned effrontery to ask a question like that when only last night he had virtually denied her the right to so much as speak of the child! He had even tossed the baby's picture away from him in open distaste!

She stood up, discarding her cup onto its saucer with the same appearance of distaste. 'Go to hell, Nicolas,' she said, and walked out of the room.

The morning stretched out like an interminable wasteland in front of her, growing more difficult to bear the longer it went on without a single telephone ringing in the house. The silence grated. The sense of utter, wretched helplessness grated. The way everyone else seemed to be getting on with their normal business grated. And the burning fact that Nicolas had locked himself away in the study and not come out again grated. Because he should be right here by her side comforting and supporting her! Worrying with her!

If he truly believed Lia to be his daughter would he be so calm and collected about it all? Would he be sitting in that damned study getting on with the day's business while the people who had stolen their baby decided to make them sweat with this long, cruel silence?

In the end, she couldn't stand it. Couldn't stand any of it any longer. In an act of desperation she ran upstairs, dragged on an old pair of washed-out and skintight jeans and a T-shirt and ran downstairs again, busily tying a dark green cotton apron about her slender waist while trying to open the front door at the same time.

'Can I help you, Mrs Santino?' A big, burly bodyguard stepped out in front of her.

'No,' she said. 'Thank you.' And she went to walk past him.

The big hand closing quite gently around her arm made her freeze. 'Take your hand off me,' she instructed him glacially.

A dark flush rushed into his face. But he maintained his grip on her arm. 'I have instructions that you are not to—'

'Nicolas!' she shouted at the top of her voice.

Doors flew open all over the place—including the study door. Nicolas appeared in the hallway, his gaze sharp-eyed and questioning as he took in the little scene being enacted on the steps of the front porch.

'Tell him,' Sara breathed, barely enunciating because of the revulsion bubbling inside her, 'to get his hands off me!'

Instead of obeying, Nicolas frowned. 'What is this, Sara?' he asked in genuine puzzlement. 'You must know that none of my men mean you any harm—'

'Tell him,' she repeated, her quivering mouth ringed by a white line of tension. '*Tell him right now!*'

His face darkened, his walk as he came down the hall towards her a statement in itself. He wasn't used to being spoken to like that, especially in front of his lackeys. And he did not like it that she was daring to do so now.

He flashed the guard a slicing look that had him abruptly letting go of her arm then melting away like ice on hot coals. 'Right,' he said shortly. 'Would you like to tell me what that was all about?'

'No,' she replied, her face still tense with anger and disgust.

He wouldn't understand if she did try to explain how no man—no man—would ever touch her again without her permission—not without her retaliating accordingly, anyway. She had learned that lesson the hard way, at Jason Castell's hands. If she had screamed then, if she'd only had the sense to scream and shout and make loud protests, then Nicolas would have known she deserved his help and not his anger. And everything else would have been so different.

He sighed, his whole manner impatient. 'Then would you like to tell me where you think you are going?'

'Out,' she said. 'Or am I under some kind of house arrest?' she then asked bitterly.

'No.' He denied that, but in a way that only helped to irk her further. 'But I would have thought your daughter's plight was more important to you than any appointment you may desire to keep.'

Sarcasm, dry and deriding. She responded to it like a match to dry wood. 'Don't you dare try telling me what should be important to me,' she flashed, 'when you have no understanding of the concept yourself!'

An eyebrow arched, black, sleek and threatening, golden eyes warning her to watch her step. 'Where do you think you are going, Sara?' he repeated smoothly.

'I don't think it, I know it!' she asserted. 'We still have the right of free will in this country in case you didn't know it. I can go where I please without answering to anyone and that includes you and your damned henchmen!'

With that she turned, hair flying out in a silken fan of sun-kissed gold, the frustration that had been building up all morning culminating in that one furious movement.

His hand circling her wrist halted her mid-step, pulling her back round to face him. 'Stop it,' he commanded when she tried to tug free. His face was dark, its angles sharpened with anger. 'Now try again,' he suggested. 'And this time come up with a suitable reply. Where do you think you are going?' He enunciated it warningly.

She glared into his predator's eyes, glared down at the place where his long fingers were crushing the bones in her slender wrist, felt the ready tears burst into her eyes and the frustration alter to despair. Felt horrid and frightened and useless and fed up and lonely and—

'To help Mr Hobbit in the garden,' she whispered thickly, and wilted like a rag doll. 'Where else would I be going dressed like this?'

He should have recognised what she was wearing! He might hate the very sight of her, and he might have come to despise her lack of sophistication and good dress sense. But did he really think she would go out into the street dressed like this?

And he really should have recognised the apron as the same kind she always wore to work in the garden!

And it hurt—hurt like hell that he hadn't.

He muttered something. What, she didn't catch, because she was too busy fighting the onset of tears. Then the grip on her wrist slackened and she slid it free to lift it into her other hand where she rubbed at it pitiably.

'Where are your gloves?' he enquired gruffly.

So, he remembered that she usually wore gloves to protect her hands! One small tick in his favour, she thought sarcastically, and indicated with a half-nod of her bowed head towards the side of the house. 'In the garden shed,' she mumbled.

'Come on, then.' His arm coming to rest across her shoulders made her stiffen in rejection, but he ignored it. 'Let's go and find your gloves.'

She went with him simply because he gave her no choice, the arm remaining where it was as they walked together around the front of the house to the side where, cleverly concealed behind a high box hedge, the big garden shed stood with its door open to reveal the multitude of gardening implements held inside.

The moment they reached it, she went to move away from him, but he stopped her, the arm remaining firm as he twisted his body until he was standing in front of her. Then he reached out to pick up her wrist—the wrist he had used to pull her back towards him. His fingers were gentle as they ran over the tiny marks already promising to become bruises in the near future.

Sara kept her face lowered and didn't even breathe. If she did breathe she would weep; she knew she would. She was feeling so raw at the moment that anything—anything—was likely to set her off.

'I'm sorry,' he said eventually. 'I'm sorry if I overreacted. But you must understand that it is not safe for you to come outside without someone with you. And I am sorry for this.' His thumb brushed a gentle caress over the fine veins in her wrist. 'I forgot my own strength, and the delicacy of yours.'

'Why isn't it safe?' she asked huskily.

He didn't answer for a moment, then gave a small sigh. 'We're dealing with ruthless people here, Sara,' he said grimly. 'They will stop at nothing to get what they want. Which means they would very much like to snatch you too if they thought they could get you.'

'Why?' She lifted tear-filled eyes to him in wretched bewilderment. 'Isn't it enough that they have my baby? What more do they think another life is worth on top of hers?'

For the first time since he had walked back into her life yesterday, she saw the Nicolas she used to know. The one who didn't slice her in two with his eyes. The one who looked almost—tender.

A tenderness that was mirrored in the way he dropped her wrist in favour of stroking a gentle finger over her pale cheek.

'When I married you I went against my father's wishes,' he reminded her. 'In their eyes that makes you my most prized possession.' He paused, looking deeply into her hollowed, anxious eyes which showed such a complete lack of comprehension, then sighed heavily. 'The child is enough. They know she is enough, but in case I decide not to toe the line some extra leverage would suit them down to the ground.'

'But you are toeing the line, aren't you?' she demanded with an upsurge of alarm. 'You won't put her life at risk by playing games with them?'

His eyes flashed, tenderness wiped out by anger. 'What do you think I am?' he muttered. 'Some unfeeling monster? Of course I won't put her at risk!'

'Then why are you trying to frighten me with all this talk of my own safety being at risk?'

'Because they have already threatened it, dammit!' he growled, then pulled her to him—as if he couldn't help himself, he pulled her to him and pressed her face into his chest. 'I shall kill them if they so much as touch you,' he vowed harshly. 'Kill every single one of them!'

'But you don't feel the same killer instinct for the baby,' she noted, and firmly pushed herself away from him.

He sighed, derision cutting an ugly line into his mouth. 'Is it not enough for you that I can feel that kind of emotion for a faithless wife?' he mocked himself bitterly.

'No,' she replied. 'It isn't enough.' And she walked into the garden shed and away from him.

He followed her, his expression harsh to say the least. 'You give no quarter, do you?' he rasped.

'No,' she agreed, rummaging through the mad clutter that decorated the workbench. 'Why should I, when you gave none to me?'

'I kept you, Sara,' he seared, 'when I should have thrown both you and your child out on the street to starve!'

'And why didn't you?' she challenged him, spinning to face

him. 'Because you were protecting your own pride, Nicolas,' she offered as the answer. 'That isn't giving anything,' she declared. 'That is just you protecting you.' With a gesture of contempt, she turned back to the bench. 'So if you're expecting eternal gratitude forget it. You did me no favours allowing me to stay here, and if anything I hold you responsible for not protecting us properly when you must have known we were at risk!'

His response to that was a short, hard, mocking laugh. 'You are amazing, do you know that?' he said in scathing disbelief. 'It is no wonder you remain so stunningly beautiful when you can shed blame as easily as you do! Your own sins are not allowed to linger long enough to place a single line of guilt or shame upon your lovely face! It must be the perfect recipe for eternal youth!'

'And what's your recipe?' she countered, then went very still, realising what she had just said.

He was still too, silent, unbreathing, pumping the wretched Freudian slip for all it was worth. Then, 'For my beauty?' he prompted silkily.

Her nerve-ends went into panic mode, forcing her hands to move again in short, jerky movements. 'Men aren't generally described as beautiful.' She dismissed his question as casually as she could.

But it was too late. She'd known it was too late from the moment she let the foolish remark slip from her lips. He was suddenly standing right behind her, bending to brace his hands on the bench at either side of her tense frame, his breath warm against her slowly colouring cheek. 'Yet beautiful was always the word you used to describe me,' he reminded her softly. 'You would lie naked on top of me with your lovely hair caressing my shoulders and your slender arms braced on my chest. You would look into my eyes and say with heart-rending solemnity, 'You are so beautiful, Nicolas,'' he chanted tauntingly.

'Stop it,' she hissed, having to close her eyes to blot out the picture he was so cruelly building. But it wouldn't be blocked out. Instead it played itself across the backs of her quivering eyelids. Beautiful hair... She could hear herself saying it in that soft, adoring voice she used to use as her fingertips had reverently touched the smooth black silk. Beautiful nose, beautiful mouth, beautiful skin...

And he used to listen—listen to every shy, soft, serious word with a solemn intensity that made her sure, so sure, that the moment had touched something very deep inside him.

You have beautiful shoulders... Her fingers would trace them, sliding lovingly over the muscular curves and hollows. Beautiful chest...

She let out a shaky sigh, her tongue sneaking out to run a moistening caress around her suddenly dry lips because she knew what her mind was going to conjure up next. And it conjured up the way her head would lower, her soft mouth closing round one of his beautiful, taut male nipples...

His response had been that of a man driven beyond anything, his eyes turning molten, the breath escaping his lungs on a harshly sensuous rasp. And in a quick, sure, purely masculine action he would lift his legs to clamp them around her slender hips then tug her downwards—down until she—

'Did you whisper those same soft, evocative words to your lover?'

The angry growl had her eyes flicking open, her whole body jumping on a sudden stinging crack back to reality. His hands came up, hard on her shoulders, to spin her around.

'Did they have the same mind-blowing effect on him they used to have on me?'

She shook her head, unable to answer, white-faced and pained, her breasts heaving on a single frightened intake of air when she saw the anger scored into his face—the hard, murderous jealousy.

'Have you any idea what it did to me imagining you lying there with him like that?' he grated. 'I loved you, dammit!' he

snarled. 'I worshipped the very ground you stood upon! You
were mine—mine!' He shook her hard. 'I found you! I woke
you! I *owned* this beautiful body and those beautiful words!'

'And I never gave either to anyone else!' she cried.

'Liar,' he breathed, and dropped his mouth down to her own.

It was punishment. It wasn't meant to be anything else. His
lips crushed hers back against her clenched teeth until, on a
strangled gasp, she gave in to the pressure and opened her
mouth. From then on it was both a punishment and a revelation. A terrible, terrible revelation because from the moment
their tongues met all sense of now went flying, and she found
herself tossed back three years into a hot, throbbing world where
this man reigned supreme. It was the smell of him, the taste,
touch, texture.

Texture. The texture of his angry lips forcing her own apart,
the texture of his moist tongue sliding against her own, the texture of his smooth, tight cheek rubbing against the softness of
hers, and there was the sensation of his breath mingling with
hers, and the drowningly sensual sound of his groan as she gave
into it all and buried her fingers in his hair, pulling him closer,
hungry, greedy for something she had not known she had been
starving for until this bright, burning moment.

When he eventually wrenched himself away she sank weakly
back against the bench behind her, unable to do anything but
wilt there while her shattered senses tried to regroup.

The air inside the shed was hot and stifling, the sun beating down on the roof filling it with the musty smell of baking
wood, old oil and earth.

He stood about a foot away, his breathing harsh and his body
tense. Violence still skittered all around them, the threat of it
dancing tauntingly in the motes of dust skittering in the musty
air.

Then came the distinctive sound of a telephone, shattering the tension like glass. He raked his hand into his trouser

pocket, came out with a small mobile telephone and pressed it to his ear.

'Right,' he gritted after listening for a moment. 'I'm on my way.'

'What?' Sara choked out, coming upright with an alarmed jerk.

He didn't answer. Did not even spare her a glance as he turned to walk out of the shed.

'Don't you dare shut me out as if I don't count!' Sara spat hoarsely after him. 'She is my child! *Mine!* If that was a call to say they are making contact again, then I have a right to know!'

His big shoulders flexed, the muscles bracing and stretching beneath the fine covering of his shirt. 'They are making contact,' he said, then walked off, out into the sunshine and away, leaving her standing there, trembling, wanting to throw something after him, wanting to scream, wanting to tear the whole world down!

'You bastard,' she whispered wretchedly. 'You cruel and unfeeling bastard.' Tears filled her eyes. 'Why can't you care? Why can't you care?'

She was sternly composed, though, by the time he opened the study door long, agonising minutes later to come to a sudden halt when he saw her sitting in a chair across the hall.

She looked like a schoolgirl who had been told to wait outside the headmaster's office, all big eyes and pensive uncertainty.

Only her mouth was not the mouth of a schoolgirl. Her mouth was the full, pulsing mouth of a woman. A woman who had recently been quite violently kissed.

She shot to her feet. 'Well?'

He shook his dark head. 'Nothing,' he said. 'It was a false alarm. A hoax caller.'

'H-hoax?' She mouthed the word in numb disbelief.

'We have had several of them.'

Her head twisted at that, the gesture sharp with pained disgust at a fellow human being who could be so cruel as to try to cash in on other people's anguish. She didn't say another word, but simply walked away, taking the stairs with her spine erect and her chin up.

Alone, as only a woman in her situation could be.

'She did that like a princess,' Toni Valetta remarked with quiet respect from Nicolas's side.

To his consternation the remark acted like a lighted fuse on a time bomb. The other man turned on him, his eyes sparking yellow murder. 'Go to hell,' he rasped, stepped back into the study and closed the door, right in Toni's surprised face.

If Toni Valetta had been present at the breakfast table that morning, he would have understood all of that. As it was, he stared blankly at the door, gave a bewildered shrug and walked away.

CHAPTER FIVE

THE AFTERNOON DRAGGED on interminably. Lunch, which Sara didn't even bother to turn up for, came and went. Then more hours, hours where she roamed from room to room, drifting out if someone else came in, wanting to be alone, needing to be alone because there was no one she could share her torment with.

Dinner that evening was another grim, silent affair, if only because none of them were prepared to pretend that there was anything even vaguely normal about it. Sara had joined Nicolas and Toni for the meal, but only because Nicolas had sent up a message to her room ordering her to attend, and she just didn't have it in her even to try to argue.

So she sat at the table, played lip-service to Mrs Hobbit's delicious chicken soup, cut up the light, fluffy omelette that must have been specially prepared to tempt her failed appetite because the other two were served thick, tender steaks, managed to swallow a couple of mouthfuls, accepted a glass of water, refused dessert and coffee then excused herself and left the two men to it without so much as uttering a single word except the pleases and thank-yous that good manners required.

'She can't take much more of this,' Toni grimly observed as the door closed behind her.

Nicolas flashed him a deadly glance. 'Do you think I am blind?' he gritted.

And that was that, the atmosphere at the table no better with Sara gone from it. They too finished their meal in silence.

A couple of hours later Nicolas Santino opened the door to Sara's bedroom to find the room empty. He frowned, eyes skimming over to the bathroom where the door stood open and its inner darkness told its own story.

He strode back down the stairs again and checked in every room before returning to the study where Toni sat at the desk with his eyes fixed on the television screen across the room. 'It's on the news,' he informed his employer. 'They're intimating Mafia connections and God knows what else. I thought you'd put a blackout on this.'

'I did.' He stepped further into the room. He had just taken a shower and had changed his clothes for buff cords and a fleecy cotton shirt. 'Has Sara been looking for me while I was showering?' he asked the other man.

'No.' Toni glanced up, frowning. 'Isn't she in her room?'

Nicolas didn't answer, his expression tightening. 'Get hold of whoever is running that bloody news station and put a block on it,' he commanded.

'A bit like locking the door after the horse has bolted, Nic,' Toni said drily.

'This whole thing is an illustration of that remark,' he clipped. 'She can't have got out of the house, could she?'

It took a moment for Toni's mind to swap subjects. 'Sara?' he said then. 'No chance. Alarm bells would have gone off, bringing ten men running and at least three dogs. And anyway, why would she want to go out?'

'I don't know,' Nicolas frowned. 'But she's not in her room and she's not in any room down here...'

Toni stood up, a mobile telephone suddenly stuck to his ear. 'I'll check with the men,' he said grimly. 'You check upstairs again.'

He went, taking the stairs two at a time then methodically opening doors and checking inside every room on the seven-bedroomed landing.

He found her in the last one—and would have missed her altogether if the shaft of light spilling in from the landing hadn't fallen on the flow of her long golden hair.

It made him still—several things made him still, but the fact that she was sitting on the floor curled up against the bars of a baby's cot had the severest effect on him, closing his lungs and tightening his chest when he realised that this was her child's room, and it was a child's pretty pink fur animal she was clutching to her breast.

Her eyes were open. She knew he was there. He had to swallow on a wave of black emotion that ripped at him inside—at his heart because of how utterly bereft she looked—and his anger stirred because he cared when he knew he should not.

'Don't put on the light,' she said when his hand reached out to do just that. 'Have they called again?'

'No.' Slowly he lowered his hand then leaned a shoulder against the doorframe. 'What are you doing in here, Sara?' he sighed out heavily. 'This can only be more painful for you.'

'It comforts me,' she said. 'I miss her. She's missing me.'

She didn't look comforted. She looked tormented. 'You need sleep,' he muttered.

'Lia won't sleep,' she countered dully. 'Not without Dandy.' Pulling the fluffy pink teddy from her breast, her fingers began gently smoothing its soft fur. 'He goes to bed with her every night. A nursery rhyme first, then a cuddle. Then she—'

'Come out of here!' he cut in harshly. Then when she went

instantly quiet he added wearily, 'You are only punishing your-self doing this.'

But she didn't move, showed no sign at all that she'd even heard him, her fingers trailing gently over the satin-soft fur.

'Sara!' he bit out impatiently.

'No,' she said. 'Go away if you don't like it. But this is where I feel closest to my baby and this is where I'll stay.'

Toni came up behind him then, catching the huskily spoken words and the way muscles began to work all over his friend and employer's face. 'OK?' he said gruffly.

'Get lost, Toni,' Nicolas responded thickly, the very fact that once again he could speak to his best friend like that a revela-tion of what he was struggling with inside him.

Toni silently moved away, his handsome face carved in a grim mask of sympathy—whether for one or both of them he wasn't sure himself. Certainly, Sara deserved sympathy for what she was having to endure. But he hadn't expected to see Nic look so damned tormented by it.

Slowly Nicolas levered himself away from the door and came further into the room, releasing the light his frame had been blocking so he could see more clearly—the pretty pink walls dressed with baby pictures, white-painted shelves decked with baby toys. The carpet beneath his feet was pink, as were the curtains at the windows.

His face tightened and he moved stiffly to stand staring out at the still, dark night, pushing his hands into his trouser pockets.

Sara allowed herself to look at him. Look at this man whose lean, lithe body she had once known more intimately than she knew her own body. A man she had loved to just look at like this, to *feel* with that warm, dark sense that resided somewhere deep inside herself, the wonder of knowing that he belonged to her. This man, this—special man.

Hers. Just as unequivocally as she had been his.

He was eight years older than she and usually it showed. He used to like that, she recalled—like the way they contrasted with each other. Whereas he was dark she was fair, whereas he was hard she was soft, whereas he was cynical with worldly experience she was as innocent and naive as a newborn babe.

They were complete opposites, he the tall, dark sophisticate with a cool maturity stamped into his lean features, she the small and delicate blonde whose youth and natural shyness made her vulnerable and therefore ignited his male need to protect.

He'd liked to have her at his side, to feel her hand clutching at one of his or resting in the crook of his arm, or simply to know that she needed to be standing close enough to touch him to feel at least bearably at ease in the élite kind of company he circulated in.

He had had the instincts of a killer shark in every other aspect of his life except where she was concerned; when he was with her his whole demeanour would soften so openly that it used to set other women's teeth on edge in envy of something she possessed that they knew they could never emulate.

An innate femininity, he'd called it—a certain fragile delicacy of mind, body and spirit that most women these days had polished out of them before they even left their cradles.

But its novelty value had worn off after a while, especially when the pressure of his workload had grown heavier by the week and she had not appeared to be learning to cope well without his being right beside her. Then the shyness that had originally drawn him towards her had become an irritant that he had, in the end, had little patience with. Adding to that the fact that she had been seriously afraid of his father, he had actually become angry with her when she'd begged him at least to let her set up house for them on their own.

'This is our home,' he'd stated. 'Is it not enough that you offend my father with your nervous attitude towards him without further insulting him by wanting to move out of this house?'

'But he doesn't like me.' She'd tried to make him understand.

'I'm not what he wanted for you, Nicolas, and he lets me know it at every opportunity he gets!'

'He teases you for your shyness, that's all. It is your own paranoia that makes you see everything he does as malicious!'

Which was just one display of his own blindness where Alfredo was concerned. For Alfredo had not been just malicious in his dealings with his son's unwanted wife, he had been downright destructive.

'OK,' Nicolas said gruffly now. 'Talk about it.'

The command made her blink, simply because she had been so lost inside her thoughts about him that she had forgotten he was actually there.

'About what?' she asked.

The profiled edges of his jaw flexed. 'The child,' he said. 'What you're feeling right now. Talk about it.'

Sara smiled wearily. 'You don't really want to hear.'

'If it helps you, I will listen.' He took a deep breath then let it out again. 'Tell me what she is like,' he invited in a low voice.

What was he thinking? she wondered curiously. What was he really thinking behind this—false facade of caring? Was he simply humouring her as his words suggested or was there something more profound going on here? Was Nicolas looking for an excuse for the right to care?

'You saw her picture. She looks like me,' she told him, wishing she could announce some clear physical evidence of the father who'd sired her child, but she couldn't. 'My features. My hair. My eyes...' She could have told him her daughter had her father's smile, his stubbornness, his ability to charm the socks off anyone. But it would not be enough, so she didn't say it. 'She was a late talker but an early walker. And she likes to be smiled at. If you frown at her she'll cry. She has done from—'

Her throat locked, choking her, because she had a sudden vision of those people who had taken her, frowning all the time and—

Oh, God. 'Nicolas,' she whispered starkly. 'I'm frightened.'

He turned, his eyes as dark as his expression. 'I know,' he acknowledged quietly.

'If they hurt my baby—' Again she stopped, having to struggle with the fear clawing at her insides. 'Would they hurt a baby?' Her eyes were dark with torment. '*Could* they hurt a baby?'

'Don't,' he sighed, but for once his voice sounded rough and unsteady, and the shoulders beneath the shirt flexed as if they could not cope with the tension attacking them. 'They will not hurt her,' he insisted. 'It will serve them no useful purpose to hurt her.'

'Then why this long silence?' She stared at him wretchedly. 'What are they waiting for?'

'It is a game they are playing with us,' he grimly replied. 'The cruel game of making us sweat. They do it to push up the ante, so that by the time they do call again we will be so out of our heads that we will agree to anything.'

'And will you—agree to anything?'

'Oh, God,' he rasped, his fingers going up to rub at his aching eyes. 'How many times do I have to tell you that I will do whatever is in my power to get your child back?' He turned on her angrily.

Remorse brought tears brimming into her eyes. 'I'm so sorry,' she whispered. 'But it's just all so...'

His harsh sigh eased her of the need to finish. 'Come on,' he said, and bent to lift her firmly to her feet. 'You are exhausted; you need rest which you will not get here.'

He was right; she was so tired that she could barely stand on her own, but she pleaded with him, 'Don't send me back to that bedroom. Please! I feel so alone there!'

'You will not be alone.' Grimly, he plucked the pink teddy from her fingers, then laid it back in the cot. 'For I shall be with you.'

'You?' She frowned in surprised confusion. 'But—'

'I will brook no protest from you, Sara,' he cut in warningly.

'You need rest. I am offering you the physical comfort of my presence. The alternative is two sleeping tablets the doctor left for just such a contingency. The choice is yours. Make it, but make it quickly or I will do it for you.'

Her luminous eyes lifted to search his, trying to discover why he was suddenly being like this. His own lashes lowered, two arcs of black settling against his cheekbones to hide what was going on in his head.

Something happened inside her—a soft flutter of yearning. A need. A memory of a time when this man had been as gentle and caring as any woman could wish for.

'You wish me to make this decision?' he prompted, at her continuing silence.

'Your accent is thickening,' she remarked, quite out of context.

He looked nonplussed momentarily, then grimaced. 'That is because I am as tired as you are,' he sighed. And in an act of failing patience he bent and lifted her into his arms. 'Your time is up,' he muttered, moving out of the baby's room and down the hallway to her own room. 'The decision is taken from you.'

He walked to the bed and allowed her bare feet to slide to the floor. Then he was grimly dealing with her robe, drawing it from her shoulders and tossing it aside to reveal a matching gown of the smoothest coffee satin, before leaning past her to flick back the covers on the bed.

'In,' he commanded.

Meekly, she did as she was told, while he turned his attention to extracting his mobile phone from his trouser pocket.

'Toni?' His voice was curt, demanding attention, not responses. 'I am with Sara. Disturb me only when it is time.' Click. The mobile was flicked shut.

'What did that mean?' she asked sharply, her wide eyes watching every move he made as he placed the mobile on the bedside table.

'Nothing,' he dismissed. 'I am expecting a call from New York.'

He began striding around the room, turning off table lamps until only the small silk-shaded one by the bed remained illuminated. Then he returned to the side of the bed, and, never once glancing at Sara, though she was sure he was aware that she never took her eyes off him, he discarded his shoes then stretched out beside her.

'Nic—' she began pensively.

'Shush,' he cut in. 'Go to sleep.'

'I was only going to say—thank you,' she whispered.

He didn't reply, didn't move, didn't do anything but lie there staring at the ceiling above their heads. Sara watched him do it, watched until her eyes began to sting and her lids grew heavy, watched until she could no longer watch, and at last drifted into sleep.

He was still lying there over an hour later, but had moved onto his side and was half dozing when she suddenly groaned and moved restlessly, throwing off the covers and twisting out of them so that she could curl herself against him instead.

'Nic,' she whispered, then placed her warm lips against his.

It was his downfall. He knew it and despised himself for it even as he gave in to it.

But she tasted so sweet. So exquisitely sweet. Like nothing he had ever tasted anywhere else in his life but from her...

It was wonderful. Like floating on a soft, fluffy cloud of rich, warm euphoria. Her body felt as light as a feather but her limbs were heavy, somnolent with the most honeyed delight. And her flesh was smiling. Could flesh smile? she asked herself wonderingly. Because hers certainly was. And since this was her dream she could let herself do and feel anything she liked. So, yes, her flesh was smiling, its outermost layer caressed by something warm and moist and infinitely pleasing.

She tried breathing not fast but slowly, savouring the sensual pull of oxygen into her lungs which seemed to set off a chain reaction throughout her body, setting her senses pulsing, slow and easy like the cloud she was floating on, the smile on her flesh, the sigh she released as she exhaled again.

'Nic,' she whispered.

That was what this was. It reminded her of Nicolas in one of his lazy, loving moods when he would lick her skin from toes to fingertips, raising a million and one sensations of pleasure all over her, rendering her lost and helpless. His to do with as he pleased.

'Sweet,' a hushed voice suggested.

Oh, God, yes, this was sweet, she agreed silently. The sweetest, sweetest sensation on earth—or in heaven. For she wasn't of this world right now. She was floating somewhere above it, stretched out, naked and basking, basking in the wonder of herself.

Her breasts felt full and heavy, her nipples stinging with impatience because he hadn't reached them yet. And they wanted him to. They wanted him to close his mouth around them, lick and suck and make them his own.

'Nic,' she whispered again, in breathless need this time.

'Shush,' the hushed voice answered.

She sighed in lazy agreement—then came fully awake with a muscle-locking, bone-clenching jerk when he slid the tip of his tongue into the delicate crevice between her thighs.

'Oh, God,' she gasped. 'Nicolas—No!'

'Yes.' He was suddenly looming over her, his face dark with passion, mouth full and moist from the havoc he had just been creating with his tongue.

And they were both naked! Her nightdress was gone—his clothes!—the crisp hair on his chest rasping against her breasts, one wonderfully muscular thigh heavy across her own.

'You want me, Sara,' he insisted. 'Your body wants me. Your subconscious mind wants me! Don't tell me no when I can feel you literally throbbing with need of me!'

'You said comfort,' she reminded him whimperingly.

'This is comfort,' he declared. 'The most exquisite comfort there is.'

'But—'

'No,' he gritted. 'I need this too! We both do.' Then he cut off any more protests with the hungry crush of his mouth.

She let out a single helpless sigh. He answered it by groaning something in his throat, then his tongue was playing with hers in the most sensuously evocative way, which brought her hands up to grasp tightly at his neck. His thigh moved against hers, rubbing a caress over the soft golden mound which protected her sex. His fingers trailed over her shoulders, her upper arms, then finally, exquisitely, her breasts.

'Do you know how sweet to taste you are?' he muttered, head coming up, hunter's eyes glowing at her in the darkness. 'How your skin secretes something onto my tongue that causes a chemical reaction inside me that drives me half-insane?' He sighed, as if he despised himself for saying all of that. 'I am addicted to you,' he admitted thickly. 'You are a fix I can get from no other source!'

'You've tried?' she asked painfully.

'Of course I have tried!' he admitted. 'Do you think I like feeling this way about you?'

'No,' she sighed on a wave of dark sadness for this man with his monumental pride which must be taking a battering because he had discovered he could not lie with her without wanting her. Wanting the woman he believed had betrayed him. 'I'm sorry,' she whispered. Sorry that fate had forced him to feel that way.

'Don't talk,' he commanded bleakly. 'I have to remember what you are when you talk. And I need this—*need it*!' he repeated hoarsely.

Then he groaned again, caught her mouth in a mind-blowing desperate kiss that brought tears to her eyes and her hands down to stroke his chest in a lame gesture of comfort to relieve his agony.

It was at that moment that she realised how much she still loved him, loved this man who could believe such vile things about her yet could still desire her as desperately as this.

The rest took place in a charged kind of silence, he arousing her with a grim sense of determination that told her he wanted the full collapse of all her senses before he would feel satisfied in taking her.

When he did eventually come into her, he did it with a ruth-less precision that brought a grunt from his throat and a gasp from hers. Then he stopped, elbows braced at each side of her, eyes closing on a tense sideways jerk of his head that was in itself a dead give-away of how close he had driven himself to the edge before allowing himself to do this.

He filled her. In that moment of complete stillness Sara lay there and felt him fill her, felt the wonder of it, the beauty, felt her own muscles close around him, draw him deeper, hold him, knead him.

'Breathe,' he gritted. 'Damn you, Sara. Breathe!'

It was only as she sucked air into her lungs on a greedy gasp that she realised she had stopped breathing, her whole body locked in a spasm of sheer sensual ecstasy.

Her hands flew out, wildly uncoordinated as they searched for something solid to hold onto. They found his shoulders. He growled something in his throat, then his body was moving, thrusting—short, tense, blunt thrusts that held his face locked in a mask of total sexual compulsion and drove her over the edge to complete oblivion.

When she eventually dragged herself back from wherever she had gone off to, Nicolas was no longer in the bed. He was stand-ing by it, pulling on his trousers with terse, angry movements, every cell in him sending out a message of bitter regret.

'Hating yourself now, Nicolas?' she taunted lazily.

He went still, then jerked his head round to look at her, the hunter's gold eyes barely brushing over her before they were flicking away again. 'Yes,' he answered flatly.

He didn't even have the decency to deny it, and that hurt. 'You seduced me,' she reminded him. 'It was not the other way round.'

'I know it.' Snatching up his shirt, he tugged it on. 'I am not blaming you for my own—'

He didn't finish. His jaw flexing with tension, he pushed buttons into holes. Sara watched him, too spent to do much else as he dropped into a chair to pull on socks and shoes. That done, he stood up, glanced at her then away again, as if he couldn't stand looking at her lying there like that, with her eyes languid and her body wearing the flush of a woman who had just been devoured.

'Will you be—all right?' he asked stiffly. 'If I leave you?'

Desperate to get away now he had disgraced himself? she wondered.

'Without you to *comfort* me, you mean?' she mocked. 'Yes, I'm sure I shall manage.' Her sarcasm bit. 'I'm used to being alone, after all,' she added bleakly. 'I've been alone since I was thirteen.'

'Not always,' he gritted. 'Once, until you spoiled it, you had me.'

'Really?' She sliced a glance at him, his bitterness igniting her bitterness, and she scrambled off the bed to reach angrily for her robe. She didn't even care that she was exposing her body to him. Nicolas hated himself for desiring her, so let him gaze at her naked body—and hate!

'Alone, Nicolas,' she repeated. 'Even with you. You gave me no support, no rights. No say in how we ran our marriage. If I dared to object, you shut me up in the most effective way you knew how.' She meant in bed, and he knew it; his grim mouth tightened. 'If I persisted, you shot me down with hard words and derision. You thought it amusing that I liked to be amongst flowers rather than people, but never once allowed me the concession that maybe I had a right to like what I wanted to like no matter how empty-headed and frivolous it seemed to you.'

'I never considered you empty-headed,' he muttered.

'You rarely considered me at all,' she countered, searching angrily around her for the tie to her robe. 'Except where it mattered exclusively to you. Then I was expected to put up and shut up, because you knew best and I was, after all, just the pretty little doll you'd had the grace to elevate onto such an exalted plateau in life! Your servants rated higher in the pecking order than I did. They—' she pulled the belt tight around her waist '—looked down on me!'

He let out a short laugh, as if he couldn't quite believe he was hearing all of this. 'I don't know whether to weep for you or applaud you for stringing together more words than I've ever heard you manage in one go before!'

'Oh, applaud, Nicolas,' she flashed. 'I deserve the applause for putting up with it all for as long as I actually did!'

He turned away, the movement dismissive. 'You are beginning to bore me.'

'Well, what's new?' she retorted. 'You were bored with me within weeks of marrying me when you discovered I was going to be just a little more trouble than you thought I was worth! But I'll tell you something, Nicolas,' she continued hotly. 'If you grew bored with the shy, timid little mouse you married in a fit of madness, then I certainly grew tired of the tall, dark, handsome god I found myself tied to, because he turned out to be just one of a very select, very well cared for but boringly similar flock of sheep!

'Oh, their coats were exquisite,' she railed on recklessly, 'and they ate off the very best turf, but what they gained in fine finish they lost in good brain cells! They did the same things. They thought the same things. And they bleated on and on about the same things! Genetic farming, I think they call it. I had no idea it went on in human society as well as—'

'Have you quite finished?' he inserted coldly.

She nodded. 'Yes.' She felt flushed and breathless, incredibly elated. In all her twenty-five years she had never spoken to anyone like that. It had been almost as good as the sex!

'Then I shall remove my—genetic abomination from your presence,' he said, giving her a stiff, cold bow that was as big an insult as the way he had hated himself for touching her again.

'After I have said one last thing,' she threw at his retreating back. 'Make a note of today's date, Nicolas. For I took no precautions against what we just did in that bed over there, and I know for a fact that the idea just would not even enter your head! If I am pregnant because of tonight, I want there to be no doubt this time who the father of my child could be.'

He'd reached the door, from which he turned to slice her with a coldly shrivelling look. 'A genetic mutation?' he clipped out curtly. 'What an appalling thought.'

Shot down. With one smooth, clever one-liner, he had managed to turn her wild tirade back on her. She didn't know whether she wanted to scream or weep in bitter, blinding frustration!

What she actually did was sit on the edge of the bed and just—wilt.

CHAPTER SIX

BY THE TIME Nicolas got downstairs he was back to being the man most people knew him to be. He entered the study to find it a veritable Aladdin's cave of hi-tech equipment. Toni, the two policemen, two men he did not recognise but knew came from some special services department—all of them stood or sat about messing with the complicated array of communications stuff.

Stone-faced, hard-eyed, he homed directly in on Toni.

Not by so much as a flicker of an eyelash did Toni's face reveal what he must be thinking, knowing how long Nicolas had been with Sara. 'Almost time,' he said quietly. 'Everything is ready.'

Nicolas gave a curt nod and moved over to the desk. The others in the room watched him like wary cats following the hunting pace of a dangerous animal. They were split into three groups—one group tracing, one group talking, one man ready to hit a command the moment they were given the go-ahead.

He sat down. 'Any problems?' he clipped.

'No.' It was Toni who answered. 'We have them pinned down

to a certain area code, but to be sure this works we need more time.'

'It has to work,' Nicolas said grimly. 'Failure means panic and panic means risk. I won't have the child's life put at risk—you understand?' It wasn't said to Toni but to the two special agents huddled in a corner across the room.

The phone on the desk began to ring. The room froze into total stillness. Nicolas sat very still in his chair, hands tense, eyes fixed on the two policemen. And waited.

Two rings. Three rings. It seemed an age. Four. He got the nod. He snatched up the phone. 'Santino,' he announced.

'Ah, good evening, *signore.*' The smooth, oily voice slid snake-like into every headphoned ear listening in. 'You have resolved the small cash-flow problem, I hope...'

Dawn was just breaking the sky when Nicolas entered Sara's room and gently shook her awake.

She sat up with a jerk. 'What's happened?' she gasped, instantly alert, her eyes huge and frightened in her sleep-flushed face.

'It's over, *cara,*' he murmured soothingly. 'Your daughter is safe.'

'Safe?' She blinked up at him, not really taking the words in. 'Safe, Nicolas?' she repeated. 'Really safe?'

'Yes.' He nodded.

'Oh, God.' Her hand whipped up to cover her wobbling mouth, her eyes, still badly bruised with the strain of it all, going luminous with tears of relief. 'How...?' she whispered. 'Where is she?'

'I will take you to her just as soon as you can get dressed and be ready to travel,' he promised.

'She's not here?' Then in a burst of alarm she cried, 'Have they h-hurt her?'

'No, to both questions,' he answered calmingly. 'Here—' He turned away, then turned back to push a cup of something hot into her hand. 'Drink this, then get dressed. I would like to leave here in half an hour. Can you be ready?'

'I... Y-yes, of course...' She was suffering from shock—a new kind of shock, the shock of deliverance from the pits of hell, which stopped her from asking the kind of questions she knew she should be asking.

'Good.' He nodded, then, turning, went quickly towards the door.

'Nic!' She stopped him, waiting for him to turn back to face her before saying huskily, 'Thank you.'

After what had happened between them the night before, there was a certain amount of irony in that. But he took it at its face value, his half-nod an acknowledgement before he was turning away again.

'Downstairs in half an hour,' he instructed, and left her alone.

She was showered, dressed and ready to leave by the specified time. Nicolas was waiting for her in the hallway. He watched her come down the stairs towards him, his eyes drifting over the simple lines of the sage-green linen trousers and cream shirt she was wearing beneath an off-white jacket. She wore no make-up—she rarely ever did. And her hair she had brushed quickly and secured back from her face with a padded green band.

Nothing fancy. Nothing couture. Like the Sara he had first met. She had reverted to that person of simple tastes the moment he'd had her banished here to his London residence. She wondered if he was making the same distinction as he watched her like that, unrevealingly, with his eyes narrowed, so that she could not read what was going on behind them. But she made no apology for her appearance. This was what she was. That other person had been fashioned like a piece of sculpture to suit the role it had been intended to play. A false role, fake like the life she had been forced to live and the marriage that should never have been.

He, by contrast, looked dynamic again, not in one of his

handmade silk suits but a pair of tobacco-coloured linen trousers and a white roll-neck worn beneath a black linen jacket—Armani, she guessed, recalling that his casual wardrobe had held mainly that designer's name.

'Where's Toni?' she enquired as he led the way outside into an early summer morning.

'He has business of mine to attend to,' he answered coolly, opening the rear door of the Mercedes saloon standing with its engine running at the bottom of the steps.

She smiled to herself as she climbed into the car. Problem solved, so Toni's attention had been turned back to business. Then she wondered how long she was to be graced with Nicolas's company before he turned his attention to other things.

For the duration of this drive? she suggested to herself as the car took off with Nicolas seated beside her and the driver safely hidden behind a wall of tinted glass. Until he had efficiently delivered Lia into her arms? Or would he feel duty-bound to see them safely back home again and maybe even hang around long enough to make sure that the security surrounding them was tight enough for something like this not to happen again?

She shivered, the mere idea of it occurring again striking like a death knell right through her. 'How far away is she?' she asked. 'Will it take long to get there?'

His dark head had been resting against the soft, creamy leather headrest, his eyes closed. But when she turned the questions on him his long lashes flickered then lifted slowly to reveal sensually sleepy pupils surrounded by a sandstorm of energy. It caught at her breath, because that look was his sexually hungry male look and—

No. She glanced away, refusing to so much as think of him in that dangerous mould. Not after last night. Never again after last night! And anyway, how could he be looking at her like that after what he had said?

'Quite far,' he murmured, answering his first question. 'A plane journey actually. She is in Sicily,' he finally tagged on.

'Sicily?' The shock of it showed in the momentary blank blue look she fixed on him. 'But how could she be in Sicily?'

'With good planning,' he drawled. 'How else?'

She shivered. Her baby had been taken so far away from her and she had been helpless to stop it. 'But I've not brought anything with me for a journey this long! No change of clothes for me, or for Lia. And my passport, Nicolas.' She turned to him urgently. 'I haven't brought my passport with me—'

'I have it,' he said. 'I recovered it from the wall-safe. Packed for you too,' he added wryly, because it wasn't a job he was used to doing for anyone, not even himself. 'For both you and the child while you were still sleeping.'

He had been in her room? Walking around it, packing for her while she slept? The very idea did the strangest things to her, filled her with alarm and a shocking sense of—

'You opened my safe?' she protested, picking on that one intrusion because the other did not bear thinking about.

'My safe,' he corrected her. 'My home.'

But she ignored the jibe because another thought had suddenly struck her, one that held the breath trapped in her lungs. 'Where is she in Sicily?' she asked.

There was a small hesitation. Then, 'With my father,' he said, watching her narrowly.

Alfredo. She stiffened, all her muscles clenching. 'After all you said,' she breathed. 'He was behind it all, wasn't he? He's the one who did this to me!'

'Not to your child, I make note,' he drily observed. 'I can at least take comfort in the fact that you are not accusing my father of wanting to hurt a child.'

Her blue eyes flashed in a bitter contradiction of that final remark. 'If he has hurt her,' she warned, 'so help me, wheelchair or not, I shall see him dead.'

'A Sicilian emotion,' he noted, 'this desire you have developed for retribution. Do you think we may have taught you something after all?'

His lazy mockery was spiked, the glinting eyes full of a cold condescension entirely aimed at previous diatribes in which she had condemned everything Sicilian. 'You people taught me many things, Nicolas,' she threw back at him. 'Not least the rule of possession. 'What's mine I keep'!' she quoted. 'And woe betide anyone who tries to lay a finger on a possession of mine, including your wonderful father, who is nothing but a—'

'Stop right there,' he inserted very softly.

She sucked in a breath of air, her heartbeat pounding in her head. But it was no use. The fact that he had actually managed to convince her that Alfredo had nothing to do with Lia's abduction only made this moment of truth more impossible to deal with.

'And you still protect him, don't you?' she derided bitterly. 'No matter how many dirty tricks he pulls on you, you still refuse to see what a nasty, cunning, evil man he is—even when the proof of it is shoved right under your very—'

His hand snaking round her neck and yanking her forcefully towards him stopped the words. 'Hold your tongue, you little shrew!' he rasped. 'Before I bite it off!'

'I hate and despise you!' she threw into his angry face.

'You were warned,' he muttered, and crushed his mouth down onto hers in a brutal kiss aimed at subduing all hint of defiance left in her.

Yet within the punishment was a dark, duplicitous intimacy that dragged pleasurably at her senses and took some fighting against to stop her from sinking greedily into the kiss.

She groaned instead, pretending he had hurt her.

'You asked for it,' he muttered as he drew away.

'I got it, didn't I?' she muttered in return, pulling shakily out of his arms.

'What surprises me,' he struck back cruelly, his hand shooting out to capture her wrist then holding onto it so they could both feel the way the blood was breaking speed records as it thundered through her veins, 'is how you were affected by it. Could it be that you're just a little in need of a man, Sara? Has the princess been locked up in her tower too long, and did last night's little—taster remind her of what she once craved?'

'Can you be so sure the tower has been locked?' she retaliated, refusing point-blank to let him diminish her as he used to so easily.

His eyes glinted. 'You're damned right I can,' he gritted. 'I've told you before: what's mine I keep. And I've kept you under surveillance enough to be sure no man has been near you.'

'Except for my gaoler,' she threw back at him deridingly. 'In the end even you—hate yourself though you do for it—couldn't keep your hands off me.'

'I have the legal right,' he declared. 'If not the moral one.'

'And the princess in the tower had the cunning to let down her hair for her secret lover to climb,' she hit back, reminding him of the old fairytale.

His eyes narrowed. She held her breath, aware that she was prodding a very temperamental animal here yet, strangely, unable to stop herself—finding it exhilarating almost.

Then, deflatingly, he dropped her wrist and relaxed. 'You have changed,' he observed. 'You would not have dared speak to me like this three years ago.'

'Oh, yes,' she agreed, subsiding angrily into the far corner of the seat. 'I've changed. Grown up. Grown tough. What did you expect me to do, Nicolas?' She flashed him a bitter look. 'Remain the same gullible fool I was when I first met you? The one who thought you loved me above all others and would stand by me whatever was thrown at me?'

'You were the one who took a lover to your bed,' he reminded her. 'Not I!'

'And you were the one who threw me to the hungry wolves then dared to be disgusted with me when I cried to you for help!'

He threw her a contemptuous look, the disgust as clear in his eyes now as it had been three years ago. 'I notice you don't deny the charge of adultery,' he jeered.

'What's the use,' she asked, 'when you refuse to believe me?'

'Believe what?' he derided. 'Your lies?'

'I never lied to you,' she asserted.

'Denying that swine's presence in your room was no lie, was it?'

'I never denied he was there,' she insisted. 'Only my acceptance of his presence.'

'I fail to see the difference.'

'And I refuse to discuss this with you now,' she countered coldly. 'Besides the fact that it comes three years too late, I find I no longer care what you think. My daughter is all that matters to me now, and she is all I want to think about.'

'My father did not steal your child, Sara,' he said grimly. 'He *recovered* her. Or, at least, he coordinated the whole thing so his people could. She is at this moment sleeping safely under his protection. And soon, very soon,' he warned gratingly, 'I shall make you eat every filthy, lying word you've spoken about him. Understand?'

She understood. Another vendetta. Another reason to punish her for being foolish enough to mess with his close-knit clan.

Nicolas could believe what he liked about his father but just the simple knowledge that her daughter was in Sicily with Alfredo told her just who had arranged for her to be there.

The Santino private jet landed at midday at Catania airport then taxied over to the far side of the runway. Away from the terminal. Away from the people.

What worried Sara now was his reason for doing so.

That was the power of the Santino name. They were met by a Customs official. Nicolas dealt with him, tiredness pulling at the lean contours of his face now, even though he had slept away the whole flight.

And despite the hostility still thrumming between them Sara experienced a sharp pang of pity. Forty-eight hours ago he had been in New York. Since then he had crossed the Atlantic, dealt with a very stressful crisis then flown another few thousand miles to get here.

'Let's go,' he instructed her, placing a hand at the base of her spine to urge her to precede him off the aircraft.

His touch sent a spray of tingling awareness skittering across the surface of her skin. She had discarded her jacket on entering the plane, and knew from past experience that the weather in Sicily would not require her to put it back on. But she wished she had now, wished she'd decided to roast in the jacket rather than suffer the sensation of his hand so close to her skin.

And it wasn't revulsion she was experiencing, not any more. In the few fraught hours she had been back in his company, her senses had been reintroduced to their lord and master! And, good grief, they were clamouring with excitement!

It was a lowering truth. And one she didn't live easily with. Could Nicolas have been right when he'd accused her of being starved of a man's touch?

She hoped not. She hoped this was only a brief reaction to the stress she had been living under. Because it was a pride-levelling concept to find herself still so violently physically attracted to the man who had hurt her so badly.

It was a perfect Sicilian day, the air hot and dry, the sun burning down from a perfect porcelain-blue sky.

A car was waiting—a white limousine shimmering in the sunlight. Nicolas saw her into it then sat beside her. They took off almost immediately, making for a pair of high, wire-fencing gates which were drawn open by two uniformed members of staff as they approached.

Neither Sara nor Nicolas spoke. Both were tense. Sara was readying herself for the moment when she would see her daughter again, impatient but oddly nervous with it. And there was Nicolas. She frowned as she stared out at the bright, shimmering coastline they were following. She didn't know how he was going to react to his first meeting with the child he saw as the living evidence of his wife's betrayal.

She saw the house the moment they rounded a bend in the twisting road. It stood on its own halfway up an acutely sloped bay. And her heart gave an odd pull of recognition as her gaze drifted over beautiful, white-painted, flower-strewn walls built on several terraced levels to hug the lush hillside all the way down to the tiny, silver-skirted beach.

Then suddenly it was gone as the car cut inland, not far but enough to take them through a tunnel of leaf-weighted trees towards the rear of the house. It was the only access unless you came by sea. A beautiful place, very private, idyllic. A high, whitewashed stone wall stood impenetrable behind the gnarled trunks of old fig trees, two royal-blue-painted solid wood doors cutting a splash of colour into it where it rose to curve over them in an arch twisted with bougainvillea heavy with paper-like vivid pink blooms.

The car stopped, gave a single blast of its horn. A small square porthole cut into the blue opened then closed again. The blue-painted doors swung open on well-oiled hinges. The car began moving slowly through them into a huge cobbled court-yard alive with colour, with the dappling shelter of several olive trees, with the delicate sprinkle of water from the simple foun-tain gushing water into a circular pond.

Sara heaved in a tense breath then held onto it. She sensed Nicolas's swift glance in her direction but ignored it. This beau-tiful place was the scene of all her nightmares, and she needed to concentrate if she was to hold on to her composure.

Lia, she told herself grimly. Just think of Lia.

The car stopped. The driver got out, stepping up to open her door. Her senses were assailed by the sweet scent of flowers and the crisp tang of fruit, the quietness, the sheer peace that enveloped her just another deception she had to do battle with.

The house from the back appeared quite humble when com-pared with its dramatic front—a mere single storey of long white wall with blue-painted shutters thrown back from small windows and a terracotta-tiled roof.

Twin blue doors stood open to offer a welcome. Sara gritted her teeth, tried to make her suddenly shaky legs move. A cicada sawed lazily, hidden somewhere in a tree.

No other sound. Nothing. Her hand reached out, unconsciously searching for and locating another, warmer, stronger hand. It closed around her trembling fingers, but she was not really aware of it as she forced herself to move forwards through the doors into a cool square hallway where she paused for a moment while her eyes adjusted themselves to the dimmer light inside.

It was all so familiar. The beautiful paintings adorning the walls, the tasteful mix of dark, well-polished furniture, delicate ornaments, and vases of flowers.

And the stony-faced housekeeper standing a couple of yards inside the hall.

But no baby to greet her. She glanced at Nicolas, eyes questioning, anxious. He stepped forward and spoke in low tones to the housekeeper then turned to come and take hold of Sara's arm.

'Where—?' she jerked out tensely.

'This way,' he said, his face stiff. He began leading her across the entrance hall and through an archway that she knew led to one of several stone staircases.

The house was built on several levels. Here on the top floor were the more functional services like kitchens and garages and servant accommodation. Then came the formal reception rooms where the Santino family entertained. Next was the floor given over entirely to the Santino empire, with office suites with all the relevant state-of-the-art equipment to go with them. The next tier housed the family's private bedroom suites, followed by the guest suites and finally the less formal pool and recreational tier where you would find the only televisions in the whole place, and the garden terrace, which stepped downwards to the tiny pebbly beach below.

There were some two hundred steps in all from top terrace

to beach. Sara had counted them once during one of her lonely periods while Nicolas had been away and his father had driven her outside to seek refuge from his constant hostility. But those two hundred steps were outside. Inside, each level had its own stairway worked in a dog-leg which took you from tier to tier.

And as Nicolas led the way down her legs began to wobble, memories she would have much preferred to keep at bay beginning to crowd her mind.

Memories of a beautiful suite of rooms with a huge, white-silk-draped canopied bed and a man lying naked and glossy brown against the pure white sheets. A man who loved to just lie there like that and watch her as she moved about the room, loved to watch her brush her hair and cream her skin and...

'Sara.'

She'd stopped. She hadn't realised she'd stopped until the sound of her name brought her jolting to the present. Her lashes fell then lifted again to reveal the glaze of pained reminiscence as she found the same man watching her.

The same man but not the same, she noted bleakly. The one who'd liked to watch her move about their bedroom had worn a look of lazy pleasure on his face. This one looked hard and cold and...

'This way,' he prompted.

He was standing by the stairway to the next level. She frowned in puzzlement. 'But...' Her hand wafted out in the vague direction of the bedrooms, her logic expecting Lia to be in one of those. Then it hit her, and if she had been up to it she would have smiled at her own stupidity. The next level contained the guest suites. Of course Lia would be there. She was not family. Just as Sara herself was no longer family—not in the true sense of the word anyway.

She followed him, her head lowered so he would not read the irony she knew must be written in her eyes. In silence they made their way down to the next level, and here, as she had expected,

Nicolas led the way to at suite of rooms, then paused by the door as if taking a moment to brace himself for what was to come.

So did Sara.

The door swung open, she stepped up beside him—then went perfectly still, heart, lungs, everything inside her crashing to a shuddering halt at the sight that met her eyes.

Across the room and to one side of the open plate-glass window which led outside was a man. His dark hair was peppered with more silver than she remembered, his once big frame radically diminished by the wheelchair he was sitting in.

But it was not just the man who held all her stunned attention. It was what he held in his arms.

Lying against his chest was a baby wearing nothing more than a disposable nappy and a white cotton vest. Her golden head was cushioned on his shoulder, her little arms clinging tightly to his neck.

Her eyes blurred out of focus then back again, the sight of her child—*her child*!—dinging to her worst enemy seeming to rock the very ground she stood upon.

Then the greying head was turning, the bright, hunter's gold eyes searching out and homing directly in on Sara's eyes. And the expression glowing in them froze the blood inside her veins.

It was possession, fierce and parental. And at last Sara began to understand what this had all been about.

The child. *Her child!*

In his illness, Alfredo Santino had seen his own mortality. He had seen himself dying without ever holding his own grandchild. It no longer mattered that the child was also Sara's child. He wanted. And what Alfredo Santino wanted he got, even if it meant stealing to get it. Even if it meant having the woman he hated most coming back into his life. He wanted Lia. And there was no longer a single doubt in Sara's mind that it had been Alfredo who had orchestrated her child's abduction.

'No!' Sheer instinct brought the thick denial bursting from her locked throat. And, almost stumbling in her haste, she went towards him, saw, with a horror that tightened like a steel clasp around her chest, his hands move on her baby in a convulsive act of ownership.

'She would accept comfort from no one else but me!' he exclaimed in glowing triumph as Sara reached him. 'See how she clings. See!'

'No,' Sara breathed again, denying it, denying his right to feel this way about her baby—as he had denied the little girl her right to know the love of her own father!

As if the baby sensed the closeness of her mother, she gave a shaky sigh against Alfredo's shoulder, bringing Sara's attention swerving back her way. And suddenly Alfredo was forgotten. Nicolas, still standing tense and silent in the doorway, was forgotten, everything was wiped clean out of her mind as she watched the head of golden curls lift and slowly turn. A deep frown shadowing her luminous eyes, her Cupid's-bow mouth cross and pouting, she looked up at her mother, released another unsteady sigh then simply stretched out an arm towards Sara.

Sara bent, lifted the baby from Alfredo, folded her to her, one set of fingers spreading across the little back, the others cupping the golden head. The baby curved herself, foetus-like, into her mother, head nuzzling into her throat, arms tucking in between Sara's breasts.

Then neither moved. Neither spoke. Neither wept. Sara simply stood there with her eyes closed and her face a complete and utter blank, the emotion she was experiencing so deep that none of it was left to show on her whitened face.

CHAPTER SEVEN

IT WAS LIKE witnessing the most spiritual communion life could offer. And no one privy to it could not be moved by the vision. Not Alfredo, who lowered his silvered head and shook it with a sharp, jerky motion that was almost pained. Not the thin, dark-haired woman standing quietly to one side of the room, whose eyes filled with aching tears. Not even Nicolas, still standing tensely in the open doorway, who had to close his eyes to block out the heart-wrenching vision.

The seconds ticked by. No one moved. Not Sara. Not the baby. Not father or son or strange woman or even the air in the room, it seemed, in those few fraught moments.

Then the small head lifted, still frowning, still cross as she fixed her mother with a condemning look. 'Not like airplanes,' she said.

Sara's legs went from beneath her. No warning. It was as if the sound of the child's voice acted like a spring on all the control she had been exerting on herself and she simply uncoiled, release flowing through her as if liquid were replacing bone.

Alfredo saw it happen but even as he let out a warning gasp, one gnarled hand lifting instinctively towards mother and child, Nicolas was there, bursting out of his statue-like posture to dart behind her so that her slender body melted against his own instead of falling to the floor, his arms snaking around both mother and child in support while the tension in his face reached crisis proportions.

The baby lifted her frowning eyes from her mother's pale face and for the first time in her life fixed them on the rigid contours of her father's.

Luminous blue met with harshly frowning gold. And while Sara fought a battle with her shattered control another communication took place—one which brought a muffled choke from Alfredo and set his son's teeth gritting behind his tightly clamped lips.

For this child was undoubtedly Sara. Sara's soft golden hair. Sara's soft mouth. Sara's pale, delicate skin. Sara's huge, beautiful blue eyes.

No hint of Sicilian. Not even a hint of the dark-haired Englishman Sara had betrayed him with. The child looked like an angel when she should have been wearing the stamp of the devil.

His instinct was to snap right away from both of them. But although Sara was still holding the child it was his arms that were taking the child's weight, his body that was keeping the mother upright.

'Take the child—quickly!' he raked out in an effort to release some of the violent emotion rushing through him right now.

But his feelings must have shown in his face, because the child's mouth quivered, her eyes growing even bigger as they filled with frightened tears.

Then, 'More bad man!' she cried, reacting to both his hard expression and the rough words which must have reminded her of her kidnap. 'Stay with Mama!' Her arms clutched tightly at Sara's neck. 'No more bad man, Mama,' she sobbed. 'Grandpa said!'

Grandpa?

Sara's eyes flicked open. Nicolas tensed up behind her. 'What the hell…?' he muttered.

'She needed reassurance,' Alfredo defended himself. 'I gave it in the only way I could think of!'

Liar! Sara's eyes accused him, and on a burst of anger that flooded the strength right back into her limbs she pushed herself free of Nicolas's supporting arms, trembling for an entirely different reason now as her hand spread protectively over her baby's head and she flashed both Santino men a condemning look.

'You vile people,' she whispered tightly, then turned and walked away—out through the open window and onto the terrace where the clean fresh air did not hold the taint of Santino.

'Sara!' Nicolas's voice, harsh with command, brought her to a shuddering halt halfway across the terrace towards the steps. 'Where the hell do you think you are going?' he muttered, catching hold of her arm.

'Let go of me,' she whispered, seething with a bitter enmity she was finding it difficult to keep under wraps.

'Don't be foolish!' he snapped.

'But you saw him, Nicolas!' she choked, turning wretched eyes on him. 'He did it! He set all of this up for some selfish reason of his own! And—'

'Be silent!' he barked. 'I have warned you before not to repeat accusations like that!' He wasn't seeing, she realised in despair—he would never see his father for what he really was.

His hard tone brought Lia's head out of her mother's throat, huge blue eyes homing in on his angry face, and the Cupid's-bow mouth wobbled a second time, the first cry leaving her on a frightened wail. 'Bad man again!'

'Nicolas!' A reprimand for his impatience came from an unexpected source. 'You are frightening the *bambina*!' Alfredo's voice, coming from the open doorway, carried above Lia's growing wails while Sara stood quivering with fury at the very idea that her child—*any* child—should have experience of what was bad in a human being!

'My father is right,' Nicolas conceded tautly. 'We are upsetting the child.' His hand tightened on Sara's arm. 'Come back inside,' he urged, taking care not to let his eyes clash with the wide, wary ones of the little girl. 'We are all overwrought. Come back inside...'

His hand urged her forward; reluctantly she went, aware that at this moment she really had no choice. They were right—both men were right and their manner was upsetting Lia. The poor baby had been through enough; she did not need her mother's hostile attitude confusing her further. But as she reached Alfredo, sitting tensely in his chair in the open doorway, she paused, her hard gaze telling him that she knew what he had done, no matter that his son refused to see it.

The hunter's gold eyes flickered then shifted from her to the baby where they softened into a gentle smile, a long-fingered hand reaching out to catch and squeeze a plump baby hand. The little girl responded immediately to the smile, offering one of her own.

'Grandpa,' she said, and once again rocked the precarious control Sara was clinging to.

It was said so affectionately.

It affected Nicolas too, his fingers tightening on Sara's arm as he urged her forward. 'You're a fool, Nicolas,' she said thickly. 'You always have been where he is concerned.'

He ignored that, jaw clenching in grim dismissal of the remark. 'Sit down,' he commanded, almost pushing her into a nearby chair, then he clicked his fingers to bring an anxious-looking woman hurrying across the room. 'This is Fabia,' he said.

Keeping her eyes away from a stiff-faced Nicolas, Sara glanced at the woman, who smiled nervously and nodded her dark head in acknowledgement. She was not much older than Sara herself, but with the luxuriant black hair of a Sicilian and beautiful brown eyes.

'Fabia is here to attend to your needs,' he continued in that same cool voice. 'And she will begin by collecting your luggage...' With a nod at the other woman he sent her scurrying on her way. Then his attention was back on Sara. 'I suggest you take the next few minutes to compose yourself and reassure the child.' Lia had taken refuge by burying her face in her mother's throat again. 'Father...?' Without giving Sara a chance to reply, he turned with that same cool, authoritative voice to Alfredo who was still sitting in the open window. 'We need to talk.'

With that he walked off, with a surprisingly obedient Alfredo in tow, propelling himself by the use of the electronic controls of his wheelchair.

Silence prevailed. Lia lifted her face from its warm hiding place. 'Bad man gone?' she asked warily.

Sara leaned into the soft-cushioned back of the chair and gently cradled the baby to her. 'He isn't a bad man, Lia,' she murmured quietly. 'Just a...' Confused one, was what she'd been about to say—which puzzled her because Nicolas had never been confused about anything in his whole life!

Life was black and white to him; confusion came in those little grey areas in between, which he did not acknowledge. Which was why their marriage had been such a difficult one, because Alfredo, knowing his son, had carefully clouded everything to do with Sara grey, causing confusion and misunderstanding all the way.

Just as he was doing again now, she realised with a small frown, and wished—wished she knew what the old man was up to this time, because every warning instinct she possessed told her he was definitely up to something dire.

What did he want? Her baby all to himself?

But he could not have Lia without making Nicolas believe himself to be the child's father. And making his son believe that would also make Nicolas question his belief in Sara's adultery. And once Nicolas did start questioning the truth would surely come out. Dared Alfredo risk it? Risk his son discovering just how ruthless his own father had been in his quest to rid him of his wife?

Or had he got some other, even more devious plan up his sleeve, one where he convinced Nicolas that Lia was indeed his child but by mere fluke rather than fidelity? Which would then lead to Nicolas claiming the child and dismissing the wife!

She began to tremble—tremble inside with a fear that came from experience in dealing with Alfredo.

Black and white. Nicolas dealt in black and white. The grey area in Alfredo's favour was that Sara would never be able to prove she did *not* take another man to her bed!

'*Signora?*' The enquiry brought her eyes flickering into focus. Fabia was standing by her chair, her smile warm. 'The *bambina,*' she prompted softly. 'She sleeps peacefully at last with her *mama's* arms around her.'

Asleep. Sara glanced down in surprise to find that Lia was indeed fast asleep, her body heavy and her limbs slack, her steady breathing a sign that, just as Fabia had pointed out, the child felt safe at last.

Tears bulged in her eyes—tears of love and fear of loss and a heart-clenching tenderness that had her trembling mouth brushing a caress over the baby's warm cheek.

'Don't cry, *signora…*' Fabia bent down beside the chair to place a consoling hand on Sara's arm. 'She is safe now. Signor Nicolas see to it that she remain safe. You need worry no more.'

Yes, she was safe, Sara silently conceded. But she suspected that, far from being over, her worries were only just about to begin.

Alfredo wanted his grandchild. He did not want her mother. He had been very clever in getting them both here with Nicolas's blessing. Was his next move to have Sara removed while the child remained?

Sara knew it was Nicolas from the moment he entered the suite. How she knew she wasn't sure, unless it was a leftover instinct from the last time she had lived here when sheer self-preservation had taught her to pinpoint him wherever he was in this many-levelled villa.

Three years ago he had felt like her only ally in a house of enemies. Even the paid staff had treated her with little respect. And, if she was honest about it, she had not known how to deal with them. They'd intimidated her—as most people had intimidated her then. Now it was a different story. Somewhere along the line she had gained a maturity that stopped her seeing everyone as frightening aliens in an alien world.

Like Fabia, for instance. Whether it was Sara's own firm, quiet manner or the fact that the servant was a new addition to the Santino staff since Sara had been here last and therefore had no idea how Sara used to be treated she wasn't sure, but far from being cold and unhelpful Fabia had gone out of her way to make Sara feel more comfortable in a situation she was so obviously not comfortable with. She'd allowed no one entry into the suite, insisting on answering each knock at the door and dealing with the caller herself.

'The whole house waited anxiously for good news of your baby, Mrs Santino,' she'd explained. 'Now they want to come and voice their concerns and their pleasure to you. But they can wait,' she'd decided firmly. 'You just be comfortable and enjoy having that warm little body close again. I will deal with the rest.'

And Sara had begun to feel comfortable—to her own surprise.

When Lia had awoken feeling hungry and fractious, it had been Fabia who had helped soothe her with the same quiet manner that Sara had recognised as the one she had used on herself. And when Lia, with the usual resilience that children had by nature, had suddenly become her usual bundle of restless energy Fabia bad come with them down to the tiny beach.

The three of them had spent a long, soothing hour down there, taking advantage of the late afternoon sun's cooler rays to simply play without fear of either mother or child burning. They'd paddled in the silk-warm water that gently lapped the sand-skirted shore, and built a sandcastle together then decorated it with pebbles from farther up the beach, Lia padding to and fro with a happy contentment that twisted her mother's heart.

She had been so close—so close to never seeing her baby like this again...

They'd come back up the long row of steps as a threesome, at first with the little girl jumping the steps between Sara and Fabia, each small hand tucked into one of theirs, and later, when she'd run out of steam, straddling her mother's hips, with her tired head on Sara's shoulder, while Fabia had paced quietly beside them, a kind of soothing quality about her presence.

That had been hours ago, though. Now the sun was setting low in the sky and Lia was fast asleep in the baby's cot which had been erected by Sara's bed. And Fabia had seemingly taken root, Sara thought with a small smile, because she was sitting in a chair beside the sleeping child, quietly stitching her delicate embroidery, quite indifferent to Sara's claims that she did not need to stay any longer.

In the end, Sara had left her to it, coming through here to the sitting room, to flop down on a sofa to watch the sunset, feeling about as drained as an electronic toy without any batteries now that Lia no longer had a claim on her attention.

The last few days, she accepted, were finally catching up with her.

'You look shocking,' was Nicolas's own observation as he arrived at the side of her chair.

'And it makes me feel so much better to hear you say it.'

He sighed at her sarcasm, stepping past her to go and stare at the sunset. 'The child is—calmer now?' he asked after a moment.

'No thanks to you, yes.' For a long while after awakening on her mother's lap, Lia had been frightened, and confused, and—

She sighed, closing her eyes and her mind to all the painful things she could only guess that her poor baby had been feeling over the last few days.

'I apologise if I—frightened the child,' he murmured stiffly. 'But you must understand that I find the situation—difficult.'

'Well, you will no doubt be pleased to know, then, that we will be happy to go back to London just as soon as you give the word.'

'So eager to leave,' he mocked.

'The sooner you transport us back out of here, the sooner the—difficult situation will be over.'

'I wish it could be that simple.'

'It is,' she assured him. 'Just call for your private limousine and your private jet aeroplane—' her voice dripped more sarcasm '—and we will be gone, I promise you.'

He said nothing to that, his attention seemingly fixed on the breathtaking sight of a vermilion sky touching a blue satin sea.

Then he turned and glanced down at her. 'Dinner will be ready in about an hour,' he informed her. 'Do you think you can make an effort and tidy yourself for it? I can understand why you must look so wrung out,' he allowed, 'but do you have to be dressed like a rag doll also?'

The criticism was aimed directly at the way she had her hair scraped untidily back into a pony-tail, and the fact that she was still wearing the same clothes she had travelled in. She looked battle-worn and travel-stained.

He had managed to change his clothes, though, she noted, and was now dressed in a snowy white shirt and black silk trousers. He looked good. Long legs, tight hips, broad shoulders.

'Blame yourself for the way I look,' she threw at him, dropping her gaze from the lean, tight attractiveness that had always been his. 'You may have kindly packed for me this morning, but only the smart couture outfits a man like you would expect a woman to wear. No day clothes,' she explained at his frown. 'Nothing to counter the hot climate, or the fact that I would be dealing with a very energetic, very messy child. And to top that,' she concluded, her voice so dry that you could have scored chalk lines on it, 'you forgot to pack toiletries, underwear or even a hairbrush.'

'That bad, huh?' he grunted. 'I am not used to packing,' he then added as an excuse.

'It showed.' Despite herself, Sara could not hold back a small smile. 'You did a little better for Lia,' she then went on to allow graciously. 'Simply because you must have just emptied each drawer containing her clothes into the suitcase. And—Oh,' she added, 'you remembered Dandy. Now that was really thought-ful. Her whole countenance changed when she saw him again.'

'And what, I wonder, will change yours?'

She went hot, then cold, then began tingling all over as his softly provoking tone sent disturbing little messages to all her senses.

'I will eat my dinner here in the suite if you don't mind,' she said coolly as a way to counteract the disturbance.

'You will eat in the dining room as is the custom in this house,' he ordained. But at least that other, more intimate tone had gone from his voice.

She shook her head. 'I won't leave Lia here alone. She may wake up and be frightened.'

'And Fabia is with her, is she not?'

'Yes.' Sara conceded that point. 'But Fabia is not the child's mother, is she? She's had enough upsets in her little life recently without waking to a strange room and a strange woman and no sign of her mother.'

'The house is equipped with an internal communications sys-tem.' He made dry mockery of all her protests. 'One call from Fabia and you can be back down here in seconds.'

'Seconds that can seem like an hour of agony to a child in distress.'

'This is foolish!' He sighed. 'The child is safe! She knows Fabia's face. She knows her mama accepts Fabia as someone she can trust. You have spent the whole afternoon together building that trust! Now you must trust Fabia to do her job without rancour from you, while you—'

'Job?' She picked up on the word with a sharp question.

'Yes.' His eyes glinted down at her, cool and unwavering. 'Fabia has been employed specifically to look after the child.'

She jumped up, a tight band of fear suddenly closing like steel around her chest. 'As a nanny, you mean?'

'Yes...' he confirmed, but in a way which tightened the band further. She was thinking of Alfredo, wondering how much of his influence was at work here. Had Alfredo employed Fabia? Was she here to wean Lia away from her mother so that the wrench when it came would not be too great for the child?

'I don't need a nanny to help me with Lia,' she stated as firmly as her quaking heart would let her. 'L-look what h-happened the l-last time you employed a nanny! Lia was taken from right beneath her nose!'

'Why are you stammering?' He frowned down at her.

Because I'm frightened, she thought agitatedly. 'Nic, please—' She resorted to begging, her hand going to clutch at his forearm in appeal. 'Don't do this to me! Don't reduce my importance as a mother! I don't need Fabia! I w-won't be here long enough to n-need her!'

'My God,' he breathed, his eyes suddenly dark with shock. 'You are terrified, aren't you?'

So t-terrified that I'm even s-stammering inside my head! she thought wildly. 'L-let me just stay quietly here in this s-suite until you are ready to send us back to London! Please!'

'But what are you frightened of?' He ignored her plea to demand an answer to his question. 'Do you think because the child's abductors were Sicilian that I cannot protect you here?' he suggested when she didn't answer but just stood there staring at him with those huge, frightened eyes and trembling so badly that he felt compelled to lift his hands to her arms to steady her. 'You are wrong, you know,' he murmured reassuringly. 'This

place is built like a fortress. Nothing moves outside it without
an electronic camera picking it up.'

But it wasn't the outside Sara was worried about. It was the
inside. And the people within it.

She took in a deep breath, and tried very hard to grab back
some self-control. 'Nic...'

She stepped closer, her fingers settling tremulously on the
centre of his wide chest. It was not a come-on; she was not trying to use female wiles on him here to get him to do what she
wanted. She was simply too anxious to know what she was
doing or how she was doing it.

'Listen to me...' she pleaded. 'I don't want to be here and you
don't want us here! If you believe it impossible to protect us in
London, then I will change my name—my identity if I have to!
Just send us back to England and I shall get right out of your
life. I promise you. You won't have to be inconvenienced like
this again on our account!'

He stiffened, the big chest expanding on a tense clenching of
its muscular flesh. 'You—love this child very much, don't you?'

Why did he keep on asking her that question? 'She is my
life!' she choked.

'And the father? Did you love him with the same strength?'

Oh, God. Sara closed her eyes on a shaft of tight pain and
wanted to drop her head onto that big chest and weep. Weep.
'Yes,' she breathed.

He stepped away from her, turning back to the window and
leaving her standing there trembling with her hands still lifted
in front of her where his chest had just been.

'Did he love you?' he enquired after a moment.

She had to swallow to remove the aching lump from her
throat. 'I think so, once,' she replied, letting her hands drop
empty to her sides.

'Then why did he never claim you both?'

Her sigh held an irony only she would ever understand. 'Because he could never be sure that my baby was his and his pride could not let him accept another man's child.'

'Could she be mine, then?'

Oh, no, she thought wretchedly. Don't ask me that question now. Not when I daren't give you an honest answer!

So instead she avoided it. 'Nic, I need to get away from here. I can't bear this place,' she murmured thickly. 'I never could.'

'Were you so unhappy here?'

Without you here with me? she thought painfully. 'Yes,' she said, and sank down onto the sofa and wished to God that they'd never begun this whole wretched scene.

He didn't say anything to that, and the silence between them throbbed with the heavy pull of her own heartbeat.

Then, quietly, he said, 'You cannot leave.'

Her stomach gave a funny lurch. 'What's that supposed to mean?' she asked warily.

He turned. 'Just what it said. You cannot leave here. The risk is too great. I can guarantee your safety here; I cannot in London.' He gave a small shrug. 'So here is where you and the child must stay.'

'No.' She shook her head vehemently. 'I don't want to.'

'I am not giving you a choice,' he grimly informed her.

It brought her back to her feet. 'Just because you refuse to divorce me does not mean you own me, Nicolas!' she cried. 'I can make my own choices. And I prefer to take my chance in London rather than live under this roof again!'

'You speak as if it were you who was betrayed!' he said derisively in response to that little speech.

'I will not be put through the kind of misery I endured here a second time.'

'Maybe you deserve to be miserable.'

That came straight from the gut, and she squeezed her eyes tight shut while she handled the blow it dealt her.

'But my baby does not,' she managed to parry. 'She is the innocent one in all of this. Punish the mother and you will punish the child. Can you be that callous? That thirsty for revenge?'

'I am not after revenge,' he denied. 'It is a simple case of logistics which decides it for us. This house is easier to guard against a repeat of what you have just been through. Therefore this is where you will live from now on. *Comprende?*'

Oh, she 'comprended' all right. The lord and master had spoken. End of discussion.

'But I don't have to eat with you,' she countered, throwing herself back onto the sofa with a defiance about her that warned him she was not going to surrender this point to him as well! 'I would rather starve first.'

'And that is being childish,' he derided.

Too true, she agreed. But there was no way she was going to sit at the same table as Alfredo Santino! No way.

'I'm tired,' she said. 'I don't want to dress up and play happy dinner hour with you and your father—can't you even allow me that one concession?'

He sighed, allowing some of his anger to escape with the sound. Then surprisingly he gave in. 'I need to speak to Fabia before I leave you,' he said. 'Then I will have something sent down to you.'

With that, he walked off towards the bedroom, leaving Sara feeling annoyingly, frustratingly let down.

Though she didn't know why.

Or refused to look at why.

CHAPTER EIGHT

SARA WAS SQUATTING by the cultivated border of one of the many white-painted terrace walls, carefully coaxing bougainvillea strands around a wire support that she had just constructed, secure in the knowledge that she could hear Lia's happy voice drifting up to her from where she played on the beach with Fabia, when an electric whirring sound behind her warned her of Alfredo's approach.

She didn't turn, did not so much as reveal she was aware of his presence. But her inner sigh was heavy. In the six days since she had arrived here, she had carefully avoided any contact at all with Alfredo. He came to see Lia each lunchtime, guiding his chair into the suite and staying long enough to share lunch with the baby, and Sara made herself distinctly scarce before he was due to arrive.

It was necessary for them to stay here, Nicolas had said. But necessary to whom? To this man in the wheelchair coming steadily towards her along the terrace? Of course it was.

It certainly wasn't what Nicolas wanted, she thought bleakly, because she hadn't even seen him since the first night she'd arrived here.

He had had his talk with Fabia, their two voices conversing in the quick Sicilian dialect Sara had never quite been able to keep up with even before her Italian had become rusty through lack of use.

When he'd come out of the bedroom again, he hadn't even bothered to wish her goodnight, but had just left.

She hadn't seen him since. The next morning she'd awoken to Fabia arriving with a manservant in tow carrying some heavy suitcases. They'd contained all her personal belongings. Nicolas must have had them flown in overnight from London. A further statement that this was to be a permanent situation. Fabia had also brought a message from Nicholas informing her that he'd had to fly back to New York.

He had been gone for almost a week now, and she refused point-blank to admit—even to herself—that she missed him.

The wheelchair stopped a couple of feet away. Sara felt his eyes on her, sensed him urging her to turn and acknowledge him. When she did not, it was he who broke the tense silence between them.

'The garden has missed your special touch,' he said.

'I have nothing to say to you, Alfredo,' she told him without pausing in what she was doing. 'You are a mean, nasty, selfish old man who doesn't deserve my attention. Or the attention of my daughter, come to that.'

Instead of taking exception to her outright attack on him, she was surprised to hear him give a soft chuckle. 'I would say that constituted saying a lot,' he remarked ruefully.

It made her turn, more out of suspicion than because she had been taken by surprise by his amiable tone. She was quite sure Alfredo could chuckle as pleasantly as that while thrusting a knife between her shoulder-blades!

Still, this first real look at him without her being blinded

by the horror of seeing her daughter clasped to his chest was
a shock.

Dressed in a cream short-sleeved shirt open at the throat
and a pair of brown trousers, he was still a remarkably daunt-
ing person—remarkable because he had been so drastically diminished in the purely physical sense.

Never anywhere near as tall as his son, he had once made up
for his lack of inches with width. Wide shoulders, wide chest,
wide hips, short, immovable trunks for legs—all of it solid-
packed and tough. But now the width had gone, the muscle
waste so dramatic that it had left behind it a mere shadow of
what once had been, replacing it with a frailty so obvious that
Sara began to understand why Nicolas was so angrily protective of what pathetic amount was left.

The sun was shining down on his silvered head—the hair was
not thinning, she noted. At least he had been saved that emascu-
lation. But his skin, though tanned, was sallow and loose, wrin-
kling his arms and his throat. And there was a lack of strength
in the way he sat hunched in his wheelchair, as if the mere act
of sitting in it was an effort in itself.

'Goodness me.' She sat back on her heels, too stunned to
hold back the next comment. 'You look terrible.'

His answering wry smile was more a fatalistic rueful grimace. 'I hate it,' he admitted, and slapped a thin hand on the
wheelchair arm. 'Hate this too.'

I just bet you do, she thought with a moment's soft pity for
this man who used to be a giant despite his lack of inches.

Then he was sending her a look that had all hint of compassion draining right out of her. For this man was still dangerous,
physically incapacitated or not. Those two bright hunter's gold
eyes were burning pinpoints of astuteness and guile, warning
her that the sharp brain behind them still functioned at its old
breakneck pace.

'You, I see, are more beautiful than ever,' he remarked. 'The child is hewn in your image. Your hair, your face, your inherently sweet and gentle nature.'

'I was a coward, Alfredo,' Sara countered, ignoring the attempted compliment. 'My daughter is not.'

Something she had discovered via listening painfully as Lia had over the last few days let little things slip which suggested that the child had not made it easy for her kidnappers.

'It will be my son's genes which give her courage.' He nodded proudly. 'Or maybe even my own.'

'God help her,' Sara responded, amazed that he wasn't even going to pretend he did not know exactly who Lia's father was. 'If she has much of you in her, Alfredo, then she will need God's help.' She fixed him with a hard and cold look. 'Have you any idea how much you frightened her having her snatched like that?'

'Me?' At last he decided to use his striking ability to fake innocence, actually managing to look shocked by the accusation. 'I did not snatch the *bambina*!' he denied. 'I would not wish to frighten a hair on her beautiful head!'

'Liar.' Blue eyes suddenly hot with anger, she stood up and went to lean over him. 'I saw your expression when you held my baby in your arms! You were glowing with triumph! With everything alive in you, you were staking ownership! Possessive and territorial! I saw it, Alfredo. I saw it!'

It made him gasp, the very fact that she could spit at him like that utterly astounding him. 'You grow brave in the face of a shrivelled old man in a wheelchair,' he murmured feebly.

'Don't try the poor sick old man routine on me,' she said scathingly as she straightened away. 'It just won't work.'

With that, she bent to pick up her coil of garden wire and secateurs and made to leave.

'Don't walk away from me, woman!' he growled. Oddly, it stopped her. Not the words themselves but the way he had said them. There was a bitter, biting frustration there—frustration with his physical disadvantage.

She turned back to glance at him just as his fist made furious contact with the wheelchair arm, his face a twisted map of angry helplessness.

'I did not take the child!' He scowled mutinously up at her. 'If I had thought of it, I would have!' he added bluntly. 'But I did not!' Then he sighed heavily because the burst of passionate anger had obviously drained his energy.

Sara saw him go a paler shade of sallow, his eyes lose the vibrant spark of life, and her bottom lip twitched in a spasm of unwanted feeling for this man who was her enemy. She didn't know whether to believe him, or even if it really mattered that much now that the deed was done. But she could not afford to relax her guard around Alfredo, she reminded herself grimly. Past experience had taught her that lesson the hardest way anyone could learn a lesson in life.

But nor was it in her nature to be cruel to the afflicted, and Alfredo was certainly afflicted at the moment.

'Are you all right?' she asked stiffly.

'Sì,' he clipped back, but he was leaning heavily on his forearms, his silvered head lowered while he seemed to be concentrating on pacing his breathing.

A child's laughter drifted up from the small beach below, tinkling around both of them and diverting their attention to the sight of Lia dressed in white cotton dungarees and a white cotton mob-cap pulled on over her hair, running as fast as her little legs could take her, away from Fabia who was chasing with a string of wet seaweed dangling from one hand.

Sara laughed too; she couldn't help it. Leaning her thighs against the terrace wall, she folded her arms and watched the chase.

Suddenly the wheelchair was right beside her, Alfredo leaning forward as much as he could to follow what was going on.

'Run, little one. Run!' he encouraged gruffly, a thin hand making a fist which he used to urge the child further.

It was miraculous. In those few short seconds he had doubled in strength, in life, in sheer vitality. And the chase was lost to Sara as she took all of this in.

A tingling on the back of her neck—that sixth sense at work again, probably—made her turn and look up—up the white-walled terraces, to see Nicolas standing several levels above them, his dark face carved in a mask of pained observation.

Pain not for the child but for the father. Her heart squeezed in her breast. He too had seen the change in Alfredo—perhaps even heard the exchange which had preceded it.

His eyes flicked to her and turned cold—as cold as yellow ice. Yes, he had heard, she realised with a small shiver. Not all of it, but enough. He had warned her not to upset his father. Now retribution was due because she had.

'Hah!' said Alfredo, sitting back in his chair with a trium-phant laugh. 'Did you see that?' He chuckled delightedly, un-aware of the other exchange going on. 'She escaped by ducking right between Fabia's legs!'

Dragging her eyes from Nicolas's, she glanced down at the beach where Fabia was now giving chase in the other direction. When she looked up again, Nicolas was gone.

'Aye, aye, aye...' Alfredo sighed envyingly. 'To be able to go down there and join in the fun...'

'Alfredo—' Impulsively, Sara knelt down to his level. 'Lia is your grandchild—'

'I know this.' He turned, eyes so incredibly softened by pride and joy that it caught at her throat.

'You love her already.'

'Si,' he confirmed. 'We—how you English say?—bonded!' he exclaimed. 'From the moment she saw me, Sara! She came into my arms as if she had known them always! I love her,' he sighed. 'She loves me! It is wonderful!'

'She is part of me too, Alfredo,' Sara firmly reminded him.

'It would be difficult to deny this when she is the image of you.' He grinned.

'She needs her mother.'

'Of course!' He looked almost shocked that she should feel the need to tell him that. 'All children need their mother...' he added, his attention drifting back to the beach where the game had now finished and Lia was busy with her bucket and spade while Fabia erected a beach umbrella over her to keep off the sun. 'Nico was entirely devoted to his mama,' he went on softly. 'They would play together—on this same beach—just like that.'

'Rosalia,' Sara prompted softly.

'Si.' The gold eyes darkened. 'You named the child after Nico's *mamma*. I thank you.' He gave a small nod of his head. 'It was—kind of you under the circumstances.'

'She was a very special woman, so Nicholas once told me. She—' Sara eyed him carefully. 'She was devoted to both her husband and her son.'

'Si.' Again the word held a wealth of tenderness. 'As we were devoted to her,' he added. 'But she took very sick. Then she died. We both grieved for her badly—still do in some quiet moments, though it was a long time ago now.'

'Would Rosalia be proud of you, Alfredo, for denying her son the right to love his own wife and child as she loved you both?'

There was a sudden stillness about him. Sara held her breath, waiting—waiting to see how he was going to respond to that blatant attempt to reach his conscience.

'You presume too much,' he said curtly then.

'Do I?' was all she answered, and stood up, deciding she had said enough for now. She had planted the seed; now it was up to him to decide whether to nurture it or just let it die. But if he did let it die then he would be shaming the memory of his beloved wife. Sara had made that point sink indelibly in. 'Just remember that Lia is my child,' she concluded. 'Try any of your rotten tricks to take her from me and I shall fight you to hell and back.'

His golden eyes flicked sharply to her. 'And how could I possibly do that?' he asked, back to being the man she used to know—the one who could terrify her with a look like that.

But not anymore, she informed herself bracingly. 'You know exactly how you can do it,' she countered. 'I am one step ahead of you, Alfredo,' she warned. 'Force me to, and I will use my ace card.'

His eyes were studying her with a gleaming intelligence. 'And what would that ace card be?' he asked silkily.

She didn't have one, but it wouldn't hurt to let him think that she might have. 'If you don't already know then I'm not going to tell you.'

'My son loves his *papà*,' he added slyly.

By that Sara assumed he was wondering if she had some way of proving her innocence and Alfredo's culpability to Nicolas.

'Your son has a right to love his own daughter too,' she responded, and turned away, preparing to leave him alone with that.

But his voice when it came to her made her skin crawl with dismay. 'He has a new woman,' he said. 'Her name is Anastasia and she lives in Taormina. He visits her twice a week when he is here.'

Her eyes closed on the words. And she had a flashback to a week ago when she had lain in his arms and heard Nicolas himself confirm that statement. 'Of course I have tried!' he had spat at her. 'Do you think I like feeling this way about you?'

Cancer. Alfredo was a cancer that lived on the weaknesses of others.

She walked away from him, feeling sick and shaken.

When she got back to her suite, Nicolas was there. Her heart sank. He was angry, his lean face stone-like and cold.

Retribution was nigh, she recognised wearily, and with a wry little smile stepped further into the suite. Then stopped dead. 'What's going on?' she asked sharply.

The bedroom door was open, and a couple of maids were busily laying all Sara's clothes out on the bed.

No! she thought on an upsurge of alarm. Alfredo had not already done it, had he? He hadn't—?

'Come with me.'

Catching hold of her hand, Nicolas all but frogmarched her out of that suite and along the hallway to the next, where he threw open the door and propelled her inside. She ended up standing in the middle of a beautiful white and blue sitting room; her eyes drifted dazedly around her surroundings without taking anything in.

The suite door shut with a controlled click. She spun back to face him. 'What are they doing with my clothes?' she demanded shakily.

'Removing them,' he replied. 'The suite was not yours to begin with. I was allowing you time to settle before moving you, but, having witnessed the way you could attack a sick old man, I do not see why I should make any concessions to you—on anything!'

'The suite was not yours...allowing you time to settle...' Her mind was too busy sorting through what he had said to worry much about the angry way he had said it.

'You mean,' she ventured at last, 'that you're moving Lia and me up a floor, to the family apartments?'

For some reason her conclusion made him frown in puzzlement. 'What have you been doing with yourself this last week?' he demanded. 'You cannot, surely, still be so ignorant of the changes that have been made here?'

Her answer was a blank look because she hadn't so much as set foot into the rest of the house since arriving here. She had eaten all her meals in her own room and confined all her recreation to the beach and the pool, which had meant her only having to walk up and down the outer steps. Other than that she had stayed put, with no interest in reacquainting herself with a place where she hadn't felt welcome the first time and was sure that that welcome would be even smaller this time.

His sigh was impatient. 'This whole house has been completely redesigned since you were here last—essentially to accommodate my father's less mobile state!' he explained. 'Oh, he gets around quite freely—as you saw just now,' he added, with a flash of that anger to remind her why she had been dragged in here like a naughty child. 'With the aid of special chair-lifts we have had fitted alongside the east stairway. But for the sake of comfort other changes were made.'

'What changes?' she prompted warily when he went grimly silent. She wasn't a fool; she knew Nicolas was angry with her. She also knew, therefore, that he was not telling her all of this for her own health!

'There has been a—reallocation of private facilities. My father now has the full use of what was previously considered the family tier. He needs specialist attention,' he went on. 'Twenty-four-hour nursing. Daily physiotherapy and so on. So rooms on that level have been equipped accordingly.'

'Like a mini-hospital, you mean,' she suggested.

'Yes.'

Alfredo must be very ill to warrant such vast and expensive care and attention in his home, she realised, and flicked a look of pained comprehension at Nicolas for what he must be feeling. His father meant the world to him.

He dismissed the look with a cold lifting of his chin. 'The guest suites, therefore, are now below us, level with the pool, recreation rooms and garden terrace,' he continued. 'Because this—' he made a short, gesturing motion with his hand, which she presumed encompassed this whole tier '—is now my own private wing of the house.'

'Ah, I begin to see,' she said with a small, bitter, wry smile. 'You want Lia and me out of your private rooms and down in the guest suites where we belong.'

'No,' he said silkily. 'You do not see at all.' His eyes narrowed on her face, his next words carefully chosen for maximum impact. 'Your child remains exactly where she is. It is you who are moving. In here. In this suite—with me.'

Silence. She met that with total, woolly-minded silence. He watched and waited, his hooded gaze glinting over her long, bare legs, which had been faintly tinted gold in the days she had spent here already. Her plain pink shorts with their loose pleated style did nothing to camouflage the slender hips beneath them. Nor did the simple crop-waisted vest-top, which gave glimpses of her flat stomach when she moved, hide the fact that she was wearing no bra beneath it. Two firm crests were thrusting gently against the thin cloth in a dusky invitation that he would have had to be totally indifferent to not to feel the hot sting of temptation that hit his loins. He remembered too well how they tasted, how they would respond to the lightest touch from him.

Provocative. That was how she looked. A fine, sleek golden creature of sensual provocation. A woman he would be happy to die inside, so long as those breasts were there for him to suckle while he did so. So long as those long golden legs were wrapped around him. So long as that pink heart-shaped mouth was fastened somewhere on his skin, warm and moistly tasting him as he knew it loved to do.

Not that she was aware of any of this, he acknowledged grimly—not of her own sexual attractiveness or what it did to him.

Unaware. Just as her hands were unaware, he was sure, of the coil of garden wire she was twisting between them, and the secateurs and the fact that her wedding ring gleamed gold on her finger.

His wedding ring. The ring he had placed there. Once a gold ring of love, now a gold ring of betrayal.

Stiffly he turned away from both the temptation and the ring, despising himself—despising her.

His movement set her long golden lashes flickering, blue eyes zooming into focus on his long, tense back.

Then, 'No,' she said in flat-voiced refusal. 'I will stay with Lia.'

He spun back, face fierce, the earlier coldness replaced by something else, something faintly disturbing. 'Are we back to arguing about choices?' he clipped. 'Because you have none,' he informed her brutally. 'You will do exactly as you are told while you are under this roof.'

'Except sleep with you,' she objected.

'You will,' he insisted. 'And you will do it without protest! You owe me that!' he rasped in a bitter rejoinder.

Did he mean by that, that she owed him the use of her body in return for his retrieving her stolen child? she wondered in horror. 'But you hate and despise me! You even hated yourself for what happened the last time we shared a bed!'

'True.' His hard face tightened. 'But if I had wanted the whole world to know that Nicolas Santino was foolish enough to marry a faithless woman,' he threw at her, 'I would have denounced both her and her child three years ago!'

She blanched at the intended insult. He took the reaction as his due.

'As it is,' he continued, 'to the world and this household, we are still very much man and wife. And man and wife share a bed and have a certain amount of marital privacy which does not include a child sleeping in the same room.'

'But you haven't been near me for three years,' she cried. 'How are we supposed to have a proper marriage with three years' separation in the middle?'

Her scornful tone made his golden eyes glint. 'You mean because until now you have preferred to spend your time at our London home where I have visited you on a regular basis?'

'My God,' she gasped as clear understanding of his meaning hit her full in the face. 'You can be as twofaced as your father when it really comes down to it, can't you?'

'We will leave my father out of this, if you please,' he said tersely.

'I wish we could!' she flared. 'But since he lives here too and he knows exactly what state our so-called marriage is in isn't he going to find it rather odd—' if not damned frustrating, if her suspicions about him were correct, she added silently to herself '—that you and I are cohabiting again?'

'He will keep his own counsel,' Nicolas coldly stated. 'For neither does he wish to see his son's pride dragged in the dirt because of this—situation we all find ourselves thrust into.'

'He said that, did he?' she challenged. 'Condoned this frankly—obscene suggestion you are putting to me?'

'It is not a suggestion,' he denied, 'and nor is it obscene. You are still my wife in the eyes of the world, and you will maintain good appearances at all costs, Sara,' he warned. 'Or so help me I will let you go, and keep the child!'

Thereby threatening to walk her right into Alfredo's neatly baited trap! she realised, and didn't know whether to scream in frustration or weep in defeat. 'I won't sleep with you, Nicolas,' was what she eventually said, and spun abruptly on her heel.

'Where do you think you are going?' he demanded.

'It's time for Lia's afternoon nap,' she informed him stiffly.

'Fabia will see to the child,' he ordained. 'We have unfinished business to discuss here.'

'Except I prefer to see to Lia myself.'

'And I am telling you you cannot!' he snapped, then made an effort to get a hold of himself. 'This is more important. So leave it,' he clipped. 'The child is as safe with Fabia as she could be with anyone.'

She spun back to stare at him. 'Even her own mother?' she challenged. Then, as a sudden thought struck her, she felt tears of hurt spring into her eyes. 'This is another punishment, isn't it?' she accused him bitterly. 'It's just one more Sicilian vendetta whereby you cruelly separate me from my baby for some nasty reason of your own!'

She had to be crazy speaking to him like that, she realised hectically as he took an angry step towards her. But she held her ground, eyes ablaze, her fingers tightening on the coil of wire and secateurs in a way that made his eyes widen in real surprise because it was so obvious that she was ready to use them on him if he gave her reason.

'Put those down,' he instructed.

She shook her head, mouth drawn in at the corners and defiant, like her blue eyes, her whole stance!

'You will not like it if I am forced to take them from you,' he warned darkly.

I know I won't, she acknowledged to herself. But for some reason I can't allow myself to cower away from you! Not any more—perhaps never again! she realised with a start, and knew the words would have surprised him if she'd said them out loud.

But maybe she didn't need to say them out loud, she noted breathlessly. Because something altered in his eyes, the anger darkening into something much more dangerous: a taste for the battle—not this mental battle whereby she was daring to defy him, or even the one involving a silly pair of secateurs that he could take from her with ease if he so wanted to, but a far more complicated one which set the tiny muscles deep down in her stomach pulsing, set her heart racing.

'Taking me on, *cara*?' he drawled.

Her fingers twitched. 'I'm not going to let you walk all over me, Nicolas,' she returned. 'Not again. Last time you broke my spirit—'

'You never had a spirit,' he countered deridingly, taking a deliberate step towards her. 'You used to jump ten miles high if anyone so much as frowned at you.'

She had to steal herself not to take a defensive step back. 'Well, not anymore,' she said determinedly. 'I am a mother now. And I shall fight you to the end of the earth if I have to but you will not separate me from my baby.'

'This has nothing to do with the baby.' He dismissed that angle, taking yet another carefully gauged step.

Her breasts heaved on a short, tense pull of air, but she held her ground.

'This is about you standing there—' he used his darkened eyes to indicate the defiant pose she had adopted '—daring to take me on...'

Another step. She quivered. He saw it and sent her a taunting smile. 'The coil of wire,' he suggested, 'would make an adequate garotte but would require a lot of physical strength for you to succeed with it. I would throw it to one side if I were you, *amore*,' he advised, 'and concentrate on the scissors instead.'

'Secateurs,' she corrected him tensely.

His mocking half-nod acknowledged the correction. 'Now with those you could do me some damage,' he observed. 'Not much,' he added. 'But some—enough maybe to make this new spirit you talk about feel better.'

'I have no wish to damage you at all!' she shakily denied. 'I just want you to stop trying to bully me all the time!'

'Then put down the weapons,' he urged, 'and we will talk about my—bullying.'

She shook her head in refusal, and the odd thing about it was that she had a feeling he would have been disappointed if she had given in to him. He was enjoying this; she could see the beginnings of amusement gleaming behind the taunt in his eyes.

'Then make your move, *cara*,' he softly advised. 'Or I will undoubtedly make mine...'

Then he did—without any more warning, her halfsecond hesitation all he allowed her before his hands were suddenly snaking out to capture her two wrists, fingers closing tightly around them then forcing them up and apart until he had her standing there in front of him with her hands made useless; then his body was taking up the last bit of space separating them, chest against wildly palpitating chest, hips against hips, thighs against thighs.

'I like it—the spirit,' he murmured. 'I used to like the soft clinging vine you used to be but I think I may like this more spirited creature a whole lot more.'

'I don't want you to like me,' she mumbled in protest.

'No?' He challenged that. The word challenged it, his eyes challenged it, and the sensual curve of his mouth challenged it. 'I think,' he said very softly, 'you want to be kissed into submission.'

'I do not!' she denied.

But it was too late; his mouth covered hers, covered it and moulded it, moulded it and parted it, and, on parting it, brought every sense that she'd been severely containing bursting into quick, clamouring life.

Her wrists he kept up and level with her head; her fingers were still clenched tightly around her 'weapons', as he'd called them. His big chest moved against her chest, making her breasts swell and tighten. His tight hips pushed knowingly against her hips, and the terrible, wonderful sinking feeling she experienced inside made her groan in denial. A denial he scorned by doing the same thing again. And again. And again—until the groan changed in timbre, gave her away, just as her breasts gave her away, her breathing, the way she sank powerlessly into the kiss.

Then her fingers slowly opened, the two clattered thuds which echoed on the tiles at either side of them announcing the final surrender, and she was tugging her wrists, urgent to free her fingers so that she could slide them into his hair, hold his mouth down on hers, move closer—even closer because her legs had turned to liquid and she needed his support to remain upright.

He let her have her way, set her wrists free so that her hands could find his head while his own hands lowered to clasp her lightly around her slender ribcage just below the trembling swell of her breasts. She gave a sensually unsteady sigh and wound her arms around his neck, moving her body closer to the source of its pleasure, sighed again as his hands began stroking her body, moving downwards until they found her hips where they closed and lifted her against the steadily growing evidence of his own passion.

It went on and on, and the one word which kept repeating itself over and over in her head was beautiful. This was so beautiful. The man, his touch, his kiss. Beautiful.

When he lifted her into his arms she did not protest. When he carried her through to the bedroom she only groaned in protest when his mouth left hers for the moment it took him to settle them both on the bed.

Then his mouth was back on hers and she was lost—lost in the beauty of deep, drugging kisses, of his hands caressing her body as they slowly stripped her of her clothes. She lost herself in the acute pleasure of helping him to remove his own, lost herself in the burning blackness of his eyes as he came over her and into her, slowly this time and deeply; mouth tense, cheeks taut with desire, he made the connection with a sombre need that brought tears to her eyes.

'Don't hate me, Nic,' she whispered.

He didn't answer, his long lashes lowering to cover his eyes, and his mouth came down to cover hers, and there in the full brightness of an afternoon sun he lost them both, lost them in the sheer beauty of a slow, slow climb to fulfilment.

When she awoke what seemed like hours later, but was probably only a few blissfully forgetful minutes, he was gone.

Gone hating her? she wondered. Hating himself?

CHAPTER NINE

AND THAT WAS IT. Sara was trapped. Trapped by necessity. Trapped by her own body, which would respond to the slightest touch from the man who had reawoken it to its pleasures. And did he pleasure her! Night after night, hungrily, devouringly. But she never woke up to him still there beside her, and that trapped her too—trapped her in a tight little world of self-disgust and helplessness because she could not do a single thing to change the status quo, his status quo, where she played the loving wife and he played the ravaging conqueror.

She was trapped by his ruthless determination to appear the master of his own household by making her sleep with him, eat in the dining room with him and his father, where she was polite to Alfredo but that was about all and Alfredo teased her with cleverly chosen words with double meanings that she did not dare react to for fear of bringing Nicolas's wrath down on her head.

And she was trapped by her daughter, who loved it here and, worse than that, adored Alfredo. A daughter whom Nicolas had managed to avoid at every possible opportunity; so they only came together on very rare occasions, when he would be coolly polite and the little girl would be warily cautious. And Sara would feel her heart break a little more each time she witnessed the guarded manner of both.

Then there was that terrible trapped feeling she experienced when twice a week Nicolas would take himself off to Taormina and not come back until late in the night. Those were the only nights he didn't touch her. And that trapped her too, because she wanted him to touch her, she wanted him to come from his mistress and still need her, still need to drown himself in her kisses, her body, her arms, her—

Love.

And, God, but she didn't know how long she could go on bearing all of this—bearing the fact that she did not dare say anything about his precious Anastasia because Alfredo's lies about herself had robbed her of the right!

Then came the big crunch, which she supposed had to do with so much pressure building up inside her. They were a month into this awful situation and Nicolas had not been away once. He worked from his office here in the villa and spent most of his time there, only appearing for the odd working lunch with his father, which Sara was not expected to attend, and every dinner, which she was. And from there he would either escort her back to their room for a night of heated passion or out to his mistress, leaving her to weep alone in their bed. Then her period came, and he added further insult to injury by disappearing to Taormina for the next five nights.

At least she had not become pregnant, she kept on telling herself as a soother for all her other aches. But it didn't help, and her bitter resentment of the whole situation just grew and grew until it decided to explode on the first night he did try to touch her again.

'Get your hands off me!' she spat at him, fighting against his grip as he tried to draw her across the bed towards him. 'If you're desperate for sex, then go to your fancy piece! I don't want you!'

'My what?' He stopped long enough to elbow himself up on the pillow to stare at her. 'Did you say fancy piece?' he asked in amusement.

'You know exactly what I said,' she flashed. 'And you know exactly who I mean as well!'

'I do? This is interesting,' he murmured, using a hand on her shoulder to keep her flat beneath him while he studied her hot, angry face. 'Does she have a name?' he asked. 'This—fancy piece I get my sex from?'

She glared at him and refused to answer. He grinned, his hand neatly fielding her fist when it came up to hit him. 'I can make you tell me,' he murmured. 'You know I can.'

'May you burn in hell, Nicolas Santino!' she spat at him.

would much rather burn inside you,' he replied.

'Or her!' she spat. 'It just depends which day of the week it is!'

His eyes widened, cruel mockery riling her on. 'Oh, I see now,' he drawled. 'You've been putting two and two together and coming up with five! That is a very English expression for someone who is totally out of order, is it not?'

'Anastasia!' she hissed up into his arrogantly mocking face. 'The lady this whole house knows you visit twice a week!' she added disgustedly. 'Now get off me!' She tried to push him away but he refused to budge. 'If you want her—have her!' she muttered frustratedly. 'But you won't have me as well!'

Suddenly all amusement was stripped from his voice. 'No?' he disputed softly, slowly, as silkily as a snake's preparation to bite. 'You did.' The biter bit. 'So why shouldn't I?'

She closed her eyes on a wave of helpless agony. 'I can't take much more of this,' she whispered.

'Yes, you can,' he gritted. 'You can take a whole lot more of it. You will take whatever it is I wish to dish out to you, *cara!* So lie back and think of England if you must,' he derided bitterly. 'But when I want you will provide, and that is not an option!'

No option. He took, she provided. But he took with such devastating sensualism that England, or anything else for that matter, never entered her head.

Afterwards, a long time afterwards, when she presumed he must think she was sleeping, he got up, shrugged on his white towelling robe and stepped over to the terrace window, quietly sliding it open enough to allow him to slip outside. The next moment she saw a flare of light through the fine weave of the full-length silk curtains and realised he'd gone out there to smoke a cheroot. A bad habit she had thought he had managed to kick. He stayed out for ages, and she wondered what he must be thinking about to want to be alone out there like that.

Was he hating himself again, she wondered bleakly for making love to her believing what he did believe? Did he do this every time—wait until he thought she was asleep then slip out there to despise himself m private?

Was it that same self-hate that made him go to the other woman for some kind of succour for his own despised lusts?

'Of course I have tried!' he had spat at her that first time in London. 'Do you think I like feeling this way about you?'

She closed her eyes to try to shut out the hurt that came with remembering the words. She hurt for herself, she hurt for him. And she hurt because of the utter hopelessness the whole situation filled her with.

When she opened her eyes again, it was to the soft sound of him stepping back into the bedroom. Under cover of darkness she watched him go into the bathroom, lay there listening to him running water, sluicing his face maybe, cleaning his teeth.

Ridding himself of the scent and taste of his supposedly adulterous wife.

Then he was back in the bedroom, a long, lean, silently moving thoroughbred who slid back into the bed beside her then lay on his back with an arm bent beneath his head, while between them lay a wide space of white linen emptiness like a huge chasm, with nothing to use to bridge the great yawning gap.

And silence—a silence that was torture.

So the scream that suddenly ripped through that silence shook the very bones in both of them.

'God,' Sara gasped. 'Lia.'

And she was up and off the bed before Nicolas had even had time to react. Snatching up her robe, she began running. By the time the next terrible scream came she was out of the bedroom, hair streaming out behind her as she raced across to the suite's main door. The child's frightened screams filled the hallway, locking the air in Sara's throat as she ran to the next door, bursting in to run across that sitting room on legs which were now shaking badly. Entering the bedroom, she found Fabia standing in a hastily drawn on robe with Lia in her arms, the little body stretching and writhing, her screams enough to turn blood to ice.

'What happened?' Sara was across to the baby in seconds, her arms reaching for her, folding her close, her voice murmuring those soft, soothing sounds mothers instinctively murmured, while the little girl's screams changed to aching sobs.

'Bad man came,' the child sobbed. 'Bad man came to take me away!'

White-faced, Sara glanced questioningly at an equally white-faced Fabia who was shaking her head. 'Dream,' she whispered. 'She has them occasionally.'

'You mean—' Sara had to swallow the rise of angry incredulity, force herself to calm her breathing and her voice before daring to go on. 'You mean this has happened before and you haven't told me?'

The other woman looked uncomfortable. 'Not so bad as this,' she said defensively, her gaze drifting over to where Nicolas had appeared in the doorway dressed in hastily pulled on shorts.

The look said more than Sara could cope with. 'Get out,' she said, and anyone who had been present the day Nicolas had cleared the room in London would have recognised the tone. It was chilling.

On a muffled choke, Fabia rushed from the room. Sara turned her back on Nicolas. It was all she could do if she wasn't to react as she was burning to react. 'Shush, darling,' she murmured soothingly to the sobbing baby. 'Mama's here now. Shush...'

'Sara—' His voice sounded thick, hoarse almost.

'Not now,' she said, and dipped her hand into the cot to get the pink teddy, gently pushed it between herself and the baby's sobbing body then began humming softly.

There was a silence behind her—then a different kind of silence. The first was filled with the battle that Nicolas was having with himself at her cold dismissal. The second was the sound of his battle won—or lost; she wasn't sure which—and she knew he had gone.

When eventually Lia drifted back into sleep, Sara did not replace her in her cot but sat down in the chair beside Fabia's rumpled bed and allowed the little girl to spread out on her lap with her warm cheek cushioned on Sara's breast.

She stayed like that for ages. How long she didn't know. It didn't matter. When Nicolas eventually came back, she barely acknowledged him. He went to stand by the window—a habit of his when struggling with something, she'd come to realise. He had pulled on a white towelling robe, and his hands were lost inside the capacious pockets. His hair was ruffled and his profile grim.

'It was I who instructed Fabia not to interrupt us after we had retired because I needed to feel our nights belonged to me.'

Those were, she assumed, the nights he did not devote to Anastasia.

'Fabia is upset,' he continued when it became clear that she was not going to say anything. 'She fears you may dismiss her if I do not make this instruction clear to you.'

'I have no jurisdiction over Fabia's employment,' she reminded him coolly.

'But she does not know that.' He turned. 'She has a genuine affection for the child, Sara. It would be wrong to punish her for something I am at fault for.'

'I have no intention of punishing anyone.'

'Then put the child back in her bed and let Fabia return to her bed,' he urged.

'While I return to yours?'

He deliberately ignored that. 'She sleeps peacefully now. There is little danger of her having another nightmare like that.'

'But I won't know that, will I?' she pointed out. 'So I'll stay here, if you don't mind, and Fabia can find herself another bed for the rest of the night.'

'But I do mind.'

'Do you know what, Nicolas?' Her chin came up, blue eyes as cold as he'd ever seen them. 'I don't really care what you mind about any more. I am staying here, with my baby, so that if she does have another dream like that I am on hand. Her mother.' She thrust that important point home. 'Not just some substitute you decided would do to keep the child quiet while you got what you wanted from me.'

'It isn't like that.' He sighed.

So did Lia, the sound shuddering on the residue of finished tears.

'It's exactly like that,' Sara maintained, soothing the child with a gentle caress along her golden hairline. 'You can barely bring yourself to look at her, never mind take her needs into consideration.'

'Can you really blame me?' he muttered gruffly.

'Yes, actually, I can,' she said. 'Lia isn't the one who offended your pride, Nicolas. I am. Yet it's the baby you punish by depriving her of her mother when she needs her.'

'I was not attempting to deprive her!' he protested, realised his voice had risen and strove to quieten it. 'I was just...'

He ran out of words. Sara provided them for him. 'Time-sharing with her.'

He gave another sigh, then surprisingly said heavily, 'Yes. She has you to herself all day. I wanted you to myself at night.'

'Unless I was time-sharing with Anastasia.'

That took him aback. 'You've developed quite a clever tongue in your head,' he observed, 'for one who used to become tongue-tied in any dispute.'

There was no answer to that, so Sara didn't offer one. She had changed, and she would have had to be a fool not to know just how much she had changed. She was no longer the shy, easily intimidated idiot she used to be.

In a weary movement he came to squat down in front of her. His hand came up, gentle in the gesture as he brushed a stray lock of hair away from Sara's cheek. 'Put the child down and come back to bed,' he urged huskily. 'I promise that Fabia will come for you the moment the child shows signs of stirring.'

But she shook her head. 'I can't,' she whispered. 'I can't share that bed with you again.'

'And why not?' he demanded. 'What has changed here that I have not already promised to put right?'

Everything's changed, she thought bleakly. Because I've just woken up to what I'm letting you do to me—again! You're tearing me apart inside—again. You're making me utterly miserable—again.

'What do you want me to do?' he muttered when she didn't answer. 'Deny the other woman's existence? Is that what this is all about?'

It was part of it, she conceded. A big part of it. 'Does she exist?'

There was a moment's silence while his face took on the expression of a man weighing up the odds. Then he got up and turned away from her. 'Yes,' he said. 'She exists.'

'Then there is no point in denying it, is there?' she replied, but his honesty had cut hard and deep.

'You are not going to insist that I stop seeing. her?' He seemed faintly puzzled by her calm, quiet attitude.

Sara compounded his surprise by smiling wryly. 'I don't have that right. I am here under sufferance, remember?' She got up, moving carefully so as not to awaken Lia, and gently lowered the child into her cot, aware of his frowning eyes following her and glad that her face was hidden from him by the long fall of her hair because she didn't want him to see what those calmly spoken words cost her.

Then she straightened and turned fully to face him. 'But I do have the right to deny you the free use of my body when you feel the need to use it,' she concluded. 'And if that causes your pride problems then I'm happy to go back to London, take my chances with the bad guys there. But I won't sleep with you again, Nicolas. That part is over.'

He was studying her narrowly. 'It may be interesting to see if your resolve is as strong as your words,' he suggested softly.

Her chin came up, eyes full of a cool blue defiance that she secretly knew wasn't more than skin-deep. 'Why bother,' she challenged him, 'when you can simply go to your—alternative comfort? It is only sex after all, isn't it? And you can get that anywhere.'

His face hardened, all of it—eyes, cheeks, jaw, lips. He knew what she was saying. He knew she was calling his bluff. If he backed down now and admitted he wanted her, not his lover, he would be revealing so much of his real self to her that she knew, just knew his pride couldn't take it.

She was right. 'You know,' he said tightly, 'perhaps I will at that.'

Then he walked out. And why that made her heart break a little more she had no idea when she'd damned well asked for what she'd got!

The next morning, Fabia was all tears and apologies, while Lia was her usual sunny self, with no idea of the trouble she had caused during the night.

It had been a long time before Sara had been able to stir herself enough to straighten Fabia's bed and stretch out on top of it, only to lie wide awake, her thoughts swerving madly from angry defiance at the way she had sent Nicolas off to wretched feelings of despair at her own stupidity in sending him right into the arms of that other woman!

It was mid-morning before she dared creep back into the other suite to shower and get dressed for the day, fairly safe in the knowledge that he would not be there. He was usually ensconced in his office upstairs by now.

So she almost jumped out of her skin when the suite door flew open just as she was coming out of the bedroom, dressed for the day in her usual shorts and T-shirt.

But it was not Nicolas who came sailing in but his father. 'Been sinking your own ships again, I see,' he remarked. 'You do not need any help to ruin a good thing for yourself, do you?' His hunter's eyes pierced her with a sly look. 'You manage so very well on your own!'

'I presume you had something specific you wished to convey in all of that,' she threw back coolly.

'My son has just left for Catania and informed me not to expect him back.'

Gone. She would have sunk down into the nearest chair in despair if Alfredo had not been there to witness the revealing gesture.

'He has taken Anastasia with him,' he added cruelly. 'And suggests you may prefer to return to the other suite. He has grown weary of you already,' he claimed with satisfaction. 'Soon you will be nothing but a spare part around here again that nobody needs.'

'Except for my daughter,' she reminded him, stung, severely stung by his words. 'Where I go she goes; remember that if you're up to your old tricks, Alfredo.'

'Me?' He looked wonderfully innocent. 'I am simply conveying messages. I am happy for you to stay here with the *bambina* for as long as it takes.'

'Takes for what exactly?' Sara enquired carefully.

'For the child to begin to show signs of her Sicilian origins, of course,' he explained. 'She is all you at the moment, I concede that. But it will not remain that way for ever. Children have a way of changing dramatically as they grow. I already see signs of her *nonna* in her.' His eyes softened. 'The smile, the way she can charm a person senseless.'

All the things Sara had noticed and likened to Nicolas. 'But Nicolas would have to be with her to see them,' she pointed out tartly. 'And since he can barely stand being in the same room as her he isn't likely to see them, is he?'

'Unless I decide to point these things out,' Alfredo said slyly. 'He is already puzzled by my affection for the child. I tell him it is because she was so frightened when she was first brought here. It—endeared us to each other and he accepts that—up to a point. But if I begin dropping little hints here and little hints there he will grow curious and begin looking carefully for himself.'

Sara went cold. 'And are you?' she asked. 'Going to start dropping your little hints?'

He gave one of his shrugs. 'If it looks like he may have had enough of you already, it leaves me with no alternative, does it? I will not allow my little girl to be taken away from me now I have her!' he stated with fierce possessiveness. 'The *bambina* will stay here—by whatever means it takes for me to keep her here! And if that means I have to convince my son to keep the child when he lets you go then so be it!'

The cold-hearted ruthlessness of the man appalled her. 'Or you could tell Nicolas the truth,' she offered pleadingly as an alternative, 'and guarantee Lia's place here in this house!'

'At the expense of my own?' He dismissed that idea with a shake of his silvered head. 'He would never forgive me. I love the *bambina* but I love my son also. I can do without neither.'

'And what Alfredo wants Alfredo gets,' Sara bitterly observed. 'Don't you care how many other lives you are hurting with all your nasty ways?'

'I am sick.' He defended his selfish behaviour. 'I have not got long on this earth. I want peace and contentment in my latter days, not trouble and disharmony.'

'What you actually are is a nasty, devious old man!' she threw back harshly.

'I know!' He actually laughed! His sallow face broke into an unholy grin that made Sara gasp. 'It does my sick old heart good to know I have not lost my brain cells along with everything else!'

The days dragged without Nicolas around to break up the tedium with long nights of passion and—just being with him.

God, she missed just being with him.

And she discovered another thing about herself that rather surprised her. Having made her big stand against him and actually won, she did not have her things moved out of his bedroom. She did not sleep in the bed—at least she saved herself from that lowering indignity. She slept in the bed next to Lia while Fabia found a bed elsewhere. But she knew that her main reason for not moving her things out of his room was that, despite the fact that he did not mind humiliating her with his open liaison with that other woman, she could not bring herself to humiliate his pride by having everyone know she was no longer prepared to live with him as his wife.

And that all revolved around the guilt she still harboured over her so-called affair with Jason Castell. It didn't seem to matter that she'd never had the affair! Nicolas believed she had. She'd hurt him and therefore she felt guilty.

It was crazy, it was stupid, but she could not do a single thing about it. She felt that she owed him somehow. She owed him his pride and he could have it for now. The time to decide what her next move would be would come when he decided to come home.

* * *

That happened a week later.

It was late afternoon and she was down on the small beach with Lia. Between them they had just constructed a rather imaginative sandcastle made up of a series of higgledy-piggledy towers moulded in Lia's red plastic bucket, which the little girl had helped fill and then energetically patted out with the back of her spade.

Kneeling there on the beach, with bare feet, legs, hands and arms liberally peppered with fine, grainy sand, something made Sara glance up—that sixth sense at work again—to see him coming slowly down the steps towards them.

And her heart flipped over with a mixture of desperately suppressed joy and a worse feeling of anxiety. He must have only just arrived back because he hadn't even changed out of his clothes. The jacket and tie were missing, but the mid-grey silk of his trousers and the bright white of his long-sleeved shirt said business.

So did his expression, and it was that which filled her with sudden anxiety. He looked like a man on a mission. A man who had made a decision and was determined to see it through.

'The man coming,' Lia murmured warily.

'I can see,' Sara said as lightly as she could in the circumstances. But it hurt to hear that wary tone in her daughter's voice, just as it hurt to know that although they had been here for over six weeks now Lia still referred to Nicolas as 'the man', as she would a stranger. 'Here,' she murmured to divert the child. 'This one is ready.' Carefully she upturned the bucket full of sand. 'You can pat it out now.'

Lia came to squat down next to her, spade in hand, eyes still on Nicolas. He had reached the final set of steps now, the longest stretch of all, made up of five sets of five cut into sheer rock, which took him into halfshadow before he reached the beach itself.

'Pat, Lia,' Sara prompted quietly.

The little girl turned her head and began to pat, but with less gusto. Nicolas's arrival had taken the fun out of the game.

The crunch of leather on pebbles. Sara gritted her teeth and pretended to concentrate on holding the red plastic bucket upright for the little girl to pat loose.

What did it mean? Was this the beginning of the end? Was she about to be banished back to London again?

As she'd requested, she reminded herself severely.

'Sara,' he said quietly, 'I need to talk to you'

And she began to break up inside, bits of her flaking and crumbling away like some of the badly constructed sandcastles in front of her.

'Of course.' She sat back on her heels and managed to send him a fleeting smile, her eyes not quite clashing with his.

It didn't matter because he wasn't looking at her either. He was glancing grimly around him, searching for something. Then, with a slight gesture of one hand, he murmured, 'Could we...?' and indicated one of the white plastic sets of tables and chairs kept down here on the beach.

'Sure,' she agreed amiably—for the wary little girl's sake more than anything, but also because she was determined to keep her own steadily deteriorating emotions hidden away.

She straightened, making a play of brushing sand grains from her hands and knees with fingers which decidedly shook. He nodded briefly and moved away.

'Me come,' Lia whispered, and took hold of a fistful of her mother's shorts just to make sure she didn't get left behind.

At least it brought a smile to Sara's tense lips. 'Of course you can come,' she assured the uncertain little face staring up at her.

If Nicolas wanted this talk in private he should have waited for a better opportunity. This was daytime, she reminded herself, Lia's time, according to his rules.

'But if you would rather build another castle I shall only be sitting over there.' She pointed to where Nicolas was now standing by the table.

The little girl took a few moments to consider that option, her big eyes cautiously gauging the distance between the sand-castle and the table. Then, 'OK,' she decided, and bent back to her bucket to begin filling it with fresh sand again.

With that, Sara carefully armoured herself, tried her best to still her racing heart, lifted her chin and walked across the few yards to where Nicolas waited.

He politely held out a chair for her; Sara took it with a muted, 'Thanks,' then waited while he settled himself into the one beside her.

'I have a proposition I want to put to you,' he informed her.

The flaking process inside her took on a new impetus. She kept her eyes fixed firmly on Lia and so, she sensed, did he. 'Go ahead,' she invited smoothly.

'I want us to try again,' he said. 'At our marriage.'

CHAPTER TEN

THE IMPACT THAT shock announcement had on Sara resulted in a complete collapse of everything inside her—just for a moment, but it showed—showed in the way her body gave an ungainly jerk, in the way her breath was sucked sharply into her lungs.

'Hear me out before you say anything,' Nicolas added quickly, obviously reading her reaction as a negative one. 'I have spent this last week trying to find some solution to this—situation we have created between us. There isn't one,' he announced heavily. 'Not one where we both keep what bit of our pride that is left, anyway.'

He turned his head to look at her, while Sara kept her glazed eyes fixed on a point somewhere between Lia and the table. 'I still want you,' he said huskily. 'I find I cannot let you go a second time. So I am prepared to wipe the slate clean and give us a new beginning. I am asking you to do the same thing.'

She couldn't breathe, couldn't swallow, couldn't even think, he had stunned her so badly with all of this. In all the time she had known Nicolas, she had never known him beg for anything, yet that was exactly what this amounted to. He was begging her to give them a second chance.

Tears clogged her throat. Tears for him, because this had to be badly hurting that pride he had mentioned. He had done nothing wrong—except believed what cruel rumour and his own eyes had told him. Yet he still wanted her—despite that. Was willing to try again—despite that.

'Lia?' she whispered thickly. 'What about Lia? She is a part of me, Nicolas. To want me, you have to also want her.'

His gaze flicked over to where the little girl was playing, and Sara's heart wrenched because she knew what he saw when he looked at her.

'I am not a bad man, Sara,' he murmured grimly after a moment. 'I have no interest in taking my own hurts out on a child.'

Maybe not, she conceded—not consciously anyway. But subconsciously? 'Nicolas, you can't even bring yourself to say her name!' she choked.

'My mother's name,' he clipped. 'I find it difficult to—' He stopped, then made a sudden move with his head that had the tears rushing from her throat to her eyes because it had been a gesture of pain, a gesture of raw pain. 'Why did you do that?' he demanded harshly suddenly. 'Why name her after my mother when—'

Because she's your daughter! she wanted to shout, but couldn't because Alfredo had denied her the right.

But her silence condemned her even more in his eyes, and he got up, hands tense, long fingers flexing at his sides. 'I will adopt her,' he said after a moment. 'Then she will legally be mine.'

Oh, God. Sara closed her eyes on a wave of despair. It wasn't enough. It could never be enough! He deserved better; Lia deserved better. She had no hope of ever proving her own innocence but she had to at least try to prove Lia's!

'I am prepared to let you have a blood test taken,' she said huskily, 'if it helps you to accept her more as your own. We can at least do that.'

He turned to look at her. 'Is that your way of saying that you agree to us trying at our marriage again?'

Was it? She pushed her two hands between her warm, sandy thighs and asked herself the same question. Could they build a new marriage when he would be constantly suspecting her of cheating on him? Could she bear it, knowing that every time they had an argument he could throw the past back up in her face? As he had done the last time they'd been together, she remembered. While she had been throwing his other woman at him.

'The past is in the past, Nicolas,' she murmured eventually. 'You have to promise to bury it there if we are to stand any chance at all.'

He nodded. 'I had already accepted that before I came to you.'

Another admission. Another climb-down. Sara sucked in a deep breath. 'Anastasia,' she breathed out heavily.

He grimaced. 'Out of the picture.'

Out of the picture. Did that mean right out of the picture or only out of the picture as far as she was concerned?

'Then—' No. Angrily she bit back that jealous thought. If she could not trust his word then what right had she to demand that he trust hers?

'Your father,' she prompted next, and waited for the expected slap-down for bringing him into this.

But it didn't come. 'I cannot lie and say he will be—happy with the situation,' he acknowledged. 'But he has developed a real attachment to the ch—' He stopped himself. Sara held her breath. 'Lia...' The name left his lips awkwardly, but at least it left his lips. She allowed herself to breathe again. 'Perhaps he sees something in her that I do not,' he then added, his eyes narrowed thoughtfully on the quietly playing little girl.

'Has he said so?' Sara asked warily.

His shrug was half an answer. 'Intimated,' he qualified.

So Alfredo had already carried out his threat last week, she noted, and couldn't stop herself from giving a small shudder. The man was incorrigible when it came to getting what he wanted.

The only difference here being that he had not gambled on Nicolas still wanting her.

'It will be enough for him, I think, to know she will remain a permanent part of his life,' he went on.

As if the little girl sensed his scrutiny, she glanced up, her big eyes clashing cautiously with his. It had the most heart-crushing effect on the mother to watch father and child warily weighing each other up in this way.

'Nic—' Her instinct was to beg him not to hurt the child by cutting her dead. But it seemed Lia didn't need her mother's protection, because she straightened up from her squatting position and, still holding that look, began walking slowly towards him.

The air was suddenly thick—so thick that Sara had a suspicion that none of them could breathe it. Lia stopped in front of Nicolas, sent a swift glance at her mother for reassurance, then slowly lifted one hand towards him and opened it.

It was nothing but a pebble, a small, insignificant little pebble. But in terms of importance it was as precious as a diamond. It was a gesture—of friendship. And, more than that, it was a test of his determination to make this proposition he had put to Sara work.

He knew all of that, of course. It was written in the fierce control he was exerting on his expression as he lowered himself to his haunches. 'Is this for me?' he asked gruffly.

Lia nodded gravely. Sara lost sight of them both as a film of moisture washed across her eyes.

'Then—thank you,' he murmured, and took the pebble. 'I shall treasure it, always.'

'Grandpa got one just like it,' the little girl informed him. 'He keeps it under his pillow at night.'

'He does?' Nicolas said a trifle curiously. 'What for?'

'To keep devils away,' Lia solemnly announced. 'No bad men come get Lia if Grandpa keep the pebble under his pillow.'

'*Dio,*' Nicolas muttered hoarsely, while Sara sat stunned into stillness. Alfredo had done that? Allayed all the child's fears as neatly and as sensitively as that? She had wondered why the nightmares had not recurred. She had thought it was because Lia had her mama sleeping beside her. But now she had to wonder if it wasn't Alfredo's doing.

A point in the old man's favour? The only one if it was.

'Will you keep this one under your pillow? Keep bad men away?' Lia then asked Nicolas.

He was having difficulty answering; Sara could see his throat working. Lia's grave little revelation had managed to reach into him and touch something raw, as much perhaps as it had her.

'If you think it will help, I will do so.' He grimly accepted the duty. Then, as if he couldn't help himself, he reached out to cup the baby cheek gently with his hand. 'No one will hurt you here,' he murmured huskily. 'I promise you.'

She nodded her head in complete acceptance of that promise. Then, with a typical childlike change of mood, she turned and trotted back to her sandcastles.

'Did you know about this?' Nicolas asked as he slowly straightened.

'About your father and the pebble? No,' Sara breathed. 'I must remember to thank him...'

'Don't cry,' he muttered, seeing the evidence of tears on her cheeks. 'She is safe here. You know she is safe! That period in her young life is over. The memory of it will fade altogether in time.'

I'm not crying out of fear for Lia, she thought achingly. I'm crying for you. You may not know it, but you've just taken the most important step in your life—bridged a link with your daughter.

'What will you do with the pebble?' she asked him, wiping her fingertips over her damp cheeks.

'As I was instructed, of course,' he said, pushing the pebble into his pocket then coming to sit down again. 'She may insist on checking,' he added wryly. 'So under my pillow it must go.'

'Thank you,' Sara said softly.

His golden gaze caught hold of hers for the first time since he had arrived here. 'For what?' he asked gruffly.

'For being so—sensitive to her feelings.'

His eyes darkened. 'I meant what I said about trying again.' It was a rebuke, and a further statement of intent. 'What I have not heard as yet is what you want.'

Well, what did she want? Could she live with him? Could she live without him? Like him, she had accepted days ago that to leave him a second time was going to hurt ten times more than the first time, and that had been bad enough. But staying could hurt too if things between them didn't improve. And what then? More pain, more heartache, with the added agony of being thoroughly trapped because by the time they discovered they'd made a mistake he would have bonded with his daughter, giving Alfredo the weapons he needed to win.

'I have conditions,' she said doubtfully.

His eyes did not so much as flicker. 'Name them.'

Just like that. She dragged her gaze away from his and sucked in a tight lungful of air. 'I need to know that you are going to be here for me, giving me your support, whether or not you believe I am right.' She glanced back at him. 'With your father.' She spelled it out carefully. 'With your servants. With any decisions I decide to make about Lia. I want your promise that you'll be on my side.'

Something flickered in those golden depths at last. 'You did not have this support the last time?'

'No.'

The flicker became a glimmer of wry comprehension. 'How bad a husband was I?' he then enquired, very drily.

'Not a bad husband exactly,' she said. 'Just a—busy one.' That seemed to explain it best. 'I've changed since then,' she felt obliged to add. 'Grown up at last, perhaps. Whatever, I can fight my own battles to a certain extent. But not without your added support.' She sent him a wry smile. 'You are the linchpin of this household, in case you don't know it,' she informed him. 'What happens here happens because you want it to happen.'

'I want you as my wife,' he murmured softly. 'My proper wife.'

That sent a flood of warmth rushing through her. 'And I want the same thing...' She had wanted to say that she'd never wanted to be anything else, but that brought up the past, and this was the future they were discussing. A new future.

'But?' he prompted.

But don't look at me like that while I'm trying to be practical, she thought, and blushed, having to turn her eyes away from him. 'Th-this house,' she said. 'B-beautiful though it is, the w-way it is designed does not m-make it ideal for creating a relaxed h-home environment for a family. I accept that, things being the way they are with your f-father, we have to live here but...'

His hand came up, a finger gently tracing the heat in her burning cheek. 'But...?' he prompted again, very softly.

'But I w-want my own space,' she told him warily. 'I w-want a kitchen of my own where I can cook the odd meal if I feel so inclined. I w-want a dining room and a sitting room and bedrooms that d-don't feel like hotel rooms, and—'

She stopped, having to swallow when the caressing finger slid beneath her chin and hooked it to make her turn and look at him. His eyes were dark, lazy with awareness. 'You can have it,' he said. 'You can have it all. Commandeer the recreational-cum-guest level. Alter it to your own specification. We will move down to it when it is ready. Anything else?'

Oh, God, yes, she thought achingly. I want you to love me. I want you to pick me up in your arms and carry me up all of those steps and throw me onto the nearest bed and love me! It was awful—so wanton that she had closed her eyes to hide the dreadful yearning. But the colour in her cheeks deepened, making her wish she could die when he emitted a husky chuckle at the sight of it.

'I did not think I would ever see you blush like this again,' he teased softly. 'What can you be thinking, *cara?*'

'It—it's time for Lia's tea,' she mumbled, and hastily got up.

So did he, lazily, smilingly; he came to stand behind her, his hands coming to rest lightly on her waist. 'That was not what you were thinking,' he taunted. 'You were thinking of me in bed, hopefully naked, with you straddled across me murmuring all those *beautiful* words you can say to send this man crazy.'

His hand moved up to squeeze gently that area of her ribcage where her heart was palpitating madly. 'And you know what I want?' he added, his chin resting on her shoulder so that he could murmur huskily in her ear. 'I want to see you smile at me again like you used to. As if I were the very joy that kept you alive.'

'Oh, Nic!' Instead of a smile, he received a muffled choke as she turned and threw her arms around him. 'Y-you were— y-you are!'

'Then why are you stammering?' he demanded. 'You only stammer when frightened of something.'

I'm frightened I am making the biggest mistake of my life here, agreeing to this, she thought anxiously. But, for him, she found that smile he'd requested. 'Or something else,' she suggested provocatively.

He muttered something, took hold of her chin, angled it to his own satisfaction then covered her mouth with his own hungry one.

Above them—way above them on one of the upper terraces— a silvered head viewed the whole situation from his bird's-eye position. His eyes were narrowed, shrewd, calculating. As they broke apart, he rolled away from the wall, as silent an observer as the umpteen security cameras positioned around the whole area.

'Let's go,' Nic muttered, turning Sara towards the steps.

'Nic, y-you've forgotten something...'

'Hmm?' He was totally nonplussed. 'I know what I want. I am absolutely sure I know what you want. What else is there?'

'Lia,' she said huskily.

He stopped, flexed his shoulders, looked down at his feet and sighed, and by then every bit of Sara's anxiety was back on show. He glanced at her from beneath his sweeping lashes, saw the anxiousness, sighed again. 'Mistake number one,' he muttered, then sliced her a look. 'OK!' he said defensively. 'I will learn, I will learn!'

Sara slewed her gaze away, not sure if he was cross or ashamed of himself. 'L-Lia,' she called shakily. The little girl glanced up, looking like Cupid bathed in a pool of golden sunshine. 'It's t-time to go back up n-now.'

'Don't stammer,' Nicolas said roughly.

'I'm s-sorry,' she choked.

'And if you start crying again I shall not be responsible for myself.'

She bit down hard on her quivering bottom lip. Lia got up, collected her bucket and spade and came towards them, big blue eyes wary because she could sense the odd atmosphere.

'Sh-shall we leave those by the bottom step for tom-morrow?' Sara suggested, doing very well at controlling the stammer.

The little girl nodded, and dutifully trotted off to place the bucket and spade where she usually left them. Then she turned, eyeing both of them warily. 'Man come too?' she asked.

Sara closed her eyes in despair because they hadn't even left the beach yet and already the problems were falling over each other to make themselves known.

'What now?' Nicolas demanded gruffly.

'She can't keep calling you that,' she sighed. 'Not if...'

'You are right,' he agreed. 'She can't.' And with a grim resolve about him that she hoped wouldn't send her daughter running for cover he walked over to Lia, squatted down to her level and said quite coolly, 'I am your papa. You know, as Grandpa is grandpa?'

The little girl frowned and pouted then gave an uncertain nod of her golden head.

'Then say it,' Nicolas instructed. 'Say Papa.'

'Pa-pa?' Lia repeated cautiously.

'Good.' He nodded and straightened and turned back to Sara. 'If she develops your stammer as well as all your other little foibles, she will be hell to every man who comes into contact with her when she grows up.'

'W-was that a compliment or a criticism?' she enquired uncertainly.

'Both,' he said, then grinned at something only he understood. 'Most definitely both. Let's go.' He offered a hand to Sara.

'I hold Mama's hand,' Lia informed him frowningly.

'Ah.' Another small lesson—in rights of possession. 'Your mama has two hands. We could have one each,' Nicolas suggested almost sarcastically.

'No!' the child protested. 'Lia want to jump!'

Sara couldn't help it—she giggled. He didn't see it, didn't recognise it, but it was his own stubborn nature he was contending with here.

'She means she needs your hand as well as mine to jump up the steps.' Still smiling, Sara came to his rescue. 'Which therefore means you cannot hold my hand as well.'

So Lia jumped. All the way up the steps to the first terrace, one small hand in Sara's, the other in Nicolas's. No one spoke; there seemed to be such an agonising poignancy in the procedure that it did not allow for mere words. But Sara couldn't stop herself from glancing at him warily, not sure if he was as relaxed about all of this as he seemed to be. It was such a novel situation for him, never mind the fact that this was his daughter he was indulging. He was a man who was not around children very much. Nor one you would expect to see helping a little girl jump twenty-five or so stone steps.

At the top, Sara turned and held out her arms. 'I'll carry you now, shall I?' she offered. It was the usual place where Lia tired of jumping.

'Man carry me.'

Sara winced, at two things—'man' and the request for him to carry her. It was one thing Nicolas making an effort with the child, but too much too soon could send him screaming for cover.

'Papa.' He took the initiative, thank goodness, because Sara found she wasn't capable of doing so. 'Papa can carry you,' he corrected Lia smoothly.

'OK.' The child turned towards him. 'Papa carry me.' And she lifted her arms.

He bent, lifted the little girl on the crook of his arm, sent her a sage look while she stared, big-eyed, back. 'May I also hold Mama's hand now?' he requested sarcastically.

He was trying to make light of the whole situation but Sara could see the tension in his features. He was not finding this as easy as it looked.

The little girl nodded. 'Good,' he said, and reached for Sara's hand. His long fingers closed around hers, and she felt the tension in him there as well.

They moved on, across the pool terrace and towards the next flight. Slowly, almost testingly, Lia slid her arms further around his neck, then slowly, even more slowly, laid her head on his shoulder.

'Don't say a single word,' Nicolas murmured gruffly when Sara could not hold back her thick gasp. 'I am not insensitive to the honour the child does me.'

'I know,' she said softly. 'And—thank you.'

His hand tightened on her hand. But he didn't say anything else. On their own level, Fabia was waiting to take the little girl off for her tea and her bath. Nicolas looked relieved, and Lia didn't protest. Sara sensed that she too had had enough of him to be going on with.

As the other two disappeared, he turned a rueful expression on Sara. 'Do I have you to myself for a while now?' he asked. 'Or does tea and bathtime take precedence?'

Normally it would do, but not today. Today he was more important. This tenuous relationship they had decided to try and build was more important.

'I'm all yours,' she smiled.

It was all he needed. The grip on her hand tightened, and the carefully controlled learner father was gone, to be replaced by the sexually very hungry predator male.

What followed was what she supposed could be called a period of adjustment, where they both tried hard to make this new beginning work for them. They were quite successful at it too— aided and abetted by the fact that Alfredo left the house only a few days after Nicolas had returned. He had been booked into an exclusive clinic in Switzerland, where he was to undergo some valve-replacement surgery.

'Is it dangerous?' she'd asked Nicolas when he'd told her about the operation.

He'd grimaced. 'It may help to ease his next few months,' was all he'd said, forcing her to acknowledge just how very ill Alfredo was.

'Are you going to stay with him?'

'No.' He'd smiled at the very idea. 'His pride would not allow me such liberties.'

That great Santino pride; she'd mocked it silently, grimly.

So Alfredo had gone off with his entourage of medical support and had seemed quite taken aback when impulsively Sara had bent down to brush a kiss across his leathery cheek when he'd come to bid Lia farewell.

'I'm coming back!' he'd snapped, sending her one of his aggressive looks. 'So don't go hoping you are seeing the last of me while you bewitch my son a second time!'

'You may be a nasty old man,' she'd retaliated, 'but I do not wish you ill, Alfredo!'

'Ah—bah!' he'd grunted, and wheeled himself off to see his granddaughter.

With Alfredo gone, some of the tension had gone with him. She presumed that this was a relaxing within herself, but maybe Alfredo had been using his clever tongue on his son also, because Nicolas too seemed more at ease within the general run of things.

Neither did Nicolas spend any length of time away from home, which must have helped. He divided his time between his office at the house and the one in Catania, and she presumed, simply on account of the fact that she hadn't seen him since they'd left London, that Toni must be running the international side of things for now.

Was this another indication of how important this new try at their marriage was to Nicolas? She hoped so. And he was trying. They both were, but he had the bigger adjustment to make because he had to teach himself to accept Lia. The baby helped. She was so easy to accept, especially with her dear grandpa gone; she needed another man to adore and Nicolas was chosen as the one.

He was cautious at first, using the same dry wit he had used with the child from the beginning to offset any real emotional bonding. But it was kindly done and, she suspected, defensive. He was treading very warily around this daughter of his who might not be his daughter.

The odd thing was that though Sara waited for the day when he would come and say he had arranged for a blood test to be carried out he never so much as mentioned it. And it was a long time before she realised just why he never brought the subject up. And by then it was too late anyway.

Sara began her redesigning project on the recreational /guest tier. She made Nicolas listen to what she had decided on, demanded his opinion, and to know his own requirements of this little house within a house that she was earnestly trying to manufacture. She made him walk the new plan with her, became irritated by his determination to find it all more amusing than anything else, and made love with him in the snooker room because that, she had told him, was where their bedroom would be and he decided he wanted to try it out first.

'What do you think?' she asked him as they lay on the hard green baize, naked and damp from their loving, their limbs so languid that neither had the energy to move.

'It may do,' he murmured noncommittally, 'but I think we should try one or two of the other rooms before making a firm decision.'

'Sex maniac,' she rebuked him.

'Sadist,' he countered. 'I will have permanently greenstained knees from this experiment! I do not think I want a snooker table for a bed, *amore,*' he decided gravely. 'So we had better try one of the other rooms.'

It was like that. Everything light-hearted, easy-going—except when they made love, of course. That was far from light-hearted; it was hot and torrid and very, very serious. They made love every time with a passion that was almost urgent. She wasn't sure why, but sometimes, if she let herself think about it, it worried her. It lacked permanency somehow, as if neither of them really believed that this—honeymoon contentment they had created around them could last.

Alfredo's operation was a success and Nicolas took a flying visit over to see him before the old man was transferred to an exclusive nursing home to convalesce for several weeks.

On impulse, Sara sent him a pebble. 'Tell him it's from Lia,' she said awkwardly. 'To keep away the devils. He will accept it better from her.'

'You two must try to mend your differences,' Nicolas commented. 'I need you to at least try.'

'OK.' She smiled brightly up at him, thinking sadly, You're telling the wrong one of us, darling. 'I'll try.'

The building alterations went ahead—and were finished before Alfredo came back home. Sara prepared a special dinner to welcome him and made a point of showing him what they'd done to the place. She showed him where Lia slept in her own little room with Fabia's off to one side and hers and Nicolas's off to the other with connecting doors in between all. She showed him, too, another bedroom, close to the stairway where the chair-lift was fitted. 'For you,' she informed him quietly. 'If you ever feel the need to be closer to Lia.'

'I'm not at death's door yet, you know,' he sniped at her. 'You do not have to make concessions for a dying old man.'

'Then I won't,' she responded. 'Forget I ever mentioned the silly room.' And don't say it's me who isn't trying, she added acidly to herself.

'Ah—bah!' he dismissed her. But he was different since going to Switzerland. Quieter, more introspective. Yet as far as his health was concerned he was much, much stronger. It made her worry that he was up to something. Something that could ruin what she and Nicolas had managed to achieve in their relationship.

Still, a few more weeks went by without anything untoward happening. The weather turned colder. Nicolas became busier, staying away from home occasionally, though not for weeks at a time. Sara began planning a playroom for Lia since she would not be able to play outside for much longer as the weather was turning less clement.

They were beginning to socialise again. Slowly. Nicolas seemed determined to reintroduce her to the old social scene but gradually as though he was trying—trying not to make the same mistakes this time as he had made the last time. And that warmed her, made her respond better towards his friends in an effort to show that she too was trying. Or maybe it was because she was a different person now and found she could cope amongst these bright, sophisticated people without feeling intimidated.

Whatever the reason, she did not feel the need to cling to him like a limpet and she did not get tongue-tied when anyone spoke to her. People were reasonably pleasant towards her—mainly, she presumed, because her new cool composure in their company gave them nothing to mock as her old nervous shyness had.

Also, they were curious. She had been off the scene for three years after all. If they'd heard rumours about her and a certain Englishman, then those rumours had never been substantiated. And her marriage to Nicolas seemed, on the face of it, firm. Which left them to assume that her absence from Sicily had been of her own volition—maybe even a result of the way they had treated her. Which meant, in their minds, that if she was back she was doing it for Nicolas's sake, not her own. And, really, no one with any sense wanted to offend him by offending his wife a second time.

So they tried—she tried. And all in all it wasn't so bad. She even found herself enjoying the company of some, her smile growing more relaxed and friendly the better she got to know them.

'You are beginning to manage them all as subtly as you manage me,' Nicolas murmured to her one evening as they were making their way home. 'You will have them eating out of your beautiful hand soon.'

'I would rather you ate my hand,' she returned softly, placing her hand over his mouth so that he could press a moist kiss to her palm. It was her way of telling him that he was what mattered most to her, not them. They never spoke of the past but sometimes, like this time, it would loom up in the silent background of what they were saying, threatening to ruin what they had managed to achieve.

While they were slowly rebuilding their marriage like this, Alfredo was growing closer and closer to Lia. He was rarely out of her company and had even started taking her out with him on some days—to visit friends with grandchildren of their own. At first Sara spent the whole time the child was out of her sight fretting in case something happened to her, but when nothing did she eventually began to relax.

If Alfredo had been behind Lia's abduction, then she was absolutely certain that the old man would now guard the child with his very life.

They were so close, grandfather and granddaughter. Much closer than Lia and Nicolas had managed to become.

Though they were getting better, she had to allow, smiling to herself when she remembered the couple of occasions when she had been about to leave the bathroom, having left Nicolas lazing in bed, only to pause on the threshold, her breath caught, throat full of aching tears at the sight of Lia sitting cross-legged beside him on the rumpled white bedding, her little face earnest while she told him some baby story of her own while he listened, as earnest as she, his golden gaze almost tender on the baby face.

Or was it yearning, that look?

She could never make up her mind. She saw it often, but could never quite catch its true quality.

But at least it was something deeper than indifference or, worse, the resentment she had feared he might harbour towards Lia.

We are getting there, she told herself bracingly. Maybe we have a chance.

Then disaster struck.

It hit on two fronts and with such devastating effect that none of them emerged unscathed. None of them.

CHAPTER ELEVEN

THEY WERE AT a party. A big one. The mayor of Taormina's annual ball. Even Alfredo had come with them, the three arriving together in his limousine, Sara dressed in an ankle-length matte black dress that slid over her slender figure as only silk could.

Her hair was down—at Nicolas's request—but she had woven two slender braids at her temples then knotted them together at her nape. Her make-up was minimal, cool, like the new manner she had adopted for her social face. And for the first time since coming back to him she was wearing the lovely diamond engagement ring that Nicolas had given her before they'd married, along with the single string of matching diamonds at her throat—again at his request.

'You're so beautiful I could eat you,' he murmured when she walked with him and his father into the main entrance hall.

'My word for you,' she scolded him. 'Stop stealing.' And she kissed him, aware of Alfredo's watching presence.

She wondered what he was thinking, this wily old man who had taken a surprisingly amiable back seat in the affairs of his son since he had returned from Switzerland. No rows with Sara. No sly taunts. No goading. She didn't understand it.

The two men were in their best dinner suits, and Alfredo looked quite handsome now that he had gained back a little bit of his weight and his skin did not look quite so sallow, since the new valves in his heart were allowing a better supply of oxygen through his system.

It was a packed affair. People milling from room to room in one of the resort's top hotels. A private villa once, dating back centuries, it had managed to maintain many of its original features, including some priceless art treasures and antiques.

She lost Nicolas quite early on, but occasionally caught glimpses of Alfredo. He was wisely remaining close to the main foyer where the crush was not quite so oppressive for a man in a wheelchair. The evening wore on. She became tired, perhaps a little bored with the affair, and decided to go and find Nicolas to tell him she would like to leave.

She found him standing just outside one of the French windows that had been thrown open so that people could take the air on the terrace outside.

And how she found him destroyed every bit of poise and serenity that she had managed to build inside herself during the last few weeks.

He was with a woman. A strange woman. A beautiful woman with thick black hair coiled high on her lovely head. She was tall and slender and wore a dress of the most exquisite blue silk. And she was standing with her hands on Nicolas's shoulders while his hands circled her slender waist. They were looking at each other. Just looking, but it was enough. The look spoke volumes.

Anastasia. It had to be. It sliced Sara apart inside.

Then came the ultimate destroyer. Nicolas smiled at her tenderly and gently touched his mouth to hers.

Sara saw no more. She turned, swaying dizzily, and stumbled away, through the crush, through the people, out into the foyer where she stood for a moment staring blankly around her, lost, completely disorientated.

'Sara?' It was Alfredo's questioning voice that pulled her round in his direction. Whatever he saw on her face made him blanch. 'What is the matter?' he asked sharply.

'I don't feel well,' she murmured vaguely. 'I need to go home.'

'I'll get Nicolas.' Alfredo was already clicking his fingers to gain the attention of a passing waiter.

'No!' she choked, then added less frantically, 'I w-would rather go by myself.' But her blue eyes were filled with anguish. 'Will you call for the car for me?'

'Of course,' he agreed, but he was frowning, those shrewd eyes of his suspicious of her excuse. The waiter hurried over. 'Get my car round immediately,' Alfredo instructed. The waiter nodded and rushed off. 'Has someone insulted you?' he then demanded brusquely.

Had they? she wondered blankly. Then, 'Yes,' she whispered. She supposed they had.

'Who?'

She didn't answer. He wasn't even sure that she'd heard him. The waiter came back. 'Your car is at the door, Signor Santino,' he told him.

'Good. Thank you.' His eyes were still sharp on Sara. 'You will find my son, please, and tell him his wife is feeling unwell and I have taken her home.'

With another nod the waiter dived into the bustling crowd.

'Sara—' Alfredo manoeuvred the chair close to her side '—put your hand on my shoulder.'

Without really knowing it she did as she was told. With his face set in grim lines, he set them both moving. At the entrance, his driver stepped forward to take the chair.

'See Mrs Santino inside first,' Alfredo ordered. The driver glanced sharply at her then jumped to take her arm; she slid into the car without making a murmur. By the time Alfredo joined her, his chair neatly stashed away in the capacious boot, she was shivering.

He took her hand and tried rubbing it. 'Now would you like to explain to me what happened in there?' he asked. 'You said someone had insulted you. Who insulted you?'

'Nicolas,' she whispered.

'Nicolas?' he repeated in stark disbelief. 'Nicolas, my son, insulted you?'

'He was with Anastasia,' she explained, then began to laugh. 'That should give you food for enjoyment, Alfredo! I caught them red-handed kissing on the terrace! Anastasia and Nicolas! Why don't you laugh?'

'Because it is not damned funny,' he muttered.

'No, it isn't,' she agreed, and stopped laughing abruptly.

'Are you sure you saw this?' he asked frowningly. 'Nicolas?' he prompted. 'Not just someone who looks like Nicolas?'

Her blue eyes swivelled onto him and they were no longer unseeing but sharp—sharper than he had ever seen them before. 'Are you accusing me of being blind as well as stupid?' she asked coldly.

'No.' He shook his silvered head. 'But,' he said slowly, 'I think you may have jumped to the wrong conclusion here—'

'Defending him, Alfredo?' she taunted. 'I thought you would be happy for me.'

'No.' He was still frowning. 'To both questions. I am puzzled,' he added. 'You see, Anastasia is—'

'I don't want to hear,' Sara cut in. 'I don't want to hear anything you have to say on the subject.' She turned her head away. 'Let Nicolas do his own explaining,' she added coldly. 'For once, this has nothing to do with you.'

He sighed, sounding at a loss, and leaned back in the seat. The car swept them around the hill and towards home. Sara stared unseeingly out of the window, her emotions on ice. Alfredo frowned at the glass partition between them and the driver and for once kept his own counsel.

Until they reached home, when he said gruffly, 'What are you going to do?'

She turned that cold look on him. 'Kill the bastard,' she said, then smiled. 'A real Sicilian answer, that, is it not?'

Despite himself Alfredo smiled too. 'I would wait until Nicolas has given you his explanation,' he wryly advised. 'Only I do not think you will feel very good about the knife in his chest when you discover this all one big mistake.'

The car door opened, the chauffeur bending to offer her a helping hand. She ignored it. 'That,' she mocked. 'From the man who first told me about that woman?'

He grimaced. 'I am a nasty old man. You know this. I say things to hurt people.'

'It hurt,' she confirmed. 'Is hurting. Congratulations, Alfredo, you've done it again.'

With that, she got out of the car.

'Will you wait one moment?' Alfredo rasped in frustration. 'I want to tell you—'

But he had already lost her. Lost her because the next disaster was already striking. Maria, the housekeeper, had appeared at the doorway, her face a frightening map of anxious concern.

'The *bambina, signora,*' she murmured shakily. 'She is very sick. Come quickly. Fabia frightened. Please, come quick!'

After that, nothing else mattered. Not Nicolas and his other woman, not Alfredo, who was yelling at his driver to get him in his chair, not the housekeeper, who paced worriedly behind Sara as she fled down the levels to her daughter's bedroom, not Fabia, who was white-faced with fright, or Alfredo's private nurse, who was worriedly leaning over the little girl, carefully examining her.

'What is it?' Sara said urgently. 'What's wrong with her?'

'Ask your husband to call for his helicopter, Signora Santino,' the nurse instructed her grimly. 'Your baby needs to get to a hospital quick.'

Quick. That word played over and over in Sara's head over

the next few nightmarish hours. Quick as in now! It rang in every brain cell. Quick, call for the helicopter. Quick, warn the hospital in Catania. Quick, Signora Santino, change your dress if you want to go with her.

Go with her. She ran to her own room to rip the beautiful black silk sheath from her body. In her haste the necklace came off with it, diamonds sprinkling all over the white-tiled floor around her. She didn't even see them as she dragged on a pair of navy ski pants and a sweatshirt, then was running back to her baby's room.

Alfredo was there, cracking out orders all over the place, throwing his weight around at people who did not listen. The helicopter arrived, sounding deafeningly loud overhead. It landed on the beach—the only place for it. The nurse gathered up Lia in a blanket and ran, with Sara running behind her.

'What the hell—?' Nicolas had arrived too late. The helicopter was already taking off. Perhaps it was fortunate. His wife was in no fit state to be wifely. His father was yelling something, banging the arms of his wheelchair in helpless frustration. Fabia was sobbing quietly in one corner. 'Will someone tell me what the hell is going on?' he bellowed at the top of his voice.

'Meningitis,' his father choked out hoarsely. 'The nurse suspects the baby has meningitis!'

Intensive Care. Lia's little body hot and swollen, an ugly red rash spoiling her beautiful skin. Sara sat beside the cot and just looked on as so many beeps and buzzes played inside her head. A nurse kept a constant watch on everything—the child, the machinery, the white-faced mother.

Hours. She didn't know how many hours. Nicolas appeared like a dark shadow on the fringes of her consciousness. Drawn, white-faced, he stared at the sick baby then swayed, bringing the nurse rushing over to grab his arm.

It steadied him. He swallowed, pulled himself up, gave a small nod to the nurse to say he was all right. She moved away again. His shocked eyes flicked over to where Sara sat. Then his face was working with a million different emotions, all of them lacerated.

It seemed to take all the strength he had in him to make him go and squat down beside her. His hand was trembling as it covered her own icy hands.

He didn't speak. He could not. So he remained like that, covering her cold hands, swallowed on the lump of utter wretchedness that was blocking his throat and watched the child with her, listened to those awful beeps and buzzes with her. At some point he sat in the chair that someone had kindly brought for him and maintained that still silent vigil with her.

Doctors came, looked, listened, checked then went. Nurses, swapping shifts. An intravenous drip fed essential fluids and powerful antibiotics into the baby via a needle in the back of her little hand. She had wires attached to her checking heart patterns, wires checking brain patterns. She wore nothing but a loosely fastened disposable nappy and looked pathetic—dreadfully, heart-rendingly pathetic.

At one point they were gently urged out of the room. Why, nobody said, but it was the first time since she'd arrived that Sara showed any real sign of life. 'What?' she breathed, startled. 'Why?'

'Just for a little while, Mrs Santino—Mr Santino.' The nurse slowly but firmly led them away to a waiting room where she poured them fresh coffee and quietly advised them to drink it.

Sara drank some because Nicolas made her. But he didn't think she was aware of doing it. In the end, and because he couldn't stand it anymore, he gently lifted her out of the chair that the nurse had guided her into and wrapped her in his arms.

But she did not hold him back. She felt fine-boned and fragile—too fragile. Was it possible for a body to lose weight because of a shock like this? He didn't know, but she felt different, as if she wasn't really there at all and it was just the shell of her that he held in his arms.

Minutes ticked by—more minutes. She didn't move but he did, pressing occasional kisses to her hairline, the top of her head, his hands gently stroking her long hair, her back, trying to instil some life in her. Something!

'Mr Santino—Mrs Santino? You can come back now.'

All in Italian. Did Sara remember her Italian well enough to understand? Nicolas wondered. They spoke mainly in English. Both of them. It was like a second language to him so he had no problem, but her Italian had never been quite up to a full-blown Sicilian conversation.

She understood, because she leaned away from his embrace.

And at last he seemed to find his voice. 'Sara...' he murmured unsteadily.

But she shook her head. White—her face was so white that he wondered if she had any blood pumping through it. 'Not now, Nic,' she said, gave him a strange little pat on his chest as if to say, Don't take offence, then walked away.

Hours, more hours. At some point, Alfredo appeared by the bed. How he got there nobody seemed to know since only immediate family were supposed to be there. But there he was. He took one look at the sick child and burst into tears.

Nicolas knew it was wrong, unfair even, but the old man's tears irritated him because they meant he had to leave Sara to go and see to him.

'I must talk to you, son,' Alfredo said hoarsely as Nicolas wheeled him away. 'I need to talk to you.'

'Later.' Nicolas nodded and glanced round for his father's nurse. She was waiting by the open waiting-room door. 'Take him home,' he instructed. 'This is no place for him—too distressing.'

'But I need to talk to you, son!'

'Later,' Nicolas said again, and went back to Sara.

Hours, more hours, and the crisis point came and went. It was just a matter of waiting now. Waiting for Lia to wake up so they would know the extent of damage, if any. But at least she was not going to die.

They moved her out of Intensive Care and into a private room next door. From somewhere Nicolas commandeered a small fold-out bed which he placed by the child's bed and gently urged Sara onto.

'It's OK,' he soothed quietly. 'I am here. I will stay by her. If she moves I will wake you but you must get some sleep now.'

Sleep. She nodded in mute acceptance and closed her eyes.

Hours, more hours. Another day, Sara suspected, but wasn't sure if that made it three days or four. Nicolas had gone back to his hotel at last to get some rest. Alfredo had been in the day before but she hadn't seen him today. She wasn't surprised; the poor old man had looked dreadful yesterday, almost as sick as the baby.

'I will never forgive myself for this,' he'd said painfully.

'You?' Sara had glanced at him. 'It isn't your fault Lia is ill, Alfredo.'

'It is.' Tears had filled the guilty old eyes. 'That friend I took her to visit with me last week, up in the mountains? Two more children from the same village have taken ill with the same thing.' He'd swallowed thickly. 'It is me who exposed her to this. I will never forgive myself. It is all my fault.'

Sara had smiled a tired smile at him. 'Even you cannot thwart fate, Alfredo,' she'd said wryly. 'This is fate's fault. Just fate. Don't torture yourself with such foolish ideas.'

But she hadn't convinced him. He had decided to take full blame upon himself and that was that. Poor old man.

Hours, more hours. Then Nicolas turned up.

He looked terrible.

He should have looked better, since he had been back to his hotel for a proper night's rest last night, yet if anything he looked worse for it, grey-faced and tense.

He muttered a muted hello. Didn't quite look at her. Pulled out the chair on the other side of the bed and sat down on it.

Looked at Lia. Looked away. Looked at where his hands rested tensely on the bed.

And where it came from Sara didn't know. But it did come. 'You know, don't you?' she said quietly.

He didn't answer. He looked at Lia again, his face hewn from rock—a rock that began to break up, slowly, uncontrollably.

'Nic—don't!' she murmured, reaching across the bed to cover one of his hands. His own turned in hers, gripped tightly until both shook, then his head went down on the bedcovers and he wept.

In all her life she had never seen or heard anything like it. It filled her own eyes with tears and sent her stumbling to her feet and over to the door to close it, her instinct at that moment to save this broken man's pride from curious eyes.

Then she stood, uncertain just what to do next. To go and hold him could well be the worst indignity she could serve him right now. In the end, she went back to her own chair, sat down and reached across the bed to slide her hand back into his.

He accepted that, at least he accepted that, his own turning again, gripping again. And it seemed to give him the strength he needed to find his self-control.

The dreadful sound stopped. Then he was suddenly getting up, swerving his face away so that she couldn't see it. He went to stand by the window and remained there just staring out at nothing for a long, long time.

'H-how is he?' Sara asked eventually. 'Your father, I mean.'

He didn't answer immediately, and she saw his jaw clench as if he was having a struggle with his emotions again. Then, 'Back at the villa, confined to his bed,' he answered. 'The—confession took it out of him.'

She nodded even though he couldn't see the gesture. But she understood now why Alfredo had not been in to see Lia today. And understood also why he had told Nicolas the truth at last. He was trying to redeem himself in the eyes of his Maker. Not Nicolas. Alfredo would already know he could never redeem

himself with Nicolas. But for the sin he believed he had committed in exposing Lia to such an illness he needed to redeem
himself by exposing a sin he'd committed when he'd plotted to
rid his son of his wife. Even if the confession would cost him
his son's love:

Poor, tormented old man.

Her fingers sought her daughter's small hand. 'I'm sorry,'
she murmured inadequately.

That made him turn. Turn to let her see the ravages that had
taken place in his face. 'You say that—to me?' he rasped. '*No,
no.*' He gave a jerked shake of his head. '*Mi scusi.* I cannot—' He
stopped and swallowed; Sara watched him helplessly work with
his throat to make it let him say what he wanted to say. Then
he gave up; she saw it happen with a surge of sudden despair,
saw he just couldn't take any more of this right now. '*Mi scusi,
cara,* but I must leave you for a while.' He was already shifting
his stiff body towards the door. 'I will come back soon when—'

My God! she thought. I've got casualties all around me! Lia
here in this bed, Alfredo sick with guilt back at the villa, and
now Nicolas is going to walk out of here sick with shock and
horror and goodness knows what else.

But she could not let him walk out in the state he was in.
'No—Nic!' she protested, jumping up to rush over to him.
'Don't go!' In an effort to get through to him she threw herself
against his chest. 'I need you here. *We* need you here!'

'God, yes,' he breathed. 'Of course you do. And once again
I was being—' His big chest heaved on the lack of words. His
arms came around her, but they didn't mould to her, didn't hold
her, not in the usual way. It was as if the shock he was experiencing had locked all his joints up; everything worked stiffly,
as if even the simplest gesture was an effort.

'Come and sit down again,' she urged. 'Please...' She began
slowly drawing him back to the bed. 'She's been moving a little today...' She managed to get him to sit in her chair. 'Fingers, toes...'

Having got him this far, she was suddenly at a loss to know what to do next. He was obviously in deep shock. When she had been in deep shock he had ruthlessly poured brandy down her throat, she remembered. But she had no brandy. And—

He was staring at Lia. Staring at her with such a wealth of vulnerable love in his eyes that she suddenly realised that the child might well be his shot of brandy.

'I w-won't be long,' she murmured carefully. 'Now you're here I can go and f-freshen up, and maybe get myself a coffee from the machine...'

Outside the door, she wilted like a wet rag against the wall, a trembling hand going up to rub wearily at her aching brow. All of this coming on top of Lia's illness was just about as bad as timing could get.

Now she had Nicolas to worry about, and Alfredo to worry about—and even herself to worry about, because she wasn't sure what all of this was going to mean.

And Anastasia to worry about.

That brought her abruptly away from the wall, a stinging, hot, bitter poison called jealousy pouring into her blood.

When she went back into the room, Nicolas's face had lost that shattered look and he seemed more—composed. He didn't mention his father's confession again. So neither did she. Nor did she mention Anastasia. But both spectres hovered in the background, waiting to swoop on them when the moment was right. The fact that the sick baby was taking priority only delayed the inevitable; it did not remove it.

More hours. Another full day and night when Sara slept on the little bed by her daughter and Nicolas went back to his hotel to sleep.

In the morning he came back, bringing a change of clothes with him for Sara. She took them gratefully and went off to shower and change into the plain jeans and white overshirt.

When she walked back into the room, she stopped dead, her

heart squeezing at the sight of Nicolas half sitting at the head of the bed with Lia, tubes and all, cradled across his chest.

'She awoke just a minute ago,' he said. His eyes were glazed with tears. 'She knew me.'

Like the last time the rigid control which stressful situations demanded had deserted her, Sara's legs went from beneath her. Only this time it wasn't Nicolas who caught her before she hit the ground but the doctor hurrying to the alarm call that Nicolas had sent out when the baby had opened her eyes.

More hours. More waiting. Tests, deliberations, during which Nicolas became Sara's constant support and Lia woke fitfully, showing hopeful signs each time that there had been no long-term effects.

Then official confirmation. 'No damage. You got her here soon enough. Another week and you can take her home.'

They arrived back at the villa on a crisp, sunny morning when everything looked brighter, clearer, more acutely defined. Lia was still weak, still slept away most of the hours in the day, but as soon as they walked into the main hallway she lifted her head from Nicolas's shoulder and smiled as if relieved to be back.

'Where's Grandpa?' she said.

Grandpa, who had not been seen by Sara in over a week. Grandpa, whom the child must have missed, though she hadn't said anything. Grandpa. Just hearing the child mention him made Nicolas's face set into a stone-cold mask.

Yet is was Nicolas who replied, 'He is here,' he assured the little girl. 'Eager to see you. If I pass you to Fabia she will take you right to him now, if you like.'

Lia went happily, leaving Sara and Nicolas standing alone in the main hallway, both tense, both aware that the spectre of truth was getting closer.

'Nic—your father...' It was Sara who decided to bring it closer.

And Nicolas who grimly pushed it away again. 'Not now,'

he said curtly. 'I have not the time.' He glanced at his watch—not at her. Nicolas had not let his eyes clash with hers for a long time—not since his father had made his grand confession. 'I have to go out,' he informed her coolly. 'To Palermo. Business—I have let it slide during all of this.'

But that wasn't the real reason why he wanted to leave, and Sara knew it. 'When will you be back?' she asked huskily.

'I cannot be sure. A few days.' He sounded impatient, eager to be gone. 'It depends on how much needs my attention—'

'I need your attention!' she bit back angrily.

'*Don't!*'

She blanched at the violence in the rough-voiced command and actually took a nervous step back from him. 'So we don't count any more, is that it?' she said bitterly. 'Crisis over, so you can now turn your attention to other things!'

Like Anastasia and how good she can make you feel! she added silently.

'That is not what I am doing,' he denied heavily. 'I just need some time—my own space while I come to terms with—with—'

'With what?' she challenged. 'With what your father's confession is going to mean to you? Your life? Your own damned lies?'

'Lies?' His golden eyes sharpened, actually focused directly on her questioningly. 'What lies?'

Oh, God, she thought bitterly. He does that as well if not better than his father does! 'Your father—'

'Leave him out of this!' he hissed, going stone-like again.

Sara sucked in a tense breath. 'We are all victims here, in case that point has escaped you,' she said tightly. 'Including your father!' His eyes flashed a warning; she angrily ignored it. 'He was a proud man, who was proud of his son and wanted the very best he could get for him. It struck right at the heart of his pride when you offered him me instead. So he went to war, and became a victim of his own desire to win over me, no matter what. He won the battle, Nicolas,' she said grimly, 'but he lost the war. Because he then had to live with the knowledge that, in alienating you from me, he had also alienated himself from his own grandchild!'

'Which is why I will never forgive him,' he grated. 'I believed in him.' And at last the real truth of it came spilling out. 'I trusted him as I trusted no other person, and he used that against me—deliberately and cynically used my unquestioning trust in him as a weapon against me!'

'Me, Nicolas. Me!' Sara corrected him. 'He used it against me, not you!'

'What's the difference?' he rasped. 'You were me! Mine!' It was fiercely possessive. 'He took the only other thing besides himself that I held dear in my life and twisted it into something ugly! *Ah, Dio!'* he choked, his dark head jerking with a wrench of disgust. 'I cannot talk about this. It offends me. It offends you! All I know is that what he did to me I did to you. I took your trust, your belief in me and destroyed it!'

Not with this, you didn't, she thought coldly. You've destroyed me with Anastasia.

'So what are you intending to do?' she asked. 'Punish a dying old man by pretending he doesn't exist in your life—just as you once punished me by pretending I did not exist?'

'I am allowing him to keep the love of his granddaughter,' he snapped. 'Which is more than he allowed me!' His expression turned hard and bitter. 'Of course,' he then added less passionately, 'you may do as you wish. I will support any decision you make about both my father's rights where the child is concerned—' Lia was back to being 'the child'! she noted angrily '—and my own rights where you are concerned.'

'In other words,' she choked, 'you're giving up on us!'

His big chest moved in a huge intake of air. 'I am giving up on the right to decide,' he amended. 'I have no rights,' he then added gruffly. 'I rescinded them the day I placed my father's word above your word.'

Or are rescinding them to leave you free to go to Anastasia!
Sara corrected him silently.

'Then go and do whatever it is you want to do, Nicolas,' she
sighed, turning away from him in disgust. 'For I rescind the
right to give a damn!'

CHAPTER TWELVE

THE INFURIATING THING about it was that he went! Just walked out of the house without another word!

And from everything seeming so wonderfully fine a couple of weeks ago it now felt as if Sara's whole world had come crashing down at her feet again!

'Alfredo,' she murmured heavily. Again it was Alfredo. Not deliberately this time, but once again he had pulled the linchpin out from under her. Her linchpin—his own linchpin!

It was time, she supposed, to go and see how much damage the old man had done to himself.

As she was making her way to Alfredo's rooms, she met Fabia on her way out with Lia fast asleep in her arms. Sara smiled at the other woman, tousled her daughter's curls and kept going.

Alfredo's nurse opened the door at her knock. She looked faintly relieved that it was her, which made Sara wonder if she had worried it might be Nicolas on the rampage. The nurse was rarely away from Alfredo's side, so it was logical to assume that she could have overheard at least part of the conversation that must have taken place between father and son when Alfredo had made his grand confession.

He was in his sitting room, his wheelchair facing out towards the window, his thin shoulders hunched, silvered head lowered. When he heard her come in, he turned sharply, those hunter's gold eyes looking hunted for a change.

'You foolish, foolish old man,' Sara scolded. 'Why did you do it?'

'I had to do it,' he said thickly. 'I owed it to the *bambina*. You have always been right about me. I am a wicked, wicked old man!'

Now a broken old man, she thought heavily, and went forward, her arms automatically offering comfort where none was expected. And for the second time a Santino male wept in front of her. It was amazing, because she had thought neither of them capable of crying.

'He will never forgive me,' Alfredo declared long minutes later when the weeping had subsided. 'But I can live with that—die with it,' he added bleakly. 'But I could not live with my own wickedness any longer.' He sniffed, and blew his nose on the handkerchief Sara produced. 'I have not been living well with it since I drove you away from here then had to witness what my plotting had done to my son!' he confessed. 'He missed you, Sara! And I had to watch it happen, watch him show the same grief he had shown when his *mamma* died and know that it was by my hand that he was feeling that bad again! By my hand that he was being denied the right to love his own daughter!'

'But you're a clever man, Alfredo!' She sighed impatiently. 'Couldn't you have found some way to put it right without having to admit the truth?'

He nodded. 'I had every intention of trying to put things right,' he informed her. 'I came to London—with the express purpose of coming to see you, to talk to you, maybe...' he sighed '...beg your help in putting this nasty business right without losing my son. But I took ill.'

Sara stared at him. 'I remember Toni telling me that you took ill in London! You were coming to see me?' she said in surprise.

'Si.' He nodded. 'Since then… Well—' he slapped the wheelchair '—you see since then. I have been in no fit state to do anything. I can barely take care of myself anymore!' He stopped to swallow thickly. 'Then the *bambina* was taken,' he continued gruffly. 'And suddenly I was being given a chance to put things right because Nicolas was having the little one flown directly out here, to me—to my safe-keeping! I could not believe my luck—'

'What?' Sara cut in sharply. 'What did you just say, Alfredo?'

He looked blank for a moment while he thought back over what he had been saying. 'You mean about Nicolas having Lia flown out to Sicily?' His shoulders moved as if he was shrugging off the fact that he was about to let out another secret.

'She was recovered in England,' he informed her. 'Nicolas was very clever,' he added proudly. 'Very cunning. He had the kidnappers tracked via satellite links with their mobile telephones, discovered their hide-out, then played a shrewd game whereby he split the gang up by agreeing to a drop-off place for the money several miles away from where they held Lia. Then a team of special agents went in to snatch back the child while Toni kept the appointment with the money. It was very clever, very slick; Lia never knew a thing about it. Nic had her safely on a plane to come here before she even woke up!'

'But…' Sara was struggling to take all of this in. 'Why did they need special agents to snatch her back if the ransom was…?' Her voice dried up, her whole blood system with it, when the look on Alfredo's face sent the answer shooting into her head. 'Oh, God,' she choked. 'The kidnappers had no intention of giving her back, did they?'

'We will never know that, *cara*,' Alfredo said grimly. 'But, on the evidence of past cases, no. Lia had too small a chance of coming back to you alive so Nicolas had to make the difficult decision to take her back himself. It was not easy for him,' he sighed. 'She was your whole life and to risk hurting her meant him hurting you too. But everyone involved agreed that he had no choice. So...' His shrug said the rest.

'Then he had her flown directly to me.' His expression showed how good that made him feel. 'Ah, it was love at first sight!' he sighed. 'Me and the *bambina* are like—that. He crossed two bony fingers, but Sara barely noticed because she was still having difficulty taking in all the rest.

'But why did he have her flown out here before I'd even seen her?' she breathed.

The old man looked at her sagely. 'I would have thought that was obvious,' he mocked. 'He had seen you again. Made love to you again. And he could not let you go a second time.'

'You know we—?' She stopped on an embarrassed gasp, a hot blush flooding up her cheeks. 'But how—?'

'Because you just told me.' He grinned, that old devilish look back on show. 'Those pretty cheeks of yours are a dead give-away, *cara*. They always were. But then,' he added drily, 'my son loves you. There was no real chance that he could be with you and stop himself from making love to you.'

'So, what is Anastasia?' she put in cynically. 'An aberration?'

'Anastasia?' He frowned. 'But did you not ask Nicolas about Anastasia?'

Folding her arms, she got up and moved away, going to stand and stare out of the window much as Nicolas did when disturbed about something. 'What was there to ask?' she said dully. 'I know what I saw.'

'As my son knew what he saw when he found you with Castell?' Alfredo prompted slyly.

She turned, blue eyes narrowed. 'Are you trying to suggest that you set that little scene up at the mayor's ball?' she quizzed him.

'No—no!' he denied, then glanced at her and grimaced. 'But I will forgive you for immediately jumping to that conclusion. Why not, after all?' He gave another one of his shrugs. 'I am a wicked old man. I tell lies. Big lies tike—my son has a new woman called Anastasia he visits twice a week. To make you jealous—you know-begin seeing him as the big, sexy man you used to see, eh?' he added roguishly.

'Sorry—' Sara shook her head at that one '—but Nicolas told me about his affair with her, so you aren't going to trick me by pretending it was just one of your meddling lies,' she warned.

'He told you?' Alfredo looked puzzled—then grinned. 'He has his *papà's* cunning, that one. He too decided to make you burn with jealousy—as you had made him burn once over Castell.'

To make her burn with—?

'Oh, I'm not staying here to listen to you twist everything into knots!' Sara sighed impatiently and moved off towards the door. 'You are too darn cunning for your own good, Alfredo!'

'But I make you think, heh?' he called after her goad-ingly. 'Your natural fair-mindedness will now make you question your right to condemn my son without a hearing.'

Well, did it? she asked herself impatiently for the umpteenth time in as many days. She was walking alone along the shore, as she had taken to doing often over the last few miserable days, even though the weather had turned cold and the skies became overcast.

Long days. Cold, empty days with no Nicolas beside her. None of his quiet, calm strength. None of his warmth in her bed. None of his kisses and mind-blowing caresses that—

And does that kind of thinking help? she asked herself sternly. Just because Lia is getting better by the day, and no longer requires your full attention, it does not mean you have to turn your thoughts in that direction!

But she missed him. And it hurt—actually hurt like a tooth-ache. And she wanted him to come home because, for all his cunning, Alfredo was right—she did not have the right to condemn Nicolas without a fair hearing.

And anyway, did one small kiss on a public terrace even begin to constitute a betrayal?

'Nic,' she whispered achingly to the cold grey sea. 'Oh, Nic...'

It began to rain, quite suddens—an absolute deluge that completely halted her miserable thoughts and sent her running as fast as she could for cover. By the time she reached the villa steps she was drenched to the skin. She began running upwards, head down to shield her face from the worst of the rain, so she was not aware of the person hurrying down the steps with a big umbrella open ready for her—until she cannoned right into the solid wall of his chest.

She cried out, almost toppling backwards with the impact, and would have done if a hand had not caught her arm to steady her. She looked up, a shaken thankyou ready on her lips, then was struck silent when she found herself staring into a pair of guarded golden eyes.

Nicolas.

Nicolas, who had come home at last while she had been down on the beach. Nicolas, who had thoughtfully snatched up an umbrella to come and shelter her from the rain.

It was Nicolas she had just cannoned into.

Déjà vu.

The sense of having been in this situation once before swept over her in a hot, tingling wave, followed by an ache so wretched that it filled her eyes with tears. Why, she wasn't sure—until the next words left her thickened throat without her even knowing that they were there to be said.

'Drop your wallet again, Nicolas,' she whispered.

He stiffened up like a board, instant comprehension lifting his big chest on a harsh inward drag of air, the eyes changing from guarded gold to a dark, molten bronze that was almost—pained.

He stood there like that, silent, unbreathing—they both did—for what seemed like an age while Sara felt the complete

breakdown of her mental processes begin. to shatter her insides because this time—this time it was she who was doing
the pleading, she who had just lowered her pride and exposed
her real feelings to him.

With those impulsively spoken words, it was she who was
asking that they try again.

And that pained look in his eyes was telling her she had
made a mistake.

Oh, God—she looked down and away—a terrible, terrible
mistake.

He breathed out at last, his body shuddering with the effort.
Then, 'Come on,' he muttered, his arm reaching out to fold her
to him. 'Let's get out of this rain.'

They went up the rest of the steps together, he holding the
umbrella over both of them, she huddled to his side, too shaken
and horrified at herself to say another word as he guided her
straight to their bathroom where he grabbed a towel and pushed
it at her.

'Get those wet clothes off,' he said, 'and dry yourself.'

He turned away to go back into the bedroom. By the time he
came back carrying her white towelling robe she was shivering
inside the big bath towel—not because she was cold but because
she was suffering from shock at her own stupid impulsiveness.

She couldn't even look at him. He said nothing, just grimly
handed her the bathrobe and waited while she pushed her arms
into it; then he silently produced her hairdryer.

But when she went to take it from him he shook his head.
'I'll do it. Throw your hair forward.'

Too appalled at herself to argue, she did as he bid. And in
the next moment heated air was being directed onto her long,
wet hair.

She said nothing—couldn't. Neither did he. And the tension
between them grew thicker and thicker as the minutes ticked
by, until, just when she thought she could stand it no longer, the
dryer was switched off, and she found herself standing there

in the sudden stunning silence surrounding them, holding her breath, trembling from head to toe, head still bent forward so that she could keep her wretched face hidden behind her hair.

Why had she said something as crazy as that? she asked herself painfully. She hadn't meant to say it. She hadn't even *wanted* to say it!

Now she felt a fool—a silly, bumbling fool. But, worse than that, she knew she had shocked him, rendered him so utterly embarrassed by her silly, stupid—

Something landed at her feet. Her eyes, glazed with wretched tears, burned into focus then just stared at the floor as Nicolas turned and walked away.

It was his wallet.

The tears came back, a muffled sob mounting in her throat. She stared at the wallet, stared until the tears blurred it out of focus again, then she was bending to pick up the fine leather, lovingly smoothing it between trembling fingers while she came to terms with what this really meant.

No mistake. And, far from being embarrassed by her silly outburst, Nicolas had understood!

This was their olive branch. Hers to him. His to her. A wonderful, beautiful olive branch!

He was standing by the bed with his back to her when she came out of the bathroom. Head down, shoulders hunched, hands thrust into his trouser pockets.

Her legs were shaking so much that she had to concentrate hard to get them to carry her over to him. 'Excuse me,' she murmured unsteadily, 'but did you drop this?' She held the wallet out towards him.

He turned, hands still in pockets, shoulders still hunched, his chin down, eyes lowered. Then he simply stood there, staring at the black leather wallet—stared at it until her throat grew thick and her fingers began to tremble.

She swallowed, eyes shining with unshed tears. 'Nic?' she prompted huskily, pushing the wallet a little closer.

He looked up, eyes so black that she could see no colour in them at all, just the reflection of her wretched self. 'Do you know what it did to me the first time you stood in front of me like this?' he asked gruffly.

She nodded, mouth quivering. Love-struck, he'd called it then. Utterly love-struck. 'Me too,' she whispered.

He breathed in—no, sucked in air, his whole body shuddering with the effort. 'Well, it was nothing compared to what I am feeling right now. Nothing—you understand?'

Did she? She nodded again, hoping she understood. Oh, hoping she did! 'Take the wallet, Nic. Please,' she begged.

He shook his head. 'I first need your forgiveness.'

What for? For not believing in her? For Anastasia?

'It is what I came back for,' he continued roughly. 'Whatever else you decide to do about us, I need your forgiveness.'

'You have it,' she said, meaning it. He could have anything he wanted so long as he went on looking at her like that. 'Anything,' she told him thickly. 'Just take back the wallet. I need you to take back the wallet!'

He took another of those deep breaths, but let this one out slowly—and at last reached out and took the wallet. Took it and immediately tossed it aside to reach for her instead.

After that, she wasn't sure how it all happened—whether it was his doing or her own—but suddenly her arms were around his neck and her legs were wrapped around his waist, and they were kissing hungrily, urgently, devouring each other as he turned to topple them both onto the bed.

Her robe fell apart, helped, she thought, by his hands, though it was difficult to say because her arms and legs were still wrapped tightly around him as if her very life depended on holding on to him like this.

It was wild, frenzied almost—the kiss, the way his hands moulded and shaped her body, her hair completely surrounding them both, their breathing completely out of control—senses completely out of control!

'Sara...' He managed to drag his lips sideways enough to murmur her name against her cheek. His mouth was warm and moist, and so necessary to her mouth that she chased it. 'Sara...' He tried again, then groaned when she captured him, their lips, tongues fusing. He allowed himself to sink down into the heat of it for another short, greedy moment before he murmured raspingly, 'You have to let go of me, *mi amore*. I cannot hold you properly while you cling like this.'

But her limbs only tightened. 'I can't let go,' she whispered shakily. 'I think I must be in shock because I just can't let go!'

His sigh shook them both as he levered himself up on his elbows, hands trembling when he tried to brush her hair away from their faces. She opened her eyes, found him gazing down at her with those blackened eyes full of grim concern.

'I am going nowhere,' he told her sombrely. 'I promise you. I will never move from this bed if this is where you want me to stay.'

'Always?' It was crazy, a stupid conversation, yet so incredibly important!

'Until the day I die if that is what it will take,' he vowed.

'Take for what?' she whispered.

'For you to feel loved by me again.'

The tears came back to her eyes. 'And do you?'

Pain dragged at his features. 'I never stopped,' he said thickly. 'How could I? You are the other part of me that is missing when I am not with you.' He lowered his mouth and kissed her again, slowly this time, lovingly. 'You feel the need to hold onto me like this,' he murmured. 'But it is I who will never let you go again. Why else do you think I came rushing back here when I heard what you were going to do?'

She frowned. 'Do?'

He nodded, his hand gentle as it smoothed the tears from her cheeks. 'When you put my father into a state of high panic by telling him you were going to leave here,' he explained, 'he called me up, weeping and wailing and yelling at me because you wanted to take his granddaughter away, and—' He stopped, his eyes suddenly glassing over as comprehension began to hit him.

It had hit Sara several seconds sooner, and if it did nothing else it allowed her to loosen the grip she had on him, her legs and arms slackening, while she concentrated on biting her kiss-swollen bottom lip to stop herself smiling.

Then, 'My God,' he gritted. 'He was lying to me, wasn't he? The manipulative old devil was putting on a pathetic act to make me jump to his bidding!'

'He assures me he knows he's a wicked old man,' Sara put in soothingly.

'I should kill him,' Nicolas muttered.

'Oh, don't do that!' she cried, looking genuinely alarmed. 'Your daughter will never forgive you! She loves that nasty old man!'

She shouldn't have said that; she realised it the moment the words left her mouth and his face suddenly darkened, his body rolling sideways out of her slackened grasp.

'My daughter,' he muttered. 'The child I rejected before she was even born, because of him.'

'Oh, don't,' she murmured, coming to lean over him, arms holding now instead of clinging. 'Blaming your father will only make you bitter. And I don't want you to be bitter!'

'I am not blaming him,' he exploded gruffly. 'I am blaming myself-*myself!*'

'But-none of it really matters now, don't you see?' she pleaded. 'I love you,' she added anxiously.

He sighed, his dark head jerking on the pillow. 'What are you, Sara?' he rasped in angry disbelief. 'Some kind of saint that you can forgive me the unforgivable? I denounced your love! Your trust! Your honesty! I even denounced our own child!'

'But you came back,' she said gently. 'Even believing all those things about me. You came back to me. You wanted to try again. I think you even forgave!'

'Forgave.' He bit the word out bitterly. 'How magnanimous of me. How—un-Sicilian! I forgave you for what?' he demanded. 'For being yourself? For remaining true to yourself despite what we Santinos did to you?' He round out another sigh. 'Well, I will tell you something,' he said grimly. 'It will be a long time before I will forgive myself.'

'Another vendetta—against yourself this time?' she mocked, and with a weary sigh sat up on her knees. 'I hope you've got them all logged on computer somewhere or you may lose track of who you are actually at war with!'

'I am not at war with you,' he said gruffly, his eyes beginning to burn again with that look which said that her angry pose aroused him.

And the fact that he had the arrogance to do that when they were in the middle of a serious discussion like this aroused her—to anger, bitter, biting anger. 'Well, I am at war with you!' she declared, tugging her robe around her to block out what his eyes were so greedily feeding on. 'And so long as you refuse to forgive both yourself and your father I refuse to forgive you!'

With that, she climbed off the bed.

'Was that an ultimatum?' he enquired.

'Yes.' Her wonderful hair flicked out as she turned to face him. 'I won't live with vendettas,' she snapped. 'If I can put my grievances aside then I don't see why you can't.'

'And have you?' he asked. 'Put your grievances aside?'

She looked down and away. 'Most of them,' she muttered. 'I can forgive Alfredo because he's old and sick and genuinely contrite. And I can forgive you because you were deliberately misled into believing what you did about me. But.'

'But?' he prompted softly when she stopped.

Yes, but, she thought, and lifted her chin to him. The blue eyes were cold, the lovely mouth tight. 'I saw you at the mayor's ball with Anastasia,' she said. 'I won't forgive you that, Nicolas. Not when you'd promised me she was out of the picture.'

'And what did you see?' He sat up, his frown cleverly giving the impression that he did not know what she was talking about.

'You, talking to her.' She turned away. 'Holding her. Kissing her.'

'Is that why you came home without me? Because what you saw hurt and upset you?'

She didn't answer, didn't need to; it was already written in the dull, throbbing silence.

'Did my father not try to explain to you about Anastasia?' he asked grimly after a moment.

She folded her arms across her chest because she was hurting inside again. 'He said I should ask you before I made judgements,' she murmured.

'And are you asking me now?'

She looked down at her feet and shook her head.

'Why not?'

She thought about that, and felt the tears sting her eyes again. 'Because I'm too frightened of the answer,' she confessed in a strained whisper.

He rolled off the bed, sighing heavily as he did so. 'As I was afraid of having blood tests taken of Lia,' he murmured. 'Because I was afraid of the answer.'

'You were?' That made her turn to look at him. He saw the tears and swore softly, reaching out to pull her against him, one hand pressing her face into his chest, the other circling her waist.

'Of course.' He grimaced. 'I wanted her to be mine so much, it was easier to simply—tell myself she was mine and leave it at that than learn the opposite.'

'She is yours,' she told him, just in case he had any doubts left in his mind.

He didn't. 'I know it,' he said. 'But Anastasia is not mine.' His eyes were dark with apology as she tipped back her head to look at him. 'Never was.' He lifted a finger to the corner of her quivering mouth. 'She belongs to Toni,' he added softly, then grimaced at her start of surprise. 'His future bride, to be exact.

But since my father took ill Toni and I have been so busy that he has barely had time to be with her, never mind arrange a wedding. She is beautiful. She is kind. And she has a very sick mother—much the same as I have a sick father.' He shrugged. 'So if I am at home and Toni is not I have got into the habit of going to visit her a couple of times a week. To break her tedium. She does not get out much.'

'But she was out on the night of the mayor's ball.'

He sighed. 'And wanted to meet you. I would not let her,' he admitted. 'Because I had used her name to hurt you and did not want to hurt you more by introducing you to what, for you, amounted to my mistress. Anastasia was angry when I had to tell her why I did not want you both to meet, so we went outside while I apologised and did a litttle—begging.'

Another grimace. 'I promised her she could have Toni back for a whole month if she would just give me a few more weeks to cement my relationship with you. She agreed, on the condition that I also promised to tell you the truth about her—straight away. To which I agreed. Only the baby took ill,' he reminded her heavily. 'And my promise went right out of my head because I had too many other things to worry about, like how did I tell Sara that I loved our beautiful daughter when the child was lying there at death's door?'

His mouth tightened. 'Too late. I had left it too late to say all the things I wanted to say to both you and Lia. Then my father came in with his grand confession—' another rasping sigh '—and broke my whole world apart. After that, I did not feel I had the right to say anything to either you or Lia. I deserved neither of you.'

'So you went away to wage a vendetta against yourself?'

His endorsing smile was wry. 'Until I received that hysterical call from my father,' he said. 'Then I was back here as quick as my car would bring me.'

'If you forgive him, I'll forgive you for lying about Anastasia,' Sara offered.

'You are asking me to be very un-Sicilian again,' he sighed.

'You want more incentive?' Her blue eyes began to darken with promises. 'Only I have this—vision, you see,' she murmured softly, her fingers beginning to slowly undo the buttons on his shirt. 'Of a man lying naked on a bed of white linen with his woman lying on top of him, saying words that would—'

The hungry crush of his mouth caught the rest of what she had been going to say. 'You win,' he muttered. 'I am the most un-Sicilian person I know. I forgive everyone!' he announced. 'Even my father, though he does not deserve it!'

'Can I tell him that?' She smiled happily.

'Later.' He bent to lift her into his arms. 'The old devil can wait his turn! For we have a vision to play out before any more forgiving is done around here.'

'You're wearing too many clothes for my vision,' Sara complained.

'Now, yes,' he agreed. 'In a moment—no.' He dumped. her on the bed and began dragging off his clothes while she watched him, her blue eyes hiding nothing as bronzed skin was exposed to her, bit by delicious bit.

'Will this do?' he enquired lazily when he was standing arrogantly naked in front of her.

'Pull the curtains,' she whispered sensually. 'Lock the doors and release the curtains around the bed.'

His eyes darkened, then blazed. He moved off like the graceful animal he was to do exactly what she had asked. As the fine white silk billowed around the bed, he was lying beside her, then beneath her, her robe gone, her hair around his shoulders, her arms braced on his wide chest, her eyes loving, solemnly loving.

'Beautiful,' she murmured. 'You're so beautiful, Nicolas...'

* * * * *

The Bridal Suite

Sandra Marton

CHAPTER ONE

GRIFFIN MCKENNA WAS a pirate.

The newspapers, and the Wall Street pundits, said he was a financial genius, but Dana Anderson knew better. McKenna was a pirate, plain and simple. He took whatever he wanted, whether it was a corporation or a woman.

What else could you call a man like that?

Gorgeous, that was what, according to the gossip columns. Dana supposed there were some women who'd find him attractive. The sapphire-blue eyes, the thick, silky black hair, the cleft chin and the nose that was almost perfectly straight except for a faint bend in the middle...all of it seemed exactly right for McKenna's broad-shouldered, long-legged body.

So what? Nobody'd ever said pirates had to be homely.

McKenna bought companies that were in trouble, scooping them up like a kid taking candy from a dish, and turned them into moneymakers. And, they said, he managed such feats because he had skill, courage and determination. They left out the fact that he'd also started life with an inheritance big enough to float a small kingdom, or that he got obvious pleasure from controlling the destinies of others.

And from having people fawn over him—especially women. But not all women, thought Dana as she marched down the hall to McKenna's office. No, definitely not all. She, for instance, was not the least bit impressed by the man. She'd seen him, early on, for what he was. Not just a pirate but a charter member of the Good Old Boys club. An arrogant, egotistical, self-important Male Chauvinist, capital M, capital C.

What he needed, instead of gushing columnists and swooning females, was the truth.

Well, she was about to deliver it.

She paused outside his office.

Not the truth about his overrated, overpublicized self. Dana wasn't a fool. She had more than a job here, at Data Bytes; she had a career, one she'd worked damn hard for, and she intended to keep it. The truth she'd tell him, the truth he needed to learn, was about the company's all-new, highly touted computer program, the one that was going to be on display at the big software convention in Miami this coming weekend—the program that was supposed to save Data Bytes from going belly-up.

But it wouldn't. It couldn't, because the code that underlay it was a disaster.

She'd already tried telling that to McKenna a week ago.

'Mr. McKenna is a very busy man,' his secretary, the formidable Miss Macy, had said. Dana had replied that The Very Busy Man himself had made it clear, during the organizational meeting he'd held, that he was also A Very Approachable Man.

She hadn't mentioned that he'd also made it clear he was a man who believed in gender equality the way a skunk believed in deodorants.

Not that it came as a surprise. What kind of man got his name into the gossip columns all the time? What kind of man was photographed with a different woman each week?

What kind of man made the sort of joke McKenna had made at that organizational meeting?

'Remember,' he'd intoned solemnly, 'we're all in this together, people. If Data Bytes is going to fulfill the vision I have for it—and I assure you, it will—it'll be because every man here works his tail off to make it happen.'

'Every man, and woman,' Jeannie Aarons had called out, and McKenna had grinned along with all the others.

'An interesting observation,' he'd said with wide-eyed innocence, and, after the laughter had died down, he'd added that he never doubted the value of the 'female of the species.'

'I'll just bet you don't,' Dana had muttered under her breath.

If she had any lingering doubts, McKenna had swept them aside when she'd met with him last week, after Macy had finally agreed to grant her an audience. She had come armed with printouts to support her contention that the new code was not going to be ready on time—but McKenna hadn't been the least bit interested in listening.

'How do you do?' he'd said, rising from behind his desk like an emperor greeting his subject. 'Would you care for some coffee? Some tea?'

'Nothing, thank you,' Dana had said politely, and then she'd launched into her speech only to have McKenna cut her off in the middle with an imperious wave of the hand.

'Yes, yes,' he'd said. 'Dave told me that he thought you might come by to protest.'

'I'm not protesting, sir,' Dana started to say, but then his words hit home. 'Dave *told* you? You mean, you already know there's a problem?' It was such a relief, knowing Dave had finally faced reality, that she smiled. 'Well, I'm glad to hear it. I never dreamed—'

'—That you'd be passed over for promotion.' McKenna nodded. 'Dave explained that to me. He understands why that's made you unhappy.'

'I *was* passed over. But that isn't why—'

'He also told me that you've complained that you haven't been given enough credit for your work.'

'Complained?'

'Politely, of course.' McKenna flashed a patronizing smile. 'He assured me you were every inch the lady when you brought it to his attention.'

'Did he,' Dana said coolly.

'He was very open,' McKenna said. He smiled again, this time with unctuous sympathy. 'You see, we go back a long way together, Dave and I. We belonged to the same fraternity.'

'Do tell,' Dana said, even more coldly.

'I assure you, Miss Anderson, your efforts will not go unrewarded. I'm going to institute a bonus plan, and—'

'Mr. McKenna,' Dana took a steadying breath. 'This isn't about getting credit for my work, or about that promotion. I came to tell you that the new code isn't going to work! If you introduce it at the Miami conference—'

'Not 'if,' Miss Anderson. When. And it won't be me introducing it, it will be Dave. I suppose you'd hoped for that chance yourself, but—'

'Oh, for heaven's sake!' Dana shot to her feet and glared at him. 'I'm not looking for a shoulder to weep on, dammit! I came to warn you that the code's a mess, but if you don't want to hear it, there's nothing I can do.'

'And why is it a mess, Miss Anderson?'

'Because...' Dana hesitated. Because Dave's a drunk, she'd almost said, but McKenna would never believe her. 'Because it's got bugs. Little bits of code that are written wrong.'

'So Dave tells me. He also tells me you wrote those little bits of code, Miss Anderson. Not that he or I hold you responsible, of course, considering your lack of experience.'

'My what?'

'But he assured me that you'll learn. He says you're bright, and quick.'

Dana stared at him in astonishment. 'I don't believe this. I absolutely don't—'.

'And now, if you'll forgive me...' McKenna had smiled politely as he rose to his feet, came around his desk and lightly grasped her elbow. 'Thank you for stopping by,' he'd said in a way that made it clear she was dismissed. 'My door is always open to my employees, Miss Anderson—or may I call you Dana?'

Dana, who'd been so angry by then that she could hardly see straight, had pulled free of his grasp.

'You may call me *Ms.* Anderson,' she'd snapped.

And what a stupid thing that had been to say. Even now, the memory made her shudder. Nobody, *nobody*, at Data Bytes was so ridiculously formal. People went around in jeans and T-shirts with funny sayings on them. Why, she was the only one who dressed in suits and tailored shirts, but when you sat down to pee instead of standing up, you had to work harder at winning a place on the team. Despite all the gender equality laws, the playing field was far from equal. Just look at how McKenna had thought he was complimenting her last week, telling her she was a lady....

'Miss Anderson. Sorry. I meant, *Ms.* Anderson, of course.' The familiar voice, a sort of honeyed growl, came from just behind her. Dana swung around and found herself facing

Griffin McKenna.

'Mr. McKenna. I didn't—I thought—'

'Tongue-tied, Ms. Anderson? How very unusual.'

Dana blushed. How could he manage that? He had a way of making her feel—what was the word? Incompetent? No. Not that. She knew her stuff; you didn't get as far as she'd gotten on the corporate ladder without being damn good at what you did. Uncertain. Yes, that was it. He made her feel uncertain. It had to do with that little smile on his mouth when he looked at her, as if he knew something she didn't.

'Were you looking for me? Or were you simply planning on skulking in the hallway?'

'I have never skulked in my life, Mr. McKenna. Yes, as a matter of fact, I was looking for you. We need to talk.'

McKenna's brows lifted. 'Again?'

'Again,' she said, holding her ground.

'Well...' He shot back his cuff, frowned at his watch, then nodded. 'I suppose I can give you a few minutes.'

Such generosity! Dana forced a smile to her lips.

'Thank you,' she said, and strode through the door ahead of him, past a surprised-looking Miss Macy, who was guarding McKenna's lair with her usual dragon-like efficiency, and into his office.

'She doesn't have an appointment, sir,' the Dragon hissed.

'That's all right, Miss Macy,' McKenna said soothingly. He paused, just long enough to give the Anderson babe time to stalk halfway across the carpet toward his desk. It was the polite thing to do, but hell, who was he kidding? What he wanted was the view.

And there it was.

Ms. Anderson had the walk of a lioness, all power and pride, and the golden hair to match. And her eyes, when she turned to face him...they were the color of emeralds. Her mouth was lush and soft-looking, made all the more tempting because she never seemed to bother with lipstick. And oh, that body, curved and feminine despite the dowdy suits she wore....

Griffin closed the door and leaned back against it, arms folded over his chest.

It certainly was a pity that a woman who looked like this should be such a cold piece of work. But then, Dave had warned him.

'The Anderson babe's a hard case, Griff,' he'd said. 'You know the type. She wishes to God she'd been born a guy but since she wasn't, she holds every man since Adam responsible for the world's woes.'

Griffin sighed, walked to his desk and sat down behind it. Why did some women want to be what Nature had not meant them to be? He'd never been able to understand it.

'Well, Ms. Anderson,' he said, 'what can I do for you today?'

Dana cleared her throat. 'Mr. McKenna——'

What was he doing? Dana frowned. He was looking through the stack of papers on his desk, *that's* what he was doing.

'Mr. McKenna?'

He looked up. 'Hmm?'

'Sir, I was trying to tell you about——'

He was doing it again! Bending that dark head of his, thumbing through what appeared to be a bunch of telephone memos, instead of paying attention to her.

'Mr. McKenna. I'd appreciate it if you'd listen.'

'Sorry.'

He looked up, and she could tell from the expression on his face that he wasn't the least bit sorry. As far as he was concerned, she was wasting his time.

Dana took a deep breath.

'I ran the new program this morning,' she said.

'And?'

'And, it's a total disaster. There's no way it'll perform properly tomorrow, when you demo it at the Miami convention.'

McKenna favored her with a small smile. 'Fortunately for me, I won't be doing the demo, remember? Dave will.'

Stupid, stupid man! Dana smiled politely in return.

'It won't matter who does it,' she said calmly. 'The point I'm trying to make is that the code won't work right. And Dave won't——'

'It's really a pity, you know.'

'What's a pity?'

'That you should be so distressed by that missed promotion.'

'That I should be…? Mr. McKenna, I told you, this has absolutely nothing to do with——'

'Your record is excellent, Miss—sorry—*Ms.* Anderson,'

McKenna leaned forward over his desk, his eyes focused on hers, his expression one of heartfelt compassion. 'I took the time to look through it, after our chat last week.'

Lord, he was condescending! Dana's gaze narrowed.

'Thank you, but I don't need reassurance. I'm good at what I do. Very good. I know that. I spent a lot of time on that code, a *lot* of time, but Dave—'

McKenna got to his feet.

'I'd hate to see this become an obsession, Ms. Anderson,' His voice was polite, but his smile, this time, was cool. 'You're a valued employee, but so is Forrester. And he's the man in charge.'

'Exactly,' Dana said before she could stop herself. 'He's the *man* in charge.'

'He is the right *person* for the job, Ms. Anderson. His gender has nothing to do with it. As for you... I suggest you rethink your position.

Data Bytes would like to keep you—but if you're not happy being part of the team, perhaps you might wish to move on.'

Dana had always prided herself on being a clear-thinking woman. She knew it was one of her best attributes, that cool, rational approach to life. It was why she'd succeeded at virtually everything she'd attempted, from the A's she'd collected in elementary school straight through to the Phi Beta Kappa key she'd proudly acquired at Harvard.

And yet, at that moment, she wanted nothing more than to tell Griffin McKenna what he could do with his advice and his job.

But she couldn't. She wouldn't. Her life, and her career, were moving forward just as she'd planned, or they had been, until the despicable McKenna came along. And she'd be damned if she'd let him derail all her plans.

'Ms. Anderson? Do I make myself clear?'

Dana forced herself to meet his cold glare with equanimity. 'Perfectly,' she said calmly. 'Good afternoon, Mr. McKenna.'

And she turned on her heel and marched out of his office without a backward glance.

* * *

Dana banged open the door to the ladies' room.

McKenna wasn't despicable, he was detestable.

'The bastard,' she said between her teeth. She stalked to the nearest white porcelain sink, turned on the faucet, cupped her hands under the flow and splashed cold water over her burning cheeks. 'The thick-skulled, insensitive lout!'

She yanked a paper towel from the dispenser, scrubbed it over her face, then balled it up and dumped it into the waste receptacle.

Was he blind? He'd bought his success with inherited money, but he did have some degree of talent. Everybody said so. Even Arthur, who knew about such things, said so.

'My dear,' he'd informed her after McKenna's takeover, 'the man is a financial genius.'

Dana had been so ticked off at hearing Arthur, of all people, say such a thing that the 'my dear' had slid past her, instead of making her clench her teeth as it usually did.

'Financial genius, my foot,' she'd replied. 'He's a spoiled brat, born with an 18-karat spoon in his mouth.'

Arthur had set her straight, explaining that McKenna had been born to money, yes, but that even the most conservative analysts figured he'd tripled his inherited wealth by now.

'If you'd read the *Journal*,' Arthur had said kindly, 'you'd be aware that the man knows all there is to know about leveraging stocks and corporate takeovers.'

Well, maybe he did. Dana leaned back against the sink, arms folded, and glared at the row of closed stalls. But he didn't know spit about computers, or computer programs, and it was painfully obvious that he didn't know spit about her boss, either. Dave was running their department into the ground, but when she'd tried to tell that to McKenna, he'd damn near laughed in her face. And why?

Because he and Forrester were pals, that was why. Because she could never qualify as anybody's 'pal,' not so long as she was a woman, and never mind McKenna's remark about gender having nothing to do with it. Dana might have come out of college naive enough to believe that sexism in the office—especially in the programming field—was a whisper of the past, but five years in the trenches had taught her otherwise.

If you were a man, the sky was the limit. But if you were a woman, there was a glass ceiling. And she had reached it.

The only kind of female the McKennas of this world could deal with were the ones who knew how to flutter their lashes. McKenna, especially. If he hadn't been linked with every beautiful female on the planet, it was only because, at thirty-five, he hadn't yet had the time to get around to them all.

One Down, a tabloid headline had read the day after John Kennedy Jr. tied the knot. One to Go.

Even Arthur had understood just who that 'one' was.

Dana stamped her foot. If she'd swooned at his feet, he'd have paid attention to her. If she'd been a man, bringing him bad news about the new code, he'd have listened. But she hadn't swooned, and she wasn't male, and so he'd shooed her off as if she were a bothersome fly.

'The idiot!' Dana said, swinging toward the mirror.

The door swung open and Jeannie Aarons walked into the room.

'Don't even speak to me,' Dana said crossly.

Jeannie's brows arched. 'And a bright and cheery hello to you, too.'

'How does that man live with himself? He is, without question, the most thick-skulled, miserable son of a—'

'Arthur? Thick-skulled, yes. Dull, yes. But miserable's going too far,' Jeannie leaned closer to the mirror, eyes narrowed, and peered at her chin. 'Wonderful. I'm getting a zit, and tonight I'm seeing that guy I met at that singles dance. What do you think, huh? Should I try popping it?'

'I'm not talking about Arthur. I'm talking about McKenna. Who does the man think he is? Who in *hell* does he think he is?'

'A hunk. That's who.'

'A jerk. *That's* who. The smug, miserable, rotten—'

'My grandma always said that repetition was the product of a non-creative mind.'

'Your grandma never met Mr. I-Am-God McKenna. Jeannie, what *are* you doing?'

'Squeezing this zit. I cannot possibly go out tonight with a zit the size of Rhode Island on my chin. It's gross.'

Dana sighed. 'No, it isn't.'

'Yes, it is. I look like the poster child for leprosy.'

'Do you have any concealer with you?'

'Does an elephant have a trunk?'

'Well, give it to me. And your compact. I'll fix it so your zit will disappear. I just wish somebody could do the same to His Majesty McKenna.'

'Now, Dana.' Obediently, Jeannie let her face be tilted up toward the light. 'Wanting to fix McKenna isn't nice.'

'Why not? Fixing that man's butt would be doing the world a favor.'

Jeannie grinned. 'Ah. Well, fixing his *butt* is okay, I guess, but fixing *him*, as in the way a vet fixes a randy tomcat, would make legions of damsels weep.'

'Frankly,' Dana said coldly, 'I don't give a hoot about his personal life, though the way he goes through women, he might just deserve it.'

'I take it you're not one of his fans,' Jeannie said cheerfully.

'If you mean that I'm not taken in by his press, his money or his looks, you're right.'

'There's no sense in arguing over his looks. Only a troglodyte wouldn't find the guy hunky. As for his press…according to what I've heard, Griffin McKenna bought up and turned around a lot of troubled companies last year.'

'Great. First Arthur and now you, giving me the same speech.'

'Please! Don't put me in the same sentence with Arthur. I'm liable to fall asleep from boredom.'

'It's garbage and you know it,' Dana said, ignoring the gibe. 'McKenna is a pirate.'

'Does he still insist on wearing bow ties?'

'McKenna?' Dana said, staring at Jeannie.

'Arthur. Somebody ought to tell him, guys just don't wear those things anymore.'

'I think his bow ties make him look distinguished,' Dana said loyally. 'Besides, I was talking about McKenna, and please don't bother telling me how many jobs he's saved because that's all secondary to his real purpose in life, which is to make himself as disgustingly rich as possible.'

'My, oh, my, is that right? He should be taken out and shot.'

'And to accumulate as many female scalps as he can manage in his spare time. Turn toward me a little, please.'

'I thought you just said you don't care about his personal life.'

'I don't. It's just that his attitude toward women spills over into his work.'

'Whoa.' Jeannie drew in her breath. 'Don't tell me,' she said in an excited whisper. 'He made a pass?'

'Ha!'

'Ha, as in yes?'

'Ha, as in I almost wish he had.' Dana's eyes glittered. 'Then, at least, I could nail him with the charges he deserves. The man is a sexist pig. He sees women only as objects.'

'I thought you said he didn't make a pass,' Jeannie said in bewilderment.

'He didn't,' Dana stepped back, cocked her head and studied Jeannie's face. 'There. If you keep your hands away from your chin, nobody'll notice a thing.'

Jeannie swung toward the mirror. 'Terrific! I'm almost human again.'

'Which is more than we can say of Mister McKenna.' Dana

curved her hands around the rim of the sink and glared into the mirror. 'Tell me the truth, please. Do I sound like an idiot?'

Jeannie looked at her friend and sighed. 'Your trouble isn't what you sound like, my friend. It's what you look like. People who design complicated computer programs aren't supposed to look like Michelle Pfeiffer stand-ins. Well, except for the hair. If you'd just go blonder, leave it loose...'

'Forget about the way I look,' Dana said sharply, 'although that, clearly, is part of the problem as far as McKenna's concerned. He looks at me, all he can see is a female.'

'How peculiar,' Jeannie said sweetly.

'Sitting there, like an emperor on his throne, giving me these solemn looks, nodding wisely as if he were really listening to what I was saying, when he'd already decided I had nothing worth listening to, thanks to my chromosomes. Oh, it was as plain as the nose on your face.'

'Or the Mount Vesuvius on my chin,' Jeannie swung toward the mirror and frowned. 'When did this happen? When did McKenna decide you had terminal PMS?'

'Last week. Well, and again just a few minutes ago. I met with him twice, and each time was a disaster.' Dana paced across the room. 'He didn't listen to me, Jeannie, he patronized me. And when that didn't work, he told me that I could look for another job, if I didn't like this one.'

'Uh-oh. That sounds ominous.'

'And why?'

'Well,' Jeannie said, 'I guess because—'

'Because I stood up to him, that's why. Because I turned out not to be the ladylike little puppet he thought I was, one that would let him pull my strings.'

'I don't think puppets have strings,' Jeannie said carefully. 'I mean, it's marionettes that—'

'It was just a figure of speech,' Dana said angrily. 'Oh, that man. How can he be so blind?'

'Dana, look, I think maybe you're going overboard, you know?'

'Well, you think wrong. There's a serious problem with the new code, thanks to my boss. Dave's screwing up, big time.'

'Are you sure?'

'I'm positive,' Dana took a deep breath. 'He's got a drinking problem.'

'You're joking.'

'I'm dead serious. He doesn't slur his speech or fall down in a heap, but there are times he's so drunk he can hardly see the monitor.'

'But—but surely, someone would have noticed—'

'Someone did. Me.'

'Did you say something about it to him?'

'Yes, of course.'

'And?'

'And, he denied it. Then he said that no one would believe me. He's the one with a name. With experience. So now I spend half my time trying to catch his errors, and the other half trying to keep up with my own work, and the result is that everything's a total mess.'

Jeannie chewed on her lip. 'Damn,' she said softly. 'What a spot to be in. Well, you'll just have to go to McKenna. I know snitching on Dave won't be fun, but—'

'I *have* gone to him,' Dana said furiously. 'What do you think I've been telling you for the last fifteen minutes?'

'You told him Dave's a drunk?'

'No. I knew he'd never believe me. But I told him the code's unstable.'

'What did he say?'

'He said he knows there are problems, and that Dave told him I was the cause, and that he realizes I'm upset because I didn't get that promotion.' Dana's eyes flashed. 'And, until he got around to telling me I might want to look for another job, he complimented me for complaining in such a ladylike way—'

The door swung open. Charlie, the custodian, beamed at Dana and Jeannie. He had a mop in one hand and a bucket in the other.

'Top o' the mornin', ladies,' he said cheerfully. 'My apologies for disturbin' you. I did knock, but I guess you didn't hear me.'

'That's okay,' Jeannie shot a glance at Dana. 'We were just about finished in here.'

'Makin' girl talk, were you?' Charlie beamed his grandfatherly smile. 'And primpin', I suppose. Well, darlins! you can rest assured that there's no need. The both of you ladies are perfect, just as you are.'

Jeannie smothered a groan as she saw the look on Dana's face.

'Indeed,' Dana said coldly. 'Whatever would we *girls* do without a man's stamp of approval?'

Charlie, blissfully unaware of the quicksand beneath his feet, grinned broadly. 'Isn't that a fact?'

'You want a fact?' Dana demanded, marching toward him. Charlie's smile faded and he flattened himself against the wall. 'We are not girls,' she said, wagging her finger under his nose, 'and we are not ladies. We are women. As for needing a man's stamp of approval—'

Jeannie grabbed Dana's arm and hustled her from the bathroom. Halfway out the door, she turned and gave Charlie an apologetic smile. 'It's nothing personal,' she hissed. 'She's just upset.'

'I am not upset,' Dana said, spinning around. 'I am just tired of pretending that I need patting on the head, as if I were a—a poodle instead of a person.'

Charlie's baffled glance went from one woman to the other. 'I never said one word against poodles, Miss.'

'Oh, for heaven's sake! I didn't... This has nothing to do with dogs. I simply meant...' Dana threw up her arms. 'Men,' she snorted, and marched off.

* * *

Moments later, Charlie stood before Griffin McKenna's massive desk, his bushy white brows still drawn together in a knot.

'So, there I was, about to mop the ladies' room—pardon me, the women's room—and the next thing I knew, the young lady said I'd insulted her dog. I ask you, sir, why would I? I like dogs. 'Course, she says it's a poodle. Try as I might, I can't claim to be fond of them little things. Can't stand their yappin' all the time, if you know what I mean.'

Griffin nodded wisely. That was the way he hoped it looked, at any rate, but he couldn't be sure he was pulling it off. What in hell was the old guy babbling about?

He liked Charlie. But his mind was on other things. Like putting on a good showing at the convention that started tomorrow in Miami. Like landing a couple of big accounts with Data Bytes's new financial database program, to put the company back in the black.

Like figuring out why a woman as gorgeous as Dana Anderson should be so impossible.

Griffin frowned. Why waste time thinking about her? She was gorgeous, yeah, but she was nothing but a pain in the rear. If only she'd admit she didn't know everything, and do what she was told.

Not that he could imagine that happening. The perfect Ms. Anderson taking orders? And from a man? He almost laughed. Still, there had to be some guy out there, somewhere, who could tame her. It wouldn't be easy, but it would be worth it to turn all that anger and fire and single-minded determination into passion, the sort of passion beautiful women were meant to experience.

'... Just said that the two of 'em were pretty little things. I suppose her poodle is, too.'

Griffin dragged his thoughts back to Charlie. The poor guy was really worked up, but about what? Griffin was no closer to an answer now than he'd been when the old fellow first came bustling through the door five minutes ago, with the ferocious Miss Macy snapping at his heels. The woman was a leftover from prior management and insisted on defending the door to his office with the zeal of a junkyard dog, despite all his reminders that Data Bytes's employees were free to see him, anytime, anyplace, about anything.

'... Wife's sister had a poodle once. Nasty little thing it was, all teeth and a bark high enough to make your ears ring.'

Griffin nodded in sympathy. He leaned forward, picked up his pen and scribbled a note on the pad Macy had centered neatly on his desk blotter.

'Early retirement package for Macy?' he wrote. 'Put junkyard dog out to pasture.' Which was a mixed metaphor if ever he'd seen one. It was just that Charlie kept going on about dogs...

Griffin focused his attention on the old man who surely deserved it, considering that he'd made it past Macy, and with his mop and scrub bucket still in his hands.

'... Best come straight to you, sir, seein' as you said there was an open door policy. Right?'

'Right. Absolutely.' Griffin cleared his throat. 'Although, actually, I'm not quite certain what the problem seems to—'

'Well, sir, the young lady thinks I insulted her and maybe even her poodle. And I didn't.'

Griffin rubbed his hand across his forehead. This was what came of defying your own advisors, all of whom thought he was crazy to go in and spend a couple of months at the helm of each company he purchased. He'd always disagreed...until now.

'Who knows what she'll do? Complain to you, I s'pose. All this nonsense I read, about sexual harrass...whatever.' Charlie looked stricken. 'She had this real angry look in her eyes— green, they are, and cold as can be.'

An icy draft seemed to waft across the back of Griffin's neck. 'She has green eyes?'

'Yes, sir. It had been on the tip of my tongue to tell her they were the color of emeralds but, thank the saints, I never got that far. Anyways, I thought I might do well to come and talk with you.'

'And the lady's name?' Griffin asked, though he knew. Dammit, he knew.

'Her friend called her—did I mention there were two young ladies, Mr. McKenna?'

'Yes. Yes, you did. What did her friend call her, Charlie?'

'Dana. And if I never see the woman again, it'll be way too soon. You understand, sir?'

Did he understand? Griffin smiled tightly as he rose to his feet and offered Charlie his hand.

'I hope I did the right thing, comin' to you, sir,' Charlie said. 'I don't want to get the girl—the woman—in any trouble, you understand.'

'Wipe her from your mind, Charlie. You won't have any more problems with Dana Anderson.'

'You'll have a talk with her, will you? Tell her I didn't mean to insult her dog?'

'Indeed,' Griffin said as he eased the old man out the door and shut it after him.

Oh, yes. He'd have a talk with Ms. Dana Anderson. Damn right, he would. The woman was trying to make Dave look bad, and now she'd upset a nice old man. She was Trouble with a capital T, and eliminating trouble was what Griffin did best.

Whistling softly between his teeth, he strolled to his desk. His glance fell on the note he'd made about Macy. With a sigh, he grabbed it, crumpled it up and slam-dunked it into the wastepaper basket.

Macy was a dragon, but she was a dragon who knew how to do her job.

Dana Anderson was a different story. Let her go make life difficult for somebody else. Let her bake cakes, or sew curtains, take dictation or type letters, let her do a woman's job instead of storming into the business world and making trouble. And if she couldn't accept her rightful place in life, then she could go find a bunch of leftover female twit-heads from the seventies, rip off her bra and burn it.

Griffin caught his breath. An image filled his mind. He saw Dana standing beside a blazing fire, her green eyes locked to his as she let down that mass of streaked golden hair and then, with heart-stopping slowness, took off not just her bra but every stitch she wore, until she had nothing on except her own soft, rose-flushed skin.

Naked, she'd be even lovelier than he'd dreamed. And yes, dammit, he *had* dreamed of her, though it galled him to admit it.

Griffin shut his eyes. The image was so real. He could feel the heat of the fire and hear the soft beat of drums somewhere off in the darkness of the night. He could see Dana smile, then run the tip of her tongue across her lips. Her hands lifted; she thrust them into her hair. Her head fell back and she began to dance. For him. Only for him...

Griffin blinked, cursed, and grabbed for the telephone.

'Miss Macy,' he barked. 'Send Dana Anderson in here, on the double.'

'Mr. Forrester's here. He wants to see you, sir.'

'All right, send him in. And then get hold of the Anderson woman.'

'Of course, sir.'

Griffin sat down. He'd give Forrester five minutes, although, to tell the truth, the man was becoming an annoyance. Still, there was no harm in a little delay. In fact, it would make what came next all the sweeter, when he finally gave the blonde with the green eyes and the disposition of a wet tabby cat exactly what she'd been asking for.

Smiling, he tipped back his chair and put his feet up on his desk.

The mere thought of the Anderson babe cooling her heels on the unemployment line was enough to make his day.

CHAPTER TWO

DANA WAS NECK-DEEP in work.

Unfortunately, none of it was hers. She was too busy fixing up Dave's disasters to pay any attention to her own stuff.

Her tiny cubicle was crowded with files, and her desk was strewn with papers. Memos fought for space with a clutter of computer disks and Styrofoam cups. 'The Neat Freak,' Dave had dubbed her long before he'd gotten his promotion, but neatness had gone the way of the dodo bird. How could you be neat, when the world was crashing down around your ears? She'd spent the past hour hunched over the keyboard, hoping to find a way to debug the latest problem in the code. Dana's fingers raced across the keyboard. Numbers scrolled down the screen of her monitor. She paused, scanned the numbers, then hit the 'enter' key.

'Please,' she said under her breath, 'let it be right.'

It wasn't.

Not that she'd expected it would be. Mistakes, not miracles, were too often the inevitable result in the wonderful world of computing.

If only Griffin McKenna could get that through his thick skull....

His thick, handsome skull.

Dana muttered a word McKenna surely wouldn't have approved hearing a woman say. She glared at the monitor. Then she sighed, sat back and reached for the closest Styrofoam cup. An inch of black sludge sloshed in the cup's bottom. She made a face, held her breath, and glugged it down. After a minute, she looked at the monitor again.

McKenna's face, complete with its smug, self-confident smirk, seemed to flicker like a ghostly apparition on the screen.

'That's right,' she said. 'Smile, McKenna. Why wouldn't you? The world is your oyster.' Angrily, she tapped the keys again, deleting the numbers, but McKenna's image still lingered. 'I should have quit,' she muttered. 'I should have told that man exactly what he can do with this job.'

It wasn't too late. She could pick up the phone, dial his office...

She was reaching for the receiver when the phone rang.

'Hello,' she snarled.

'Dana?'

It was Arthur. Dana shut her eyes.

'Oh,' she said. 'It's you.'

'Were you expecting someone else, my dear?'

Dana shot a glance at the monitor, as if she half expected to find McKenna's face still etched onto the glass.

'No,' she said. 'No, not at all. I just—I'm, ah, I'm awfully busy just now, Arthur, so if you wouldn't mind—'

'Of course, Dana. I only wanted to say hello.'

'Hello, then,' she said, trying not to sound brusque, 'and now, if you'll excuse me...'

'Will I see you this evening?'

'No,' she said. 'I mean, yes. I mean...'

Dammit. She was being rude, and she was babbling, and it was all because of McKenna. She flashed another quick look at the screen. He was still there, smirking. She stuck out her tongue, then rolled her eyes. What had happened to the rational thought process she was so proud of?

'Arthur.' She took a deep breath. 'Are you free for lunch? Because if you are, could you meet me at...' Dana paused and did a mental run-through of the restaurants between Arthur's office and hers. McKenna might eat in any one of them, and he was the last person she wanted to see right now. 'At Portofino,' she said, plucking the name out of the air. It was a name she recalled from a recent review in the *Times*.

'Portofino. Of course. But...all you all right, Dana?'

'I'm fine. It's just... It's just that I need you.'

'Oh, my dear,' Arthur said, and she didn't realize he might have gotten the wrong impression until she was on her way out the door.

But by then, it was too late.

Griffin had been in a lot of restaurants in his life, but never in one that reminded him of a chapel.

If only he'd been paying attention when Cynthia had turned up unexpectedly at his office, smiling her perfect smile, looking as if she'd just stepped out of a bandbox—whatever the hell that might be—asking if he'd like to join her for lunch.

Sure, he'd said, even though he knew he should have come up with some excuse because Cynthia was beginning to push things a little too hard. But his thoughts had been on Dana Anderson, and how much pleasure there'd be in firing her, and the next thing he'd known, he and Cynthia had been standing inside this super-trendy, self-conscious watering hole where violins violined and trysters trysted.

'What *is* this place?' he'd muttered.

'It's called Portofino,' Cynthia had whispered, giving him a tremulous smile. 'Your mother said the *Times* gave it a terrific write-up.'

My mother, the matchmaker, Griffin had thought grimly, but

he'd managed to smile. Apparently, it was time for another little chat. Marilyn McKenna was wise, sophisticated and charming…but she never gave up. She had decided, a couple of years before, that it was time he married and settled down, and she'd switched her considerable energies from her newest charity to getting him to do just that. Poor Cynthia didn't know it, but she was his mother's latest attempt at moving him toward the goal.

'If you'd rather go someplace else,' Cynthia had said, her perfect smile trembling just a little…

'No,' Griffin had said, because that was exactly what'd he been thinking. 'No, this is fine.'

It wasn't fine. The *Times* might love Portofino but as far as he was concerned, the place was a total loser. He liked being able to identify the food on his plate, something you could not do in the artificial twilight of the restaurant, and if the captain or the *sommelier* or the waiter slid by one more time, smiling with oily deference and asking, *sotto voce*, if everything were all right, he was going to say no, by God, it wasn't, and would somebody please turn up the lights, dump half the bordelaise sauce off what might yet prove to be a slab of rare roast beef, and take away these flowers before he started listening for a Bach fugue to come drifting from the kitchen?

Griffin smothered a sigh. The truth was that he'd do no such thing. He'd come here of his own free will, which made paying the consequences for his stupidity an obligation.

The captain had seated them at a table for two behind the perfect fronds of an artificial palm tree. The fronds had dipped into his soup and his salad. Now, they were dipping into his beef.

'Isn't this romantic?' Cynthia sighed.

'Yes,' Griffin said bravely, brushing aside a frond. 'Yes, it is.'

'I just knew you'd like it,' Cynthia said, batting her lashes.

He'd never noticed that before, that she batted her lashes. He'd read the phrase in books but until this moment, he hadn't thought about what it meant. Blink. Blink, blink. It looked weird. Did all women do that, to get a man's attention? He

couldn't imagine the Anderson woman doing it. She'd probably never batted a lash in her life.

'Griffin?'

Griffin looked up. Cynthia was smiling at him. Nothing new
there; she almost always smiled at him. Not like the charming
Ms. Anderson, who always glared.

'Griffin.' Cynthia gave a tinkling little laugh and cocked her
head at a pretty angle. 'You seem to be a million miles away.'

'I'm sorry, Cyn.' Griffin cleared his throat. 'I, ah, I keep
thinking about that conference.'

'The one in Florida? Your mother mentioned it.'

Give me a break, Mother!

'Yes,' he said pleasantly. 'It should be interesting. I've never
been to a software convention before.'

'I envy you,' Cynthia said, and sighed.

Griffin's dark brows angled upward. 'I didn't know you were
interested in computers.'

She laughed gaily. 'Oh, Griffin! Aren't you amusing? I meant
that I envied you for getting away from this cold weather to
spend a long weekend in Florida. I only wish I had that opportunity.'

Griffin's jaw clenched. Marilyn the Matchmaker was really
pushing it this time.

'Yes,' he said politely, 'I suppose it sounds terrific, but I doubt
if I'll even get to set foot on the sand. I'll be too busy rushing
from meeting to meeting.'

'Ah,' Cynthia gazed down at her plate. 'I see.'

Griffin sighed. No. She didn't see. She was a nice girl, but
she was wasting her time. Sooner or later, he was going to have
to find a way to tell her that.

It was true, she would undoubtedly make some man a fine
wife. She was pretty. Actually, she was beautiful. She was well-
educated, too, but she wasn't the kind of woman who was bothered by the fact that she *was* a woman; she understood that there
was a difference between the sexes. Griffin had had enough of

male-bashing broads to last a lifetime. Any man would, who'd come of age within the past couple of decades.

Cynthia was like a breath of fresh air. She had no agenda and no career goals. She didn't look upon men as the enemy. She liked being a woman. She understood the difference between the sexes, and the difference pleased her.

There was no question as to what would make Cynthia happy. She would be content to be a man's helpmate. To bear his children. To stay at home, cook his meals and clean his house... metaphorically, anyway, because, of course, there'd be a staff of servants to do all of that. The point was, Cynthia would not want the rules bent to accommodate her. She wouldn't leave you wondering if she'd say 'thank you' if you opened her car door for her or accuse you of trying to treat her as if she were the weaker sex.

Griffin knew that if he'd been looking for a wife, he'd have looked no further.

But he wasn't looking for a wife. Not yet. Maybe not ever. His life was full and exciting, just the way it was. He loved his work, and his freedom, the right to come and go as he pleased, when he pleased. Not that he didn't enjoy curtailing that freedom from time to time. The world was full of gorgeous women who were eager to share his life for a few weeks or months, no commitments asked. They were not wife material, his mother had said more than once, and each time she did, Griffin nodded thoughtfully and breathed a silent prayer of thanks that they were not.

But—and it was one hell of a big 'but'—if he ever did decide it was time to settle down, and if Cynthia was still available, he might just look her up. He liked her well enough; he supposed he could even learn to love her...and if he couldn't imagine taking her in his arms, the way he'd thought about taking Dana Anderson in his arms, and making love on the warm sands of a tropical beach, so what? Wild passion wasn't what married life was all about.

Griffin frowned. Dammit, it wasn't what the Anderson woman was all about, either. Why did he keep thinking about her and that silly beach?

Ms. Anderson, making love on a beach. The very idea was laughable. She'd probably never had a date in her life. She'd probably never...

Griffin jerked back in his seat.

No. It couldn't be!

But it was. There, directly across the restaurant, tucked away in a cozy little nook, sat Dana Anderson...and a man.

What was she doing here? Griffin would have bet anything that she had her lunch in a health food store, or quaffed yogurt at her desk. Instead, here she was amidst the palm fronds and velvet drapes in the pseudo-romantic, sickeningly phony confines of Portofino. And she was with a guy.

An attentive one.

Griffin's frown deepened.

The man could have been chosen for her by central casting. He was perfect, from his tortoise-shells to the bow tie that bobbed on his Adam's apple.

'Monsieur?'

Griffin looked up. The waiter hovered beside the table.

'Do *monsieur* and *madame* wish dessert? A *tarte*, perhaps, or a *Madeline Supreme*?'

What Griffin wanted was to keep watching the Anderson babe and her boyfriend, but Cynthia had that I'm-hurt-but-I'mbeing-brave look on her face again. The waiter, who seemed to see nothing strange in a French menu and a French accent in a restaurant named for a town in Portugal and warned, perhaps, by the look on Griffin's face, drew back as if expecting to be attacked.

Griffin did his best to smile politely.

'Nothing for me, thank you,' he said. 'Cyn? What will you have?'

Cynthia listened attentively while the waiter made his way

through a seemingly endless list. Anderson—*Ms*. Anderson—wasn't doing much of anything. She certainly wasn't eating. Griffin couldn't fault her for that. He couldn't see her plate very clearly, thanks to the near-darkness that hung over the room like a pall, but from what he could observe, she was eating what looked like a taxidermist's special.

And the Bow Tie was worried. You could see it on his face. He was looking at Anderson the way a puppy looks at an out-of-reach bone.

Well, who could blame him? Despite the plastered-back hair, the tweed jacket and the loose-fitting twill trousers, Dana Anderson was something to look at.

Griffin frowned. Yeah, well, piranhas were interesting to look at, too.

The guy said something. Anderson started to answer, stopped, then began to speak. She was really getting into it now, gesturing with her hands, leaning forward and risking immolation from the candles flickering in the floral centerpiece. She took the guy's hand in hers, and the idiot positively beamed. There was no other way to describe it.

He was smiling so hard it looked as if his ears might start glowing, and why wouldn't he? Anderson was looking at him as if he were St. George standing over the dead body of the dragon when, in reality, the guy looked as if a strong breeze might blow him over.

One corner of Griffin's mouth turned down. This was the Anderson babe's sort of man, all right. A guy she could lead around by the nose. Somebody who'd never want her to dance for him on a deserted stretch of sand, while the moon looked down and the drums pulsed out a beat that matched the fire in his blood...

'Griffin? Griffin, are you all right?'

Griffin pulled back from the edge of the precipice and looked across at Cynthia. 'Yes,' he said calmly. 'Yes, I'm perfectly fine.'

And he was.

It was just curiosity that had him wondering what could be keeping Dana Anderson's attention so tightly focused on the man she was with.

'You aren't eating, Dana. Is something wrong with your fish?'

Dana sighed. Arthur was looking at her with concern. Well, no wonder. She'd called and asked him to meet her for lunch, and now she was sitting here like a piece of wood, saying nothing, doing nothing, just watching her own grim reflection in the lenses of his horn-rimmed glasses.

'No,' she said, forcing a smile to her lips. 'No, the fish is fine, Arthur. Just fine.'

It *was* fine. She assumed so, anyway, because the truth was that she hadn't eaten enough of it to know. It was just that Portofino served fish complete with head and tail. The tail didn't bother her but the head was another story. The finny creature lay draped across her plate on a bed of something that looked suspiciously like kelp, its thin mouth turned down, its glassy eye turned up and fixed on the cherubim painted on the gilded ceiling.

Dana repressed a shudder. She'd never been good with food that looked as if it might get up and walk off her plate—or swim off, as the case might be. Besides, if this morning's runin with McKenna had dimmed her appetite, the atmosphere in Portofino had finished it off completely.

She'd had no idea the place dealt in such overblown decor. If she had, she'd never have suggested it.

No wonder poor Arthur kept looking at her that way, with a little smile on his lips and his gaze expectant and misty behind his horn-rims. Her phone call, her choice of words, even her choice of restaurants, must have convinced him that romance was in the air.

Dana cleared her throat, lay her knife and fork across her plate, and folded her hands in her lap.

'Arthur,' she said gently, 'I'm afraid I may have misled you.'

'I knew it,' he said, 'you really *don't* like the fish! Where is our waiter? I'll ask him to bring you something else.'

Dana sat forward and put her hand on his. 'The fish isn't the problem.'

Arthur's brows lifted. 'It isn't?'

'The problem's...' She frowned. McKenna, was what she'd thought. But what she'd almost said was, me. Me, you, us, Arthur. We're just not right for each other.

But it wasn't true. They *were* right for each other; it was only that she was in an insane mood today. Just look at how she'd treated that poor custodian. She owed him an apology, and she'd give it to him first thing this afternoon, but right now, she was going to let Arthur help her get back on an even track.

He could do it, if anyone could.

'The problem,' she said, clearing her throat, 'is Griffin McKenna.'

Arthur blinked. Just for a moment, it made him bear an uncanny resemblance to her glassy-eyed fish.

'Your employer? My dear Dana, I don't understand. What has he to do with our lunch?'

'Nothing, Arthur. He has to do with me. With my job, with my self-respect, with my responsibilities at Data Bytes.' She drew back her hand and sat upright. 'You cannot imagine how much I despise that man.'

Arthur sighed. 'My dear Dana—'

'Do you think you could stop saying that?'

'Saying what, my dear?'

Dana forced a smile to her lips. 'Nothing. I'm sorry. I just— I've had a bad morning, that's all. My nerves are shot. That's why I called you. I need your advice.'

'You need...' Arthur's smile dimmed just a little, then brightened again. 'I'm at your disposal, of course.'

'There's a problem at work, with my boss and the code we've been working on. I tried to tell McKenna about it, but he wouldn't listen.'

'That's surprising, Dana. Griffin McKenna is a brilliant strategist. According to the *Journal*...'

'The *Journal* doesn't bother mentioning that he's a pompous ass! I hate working for him.' Dana paused. 'So, I'm asking for your opinion.'

Arthur's bow tie rode up and down his Adam's apple. 'I'm flattered, my dear.'

'Should I start looking for another job?' 'Well, if you ask me—'

'Or should I ride it out? McKenna won't stay at Data Bytes forever, but Dave Forrester probably will.'

'True. And—'

'But, if I quit, what kind of references would I get?' 'An excellent ques—'

'On the other hand, what can I accomplish by staying on? Forrester's just going to keep screwing up and McKenna's going to keep treating me as if I'm a troublemaker.'

'I see. If you think—'

'He'll fire me anyway, when the new code blows up tomorrow. But if I quit before then, he'll think he forced me out.' Dana's eyes narrowed. 'I refuse to give him that satisfaction.'

'Well,' Arthur said quickly, 'if you really want my opinion—'

'I might not need references. I know lots of people in this business. I could find a job, a better job, then tell McKenna what he can do with this one!'

'True. But—'

'But that would be giving in. And I won't do that. I'll never do that!' Dana seized Arthur's hand. 'Oh, I'm so glad I asked your advice! Thank you for helping me come to a logical decision.'

Arthur blinked. 'Ah...you're very welcome.'

'You're wonderful, you know. You're so clear-headed.'

A pink glow suffused Arthur's cheeks. His fingers tightened on hers, and he leaned forward until his bow tie lay nestled among the daisies and tea roses that separated them from each other.

'Thank you, my dear.'

'Thank *you.*'

Beaming with delight, Arthur lifted her hand to his lips.

'Monsieur.' The waiter favored them with the hint of a smile. 'Would you and mademoiselle care for some *cafe* and dessert? Some *sorbet*, perhaps, or an excellent *tarte...'*

'Nothing, thank you,' Dana said. She smiled at Arthur as she rose to her feet. 'I feel rejuvenated, thanks to you, Arthur. And I'm really eager to get back to work.'

Cynthia was talking, something about a luncheon she'd attended with his mother. Griffin was trying to pay attention, but how could he, after that incredible display? The Bow Tie had kissed Anderson's hand, and she'd given him a thousand-watt smile in return.

Anderson rose to her feet. So did the Bow Tie. And they headed straight in his direction.

Griffin's jaw tightened. He tossed his napkin on the table and shoved back his chair.

'Griffin?' Cynthia said.

Anderson was holding the guy's arm as they came down the aisle, looking at him as if he were the only man alive.

'Griffin?' Cynthia asked, 'are we leaving already?'

Griffin stepped away from the table, folded his arms and waited. The estimable Ms. Anderson was still chattering away, smiling brightly, her head tilted toward the Bow Tie.

Griffin felt a tightness in his belly. She had never looked at him like that. Not that he'd want her to, but still, it was infuriating. She'd given him the kind of look you gave tapioca pudding when you had it shoved in front of you. How come she was gazing at Bow Tie and damn near glowing?

'... Don't know what I'd do without you,' she was saying. 'You're so good for me.'

They were going to walk right into him. Griffin almost smiled as he anticipated her shock. But at the last second, Bow

Tie pulled his adoring gaze from Anderson's face, looked up, and saw Griffin standing, immobile, directly in their path.

To say he blanched was to be kind. The guy turned as white as paper.

'Mr. McKenna!'

Anderson nodded. 'That's right,' she said. 'That's all you hear around the office. Mr. McKenna this and Mr. McKenna that, spoken in such hushed tones that, frankly, sometimes I just want to—'

'Now, now,' Griffin said coolly. His lips curved into a tight smile as she skidded to a dead stop not more than six inches off his chest. 'Be careful what you say, Ms. Anderson. We're in a public place, after all.'

Dana's heart slammed into her throat. 'You,' she croaked as she looked into the scowling face towering above her.

'Indeed, Ms. Anderson. What a small world.'

Dana's thoughts were whirling. McKenna? And a woman who looked as if she'd just stepped out of the fashion pages? But that was impossible. She'd chosen this restaurant with such care! McKenna wasn't supposed to be here.

And why didn't he step back? Why didn't *Arthur* step back? Then, at least, she'd have room to breathe. She wouldn't have to stand so close to McKenna's hard body that she had to tilt her head at a neck-breaking angle just so she could look him in the eye.

'Introduce us,' Arthur hissed in her ear.

'Did you enjoy your meal, *Ms.* Anderson?'

'Dana,' Arthur whispered, 'please. Intro—'

'What are you doing here?' Dana said.

Griffin's scowl deepened. 'Having lunch, Ms. Anderson. And you?'

'I don't mean *what* are you doing here, Mr. McKenna, I mean…' God! What *did* she mean? Dana straightened her shoulders. 'Excuse me,' she said coldly, 'but I'd like to get by.'

'Oh, I'm sure you would.'

'Mr. McKenna. I am on my lunch hour.'

McKenna's brows rose. 'Is that a fact,' he said pleasantly.

Dammit all, why didn't Arthur step back and give her some room? Dana shoved her elbow into Arthur's middle and shot him an angry look, but he didn't notice. How could he, when he was staring at Griffin McKenna with the look of a deer caught in the headlights?

Dana firmed her jaw, stepped back and planted her foot firmly on Arthur's toes. That made him move, all right, not much but enough so that now she didn't have to inhale faint whiffs of McKenna's cologne with every breath she took.

'It is,' she said. 'And now, if you'll excuse us, Mr. McKenna, I'll see you back at the office.'

Griffin nodded. 'Indeed you shall, Miss—oh, sorry—*Ms.* Anderson.'

How could the man make the correction of her name sound like an insult? Dana's cheeks burned as she maneuvered past him and headed for the door.

Arthur stepped in front of her when they reached the sidewalk.

'Why didn't you introduce me, Dana?'

She glared past him, at the restaurant, as if McKenna might materialize at any moment.

'The nerve of him,' she said, 'the damned nerve!' 'You should have introduced us. It was a wonderful oppor—'

'Did you see him? Did you *see* him?'

'Of course, I saw him.'

'Don't be dense, Arthur. I mean, did you see him? The way he stood there, with that look on his face!'

'What must he be thinking? Common courtesy demands—'

'Courtesy is uncommon, Arthur, haven't you figured that out yet?' Dana blew a strand of streaky blond hair out of her eyes. 'And that woman with him. Miss Perfection.'

'Actually, I thought she was rather attrac—'

'The polite little smile. The perfect hair. The elegant suit. The la-di-da air.'

Arthur frowned in bewilderment. 'La-di-da air?'

'So ladylike. So unruffled. So—so unthreatening, to the master's masculinity!'

'Dana, really, I fail to see what you're so upset about.'

'That's just the point, Arthur. You fail to see, but that's because…because…'

Because what? What *was* she so upset about? McKenna had been in the same restaurant as she'd been, he'd been having lunch with a beautiful woman. So what?

'If I have to explain it,' she said loftily, 'there's no point. Goodbye, Arthur. Thank you for lunch.'

She swept past him, chin lifted, and started toward the corner. Arthur stared after her for a couple of seconds before hurrying to catch up.

'Dana, my dear, let's not quarrel.'

'We haven't quarreled. I just don't see how you can let yourself be taken in by Griffin McKenna.'

'I haven't been taken in. I just…' Arthur sighed. 'Never mind. Are we still on for dinner this evening?'

'Yes. No. I'm not sure. Why don't you phone me later?'

'Dinner,' Arthur said more firmly than usual. 'All right?'

Dana sighed. 'All right,' she said. 'I'll see you at seven.'

Dave Forrester, who had not yet succumbed to his afternoon ration of vodka, was lounging in the doorway to Dana's office when she returned. He greeted her with an enigmatic look.

'Had a good lunch, did you, Dana?'

'What's that supposed to mean?'

Forrester grinned. 'Boss wants to see you.'

Dana didn't reply. She turned and walked down the hall to McKenna's office, telling herself as she did that she was not about to take any more nonsense from the man and telling herself, too, that it was a good thing she'd spoken with Arthur because now she was calm, she was very calm, and nothing Griffin McKenna did or said could get under her skin anymore.

Miss Macy greeted her with a look that mimicked Forrester's. Were enigmatic looks the order of the day?

'Mr. McKenna is waiting for you, Miss Anderson.'

'It's Ms.,' Dana said, and stepped into McKenna's office. He was sitting behind his desk, looking the length of the room at her, like an emperor on his throne. 'You wanted to see me, Mr. McKenna?'

'Shut the door please, Ms. Anderson.'

Dana complied, then faced him again. 'Mr. McKenna. If this is about our bumping into each other at that restaurant—'

'Where you eat is no concern of mine. You may eat what you wish, where you wish, with whomever you wish.'

'How generous of you, sir,' Dana smiled sweetly. 'In that case, what did you want to see me about?'

McKenna smiled, too, like a cat contemplating a cageful of canaries.

'You're fired.'

'I beg your pardon?'

'Fired, Ms. Anderson. As in, clean out your desk, collect your severance pay, and don't come back.'

Fired? *Fired?* Dana's vision blurred. All the logic of the last hour fled in the face of Griffin McKenna's self-indulgent smile.

'You can't fire me,' she snapped. 'I quit!'

Griffin tilted back his chair and laced his hands behind his head.

'Have it your way, Ms. Anderson. Frankly, I don't give a damn, just as long as we agree that you are no longer in my employ.'

Maybe it was the way he said it, in that know-it-all, holier-than-thou tone. Maybe it was the insufferable smile, or the way he tilted back that damn chair. All Dana knew was that, suddenly, she'd reached the breaking point.

She stomped across the room, snatched a stack of papers from his desk, and flung them high into the air.

'You,' she said, 'are a complete, absolute, unmitigated jerk.'

Griffin looked at Dana. She was breathing as hard as if she'd just finished a five-mile run. Her eyes blazed with green fire, and she looked as if she could happily kill him.

Something in his belly knotted. Slowly, his eyes never leaving hers, he kicked back his chair, rose to his feet and came around the desk.

'And you,' he said, 'are a woman in need of a lesson.'

'In what?' Dana said furiously.

'In the fact that the world is owned by men like you?'

A dangerous smile curved across Griffin's mouth. For the second time in her life, and the second time that afternoon, Dana wanted to step back. But she didn't. To give way would have been a mistake.

Standing her ground turned out to be the bigger mistake. It meant that when Griffin reached for her, he had no trouble pulling her straight into his arms.

'In the fact that women have their uses, Ms. Anderson,' he said, and then he bent his head, laced his fingers into her hair, and kissed her.

CHAPTER THREE

IT WASN'T MUCH of a kiss, as kisses went.

No bells. No fireworks. No explosion of colors behind Dana's closed eyelids.

Not that she'd deliberately shut her eyes. It had been reflex, that was all. And she certainly hadn't expected bells or fireworks. That was the stuff of women's novels, those silly books that were all fantasy.

It was only that somehow, when a man like Griffin McKenna kissed you, you thought—you sort of assumed—dammit, you *expected*...

Expected?

She *hadn't* expected. That was just the point. McKenna had hauled her into his arms and sent her straight into shock. And that, plain and simple, was what he'd counted on.

Dana exploded into action, twisting free of McKenna's grasp, balling her hand into a fist and whamming it into his middle. It was like pounding her knuckles against a rock but it was worth it. Oh, yes, it certainly was, just to see the look of astonishment spread across that too-handsome-for-its-own-good face.

'Hey,' he said, sounding indignant. Dana's blood pressure soared.

'Hey? *Hey?*' She jabbed her forefinger into his chest. It was steely, too, like his middle, so she jabbed again, a lot harder. 'Is that all you have to say for yourself, you—you beetle-browed Neanderthal?'

'Now, wait just a—'

'How dare you, McKenna? How *dare* you kiss me?'

She paused for breath and Griffin opened his mouth, determined to get a word in while he could...and then he shut it again. She was waiting for an answer. She *deserved* an answer. Unfortunately, he didn't have one.

Why *had* he kissed her? It was an excellent question. She'd stood there, glowering at him, drawing a line in the dust, so to speak, women on one side, men on the other. So what? You didn't kiss a woman because she didn't like men. You didn't look at the sexual chip on her shoulder and see it as a dare.

On the other hand, that was damn well what it was. And facing down dares had been the story of his life, starting with the day he'd inherited his father's fortune along with a note handed over by John McKenna's embarrassed attorney, a note that had contained a line he'd never forget.

Here's my fortune, Griffin, his father had written. *I worked a lifetime to build it. How long will you take to waste it?*

That challenge, even though it had been given by a man who'd never had time for his wife or son, had driven a knife into Griffin's heart. But he'd risen to it, perhaps beyond it, and built an empire he was proud of, one that might even have impressed his father.

But what kind of dare was there in hauling an unwilling woman into your arms?

None. Absolutely none whatsoever. So, why had he done it?

Griffin frowned. Damned if he could come up with a reason. A lesson, he'd said, but what lesson? Not even he believed in all that old crap he'd spouted about a woman's place being in the kitchen and in the bedroom.

Okay, so he didn't like the kind of female who saw men as the enemy. Who eagerly awaited the day they could reproduce by cloning and let the opposite sex kill themselves off, trying to gather a harem.

That didn't mean he belonged to the 'knock 'em in the head, toss 'em over your shoulder, drag 'em off to the cave' crowd, either—and yet, how else could you describe what he'd just done?

'Your silence is eloquent, McKenna.'

Griffin focused on Dana's face, still flushed with anger.

'I take it to mean that even you are aware that the days are long gone when a man could get away with coming on to a woman as if they were both decked out in animal skins!'

Griffin's frown deepened. She was right, that was the damnedest part. It was what had kept him from *really* kissing her, the sudden realization, once he'd had her in his arms, that there was absolutely no rational explanation for what he was doing, that the 'Me man, you woman' thing had never held any appeal for him.

By God, much as he hated to admit it, he owed her an apology.

He cleared his throat.

'Miss Anderson—'

'*Ms.*,' she said, her tone frigid enough to freeze water. 'Or are you memory-impaired, as well as hormonally imbalanced?'

A muscle ticked in Griffin's jaw. 'Ms. Anderson,' he said, telling himself to stay calm, 'I suppose I— I mean, I guess, maybe—'

He couldn't say it. Why should he apologize, when she was glowering at him as if he were something that had just crawled out from under a rock?

Because it's the right thing to do, McKenna, that's why.

Hell, he thought, and he thrust his hand into his hair, shoving the dark locks back from his forehead, and told himself to try again.

'Listen,' he said. 'Listen, Ms. Anderson—'

'No,' Her eyes, those green, green eyes that could be so filled with heat one second and so icy cold the next, fixed on his. 'No,' she repeated, punctuating each word with a poke to his sternum, '*you* listen, Mr. McKenna!'

Griffin caught hold of Dana's wrist. 'Ms. Anderson, if you'd just calm down—'

'Unhand me, Mr. McKenna!'

Unhand me? Griffin stifled a chuckle. It didn't take a genius to know that laughter would only make her more furious, but hell, *unhand me...*

'I said...'

'I heard you,' He let go of her wrist, screwed his face into an expression he hoped would communicate apology, and started over. 'Ms. Anderson, I'd like to tell you—'

'I'm not the least bit interested in anything you have to say, McKenna—but you might be interested in what *I* have to tell *you*,' She smiled, put her hands on her hips, and tilted back her head so that their eyes met. 'In fact, I'm certain of it. It's going to wipe that—that stupid grin right off your face!'

'Ms. Anderson. I can assure you, I am not grinning. I am not even smiling. If you'd just keep quiet for a minute and let me talk—'

Her index finger made another dent in the front of his shirt. 'Your lawyers will have to do the talking, because I, Mr. Mc-Kenna, am going to see to it that every woman in New

York knows exactly what kind of man you are!' Griffin's eyes narrowed. 'Stop poking at me.'

'Did you hear what I said? I'm going to sue the pants off you!'

His hand clamped down on hers. 'Did you hear what *I* said, Anderson? I am not a human pincushion!'

'Let go of me!'

'When you calm down, I'll let go.'

'I am calm. Completely calm. Calm enough to assure you that the Griffin McKenna who—who swashes his way through life is in deep trouble.'

'Swashes?' Griffin couldn't help it. This time, he did laugh. 'What in hell does that mean?'

'Go ahead. Laugh. Laugh all the way to court because you'll never laugh again, after I get done suing you for sexual harassment.'

'You're joking.'

'Do I look as if I'm joking?'

Griffin considered. What she looked was furious. Indignant. Righteous...and out and out gorgeous. He could feel her pulse leaping just under the soft skin at her wrist. Her eyes were the color of the Atlantic off Cape Cod, just before a storm. Her cheeks were the tender color of new roses. And, somehow or other, her hair had come undone.

Somehow or other? His body tightened. Why was he being so modest? He knew how her hair had come undone. He had done it, plunging his hands into it when he'd kissed her.

But he hadn't kissed her. Not really. The thought had been there, even the intention, but before he'd had time to get started, the knowledge of exactly what he was doing had broken through his anger and he'd clamped down on the kiss so that it had been nothing more than a touch of his mouth against hers.

If he'd kissed her, really kissed her, it would have been more than that. He'd have drawn her close against his body, held her so that he could feel the softness of her breasts against his chest. He'd have parted her lips with his, tasted all the heat bottled inside her, savored the silkiness of her mouth—that soft-looking, sweet mouth. He'd have inhaled her scent, whispered her name, accepted her surrender as she wound her arms around his neck....

'—anything to say?'

Griffin blinked and let go of her hand. 'What?'

'For a man who's always barking orders, you don't seem to

have much to say right now.' Dana glared. 'Maybe you think I'm joking about slapping you with a lawsuit for sexual harassment!'

'Look, Anderson, if you want an apology—'

'An apology?' Dana said in a way that made his hackles rise. 'You've got to be joking. What I want is your neck in the noose of the law,' She shot him a smile that would have bared her fangs, if she'd had any. 'And believe me, that's just what I'm going to do. I am going to sue you for every cent you've got, McKenna. And when I'm done, the entire world will know just what a sexist rat fink you are.'

Gorgeous, but nuts, Griffin thought, and folded his arms over his chest.

'Listen here, lady—'

'I am not a lady!'

'Damn right, you aren't.'

'Don't twist my words, McKenna! You know what I mean. I am *not* a lady, I am a human being. A person. And I don't have to take any nonsense from the likes of you.'

'If you'd just shut up for two minutes, you'd know that I've been trying to apologize.'

'For what?'

'For kissing you, that's for what.'

'It's too late. You've already done it.'

Griffin swore. 'Of course, I've already done it! How in hell could I apologize if I...' He stopped, counted silently to five, and tried again. 'Look, let's not make a mountain out of a molehill.'

Dana folded her arms, too. 'You're the mole who's building the mountain, not me.'

'Okay. Okay, you want to sue me?' Griffin glared at her. 'Sue me, then.'

'I intend to.'

'Assuming, that is, you can find some shyster lawyer to take the case.'

'Any lawyer worth her salt will jump at the chance, McKenna.'

'Any lawyer with half a brain will burst your bubble, Anderson.' He smiled smugly. 'You can't sue me.'

'Says who?'

'Says logic. You don't work for me anymore, remember?'

Was he right? Dana felt a moment's panic. She couldn't let him get away with what he'd done...or with that one instant when she'd wished he'd done more.

'That has nothing to do with it,' she said. 'This is America. I can sue anybody I want to sue.'

'Dammit, don't wag your finger in my face!'

'I'll wag it anywhere I choose. I don't work for you anymore, as you so generously pointed out. I don't have to take orders.'

'You're right,' he said grimly. 'You don't have to take orders. And I don't have to be polite.'

'Polite? You?' Dana laughed. 'You wouldn't know how to be polite if Emily Post gave you private lessons!'

'Emily Post is dead!'

'Your reputation will be, too, when I'm done with my lawsuit!'

'Do you ever step down from that soapbox, Anderson?'

'What soapbox?'

'The one marked 'neuter' where it says 'gender.''

'That's pathetic, McKenna.'

'It's the truth. Forrester was right about you.'

'Forrester?' Dana frowned. 'What does he have to do with this?'

'He tried telling me what you were, from day one. He said you were a frustrated broad who hated all men as a matter of principle.'

Dana's face flushed crimson with anger. 'I won't even justify that with a response.'

'Why? Does it hit too close to home?'

'Step into the twenty-first century, McKenna. Women who choose careers over marriage are not frustrated.'

Griffin smiled coldly. 'Got a torrid thing going with the Bow Tie, do you?'

'You are truly pathetic!'

'I'm a man, is what you mean.'

'You're an anachronism, and since there are too many syllables in that word for you to understand it, let me explain it to you.'

'Oh, by all means, Anderson. Please do.'

'You, Mr. McKenna, are a man who still thinks a woman's place is in the home.'

Griffin looked at Dana. Her hair, so neatly arranged until he'd touched it, flew wildly about her flushed cheeks. Anger had put glints of fire in her eyes, and her breath was coming so fast that not even the dowdy blouse and tailored jacket could disguise the upthrust roundness of her breasts.

Something dark and dangerous seemed to uncoil deep within him. Don't, a voice inside him warned. But Griffin was a man who'd never refused a challenge, especially one he'd imposed on himself.

'You're wrong,' he said in a tone as cold as his blood was hot. 'I've always known exactly where women really belong.'

He reached out, tugged her into his arms, and kissed her again.

It was nothing like the kiss of minutes ago. That was Dana's first thought.

Her second was that New York had to be undergoing an earthquake, because she could feel the floor tilt beneath her feet.

His mouth had been cool when he'd kissed her before. Now it was hot. Hot, and hard—though, even as she thought it, his lips softened, shaped hers, and opened her to him.

The rotten bastard, she thought…and then, with absolutely no warning, she was tumbling into heat and darkness, the floor was not just tilting, it was turning, and the only thing she could do was curl her fingers into the lapels of Griffin's jacket and hang on.

Someone made a soft, moaning sound. Was it she? It had to be, because Griffin wasn't moaning. He was making a low sound in the back of his throat, something between a growl and a purr. And he was drawing her closer against him, holding her tightly in his arms, so that their bodies were meshed, breast to breast, belly to belly, toe to toe.

His hands swept down her back, cupped her bottom and lifted her against him. She felt the hardness of his erection press against her.

What am I doing? she thought crazily, and she lifted her arms and wound them tightly around Griffin's neck. Her fingers plunged into his hair; her breath quickened. She whimpered as his teeth closed lightly on her bottom lip, as he sucked the tender flesh into the heat of his mouth...

And then, as suddenly as he'd taken her in his arms, Griffin cupped her elbows, put her away from him, and stepped back.

Dana swayed, blinked her eyes open—and looked straight into his expressionless face.

'You see?' he said very calmly. 'Women do have their uses.'

'What?' she said in a hoarse whisper.

'I said, you have no case, Ms. Anderson.'

'No...' Dana swallowed dryly. 'No case?'

Griffin's smile crooked at the corner of his mouth. He rocked back on his heels and tucked his hands into his trouser pockets.

'None at all. Unless, of course, you're prepared to have me describe, in excruciating detail, every last second of our little encounter.'

Dana put her hand to her throat. 'You mean—you mean, you deliberately...'

'Did you think I was overwhelmed by passion, Ms. Anderson?' The arrogant smile became an egotistical grin. 'Perhaps I should refresh your memory. You sighed. You moaned. You—'

Color flamed in her face. 'I did not!'

'Moaned,' he said pleasantly. 'And you damn near strangled me when you wrapped your arms around my neck.'

'You rat! You swine! You no good—'

'And then, of course, there's the way you opened your mouth. And kissed me back. Very effective move, Ms. Anderson. And nicely done.'

'You—you—you—'

He caught her wrist as her hand flew toward him, and drew it down to her side.

'Think about it,' he said softly. The smile was gone from his face now. In its place was a look so cold it made Dana's breath catch. 'Do you really want to pursue a lawsuit that will only prove my point?'

'What point?' Dana said, her voice trembling with anger. 'That you're detestable?'

'That you're exactly what I said you were, Anderson. A frustrated female, in desperate need of...' He paused delicately. '... Male attention.'

She struggled, desperately, to control herself. She knew what he wanted, that she should weep or rage or do whatever he thought women were supposed to do when things went against them. In his mind, she'd already become a stereotype. She'd behaved as he'd expected because, somehow, he'd managed to put her off balance more times than she'd have thought possible.

But it wouldn't happen again. Women—strong, independent women—should always be in firm control of themselves, and of their destinies. Hadn't she learned that in childhood, watching her mother tolerate her stepfather's ugly domination? Dana had vowed, years ago, that she would never bend to any man's will.

But she'd bent to this man. He'd gotten her to lose her composure. Her sanity. Why else would she have returned his kiss? And that was what she'd done; there was no sense lying to herself about it.

How could she have done that? How *could* she?

'Nothing to say, *Ms.* Anderson?'

His tone mocked her. Dana stiffened and looked into that handsome, self-assured face.

'Nothing at all,' she said calmly. 'Except that if I ever have the misfortune to set eyes on you again, Mr. McKenna, I won't hesitate to wrap a crowbar around your thick skull.'

Griffin turned his back and strolled to his desk. 'I'll be sure never to give you the opportunity. Now, if we're finished here, I'll phone Payroll and have them draw your check.'

'Be sure to include the three weeks severance pay that I'm entitled to.'

He glanced up. It pleased her to see a glimmer of surprise in his eyes.

'I'll do that.'

Dana nodded. She turned briskly and walked to the door. At the last second, hand on the knob, she looked back. McKenna, seated behind his desk, had already put her out of his mind. He was concentrating on a paper in front of him, frowning and making quick notes on it with his pen.

'McKenna?' He looked up, and she smiled tightly. 'Just for the record...'

'Yes?'

'That moan you thought you heard?' Her smile widened until it glittered. 'Actually, it was me, trying not to retch. I guess we're both fortunate that you let me go when you did.'

It wasn't much, as curtain lines went, she thought as she slammed the door and marched past a startled Miss Macy. But anything was better than letting Griffin McKenna think his kiss had affected her. It was the suddenness of it that had affected her, that, and all the emotional ups and downs of the last few weeks.

Why hadn't she realized that so she could have told him so a few minutes ago, when he was standing there and gloating?

Not that it mattered. She had seen the last of Mighty McKenna.

'Goodbye, and good riddance,' she muttered, and she picked up her pace and headed down the hall to Payroll.

Safe inside his office, Griffin let out his breath as the door slammed shut.

He put down the paper he'd pretended to read, tossed aside his pen, and ran his fingers through his hair.

What had gotten into him?

Kissing Anderson once had been stupid, but kissing her twice? That had been insane. She hadn't wanted him to kiss her, and he was not a man whose ego was so big that it kept him from understanding that when a woman said 'no,' 'no' was what she meant.

Besides, he didn't even like Dana Anderson.

Griffin shoved back his chair and got to his feet. Didn't like her? He almost laughed as he stood at the window, staring down into the canyon of skyscrapers around him. That had to be the understatement of the year. The redoubtable Ms. Anderson would never, not in a lifetime, make it onto a list of women he'd hope to be stranded with on a deserted island, not even if every female on the planet suddenly vanished, except for her.

So, how come he'd kissed her the second time? How come that second kiss had left him feeling as if all the air had been sucked out of his lungs? And when she'd risen up on her toes, looped those slender arms around his neck...when she'd done that, what little remained of his control had all but fled. He'd wanted to carry Dana Anderson to the sofa, lay her down upon it and make love to her until neither of them had the strength to move.

Griffin shuddered. At least he'd come to his senses in time. He'd been a breath away from tearing off her clothes—and she'd have let him, he knew that as surely as he knew his own name—when his brain had said 'hello' and his hormones had said 'goodbye.' He'd shoved her away, come up with an explanation fast enough to make his head spin, and then he'd had to climb out of the hole he'd been busily digging under his own feet.

'Damn,' Griffin said softly, and shook his head.

'Sir?'

He swung around. Miss Macy was standing in the doorway, her bushy brows raised in inquiry.

'I knocked, sir, but—'

'What is it, Miss Macy?'

'Payroll telephoned, sir. Miss Anderson is there, asking about a check.'

'Yes,' he said briskly, 'that's correct. Miss Anderson's been terminated. Tell Payroll I said they're to write her a check for the week, and to include whatever severance pay she's entitled to.'

'Certainly, Mr. McKenna. Will that be all?'

No, Griffin thought. Get me the number of a good psychiatrist.

'Yes,' he said, 'thank you, Miss Macy. That will be all.'

The dragon turned, hurried to the door, then paused and looked back at him.

'Oh, Mr. McKenna? I have those documents ready for you, sir. Do you want to go through them, or shall I put them into your attache case?'

Griffin tried to figure out what in hell she was talking about, and failed.

'Documents?'

'Yes, sir. For your trip to Florida tomorrow. The work-ups, the specification sheets... Did you want to see them again?'

Florida. Tomorrow. Griffin almost groaned. He'd managed to forget all about the convention, the appointments, and the new program—a program that was still flawed, thanks to the bumbling efforts of the charming Ms. Anderson.

'Sir?'

'I suppose I'd better take one last look, Miss Macy. Yes, please, bring me the papers. And phone Dave Forrester. Tell him I'd like to see him ASAP.'

Moments later, Griffin was elbow-deep in printouts of what might as well have been gibberish. After a while, he shoved everything aside and massaged his temples with the tips of his fingers.

Who was he kidding? Reading this stuff was like reading Sanskrit. He knew how to use computers, not how to program them. He'd just have to rely on Dave's expertise. He'd have to rely on him for a lot of things, if this program wasn't up and running by tonight, which was just one more thing to lay in Dana Anderson's lap.

It was too damn bad he hadn't fired her the minute Dave had launched his first complaint.

Griffin frowned and looked at his watch. Where was Forrester, anyway?

Leaning forward, he hit a button on his telephone.

'Miss Macy,' he said. 'Would you please ring Dave Forrester again, and—'

The door swung open. Griffin looked up. Miss Macy looked back at him, her hands clasped tightly against her flat bosom.

'Mr. McKenna,' she gasped, 'I tried to stop him, sir, but—'

A man shoved past her. Griffin rose to his feet.

'Dave?' he said.

It was Dave, all right, but a Dave he'd never seen before. Forrester's eyes were red and shiny, he had a stain down the front of his shirt, and he was wearing a big, loopy grin.

'Dave?' Griffin said again, 'what is this?'

'You fired her,' Forrester said, listing to the right.

Griffin nodded. 'Anderson? Yeah. I did. I just wish I'd listened to you all along and... What's going on here, Dave? Are you sick?'

'I'm fine. I'm A-OK, ol' buddy,' Dave grinned again and listed to the left. Griffin hurried forward and grabbed his arm. 'Good riddance to bad rubbish, is what I say, ya know?'

'Dave,' Griffin said cautiously, 'come and sit down. Miss

Macy? I wonder if you might check and see if there's a doctor in the building.'

'I doan need a doctor,' Forrester said, and hiccuped.

It was the hiccup that did it. Griffin drew back, grimacing. 'Dammit, Forrester, you smell like a brewery!'

'A distill'ry,' Forrester said, and chuckled. "At's twelve-year-old Scotch, Griff, old man.' He winked and leaned in close. 'Ran outta vodka a li'l while ago. Wouldn't put it past that busybody to have stolen my stash 'n tossed it out.'

'Busybody?' Griffin said, trying not to inhale as he half dragged Forrester toward the sofa.

'The Anderson broad. She's always pokin' her nose where it doesn't belong.'

Griffin felt himself grow cold. 'She said you were a drunk,' he said, looking at his old friend. 'And I didn't believe her.'

'Me? A drunk? Doan be sil...'

Forrester groaned. His eyes rolled up in his head and he tumbled, backward, onto the cushions.

CHAPTER FOUR

DANA PHONED ARTHUR from the lobby of the Data Bytes building.

He was in a meeting, his secretary said, but if it was urgent...

Urgent? Dana almost laughed. She'd lost her job, been humiliated...

'Ms. Anderson? Is it urgent? Because if it is, I can beep him for you.'

'No,' Dana said quickly. 'No, it isn't urgent. Not at all. Just tell Mr. Coakley that I phoned, please, about our dinner appointment, and—'

'Oh, that reminds me. Mr. Coakley asked me to phone *you* and say that he's made reservations for six o'clock, at someplace called The Arbor. It's on—'

'I know where it is, Ms. Costello, but I can't—'

'Ms. Anderson, I have a call on another line. Would you mind holding for a moment, please?'

Dana leaned her forehead against the frosted glass partition of the telephone kiosk.

'That's all right,' she said wearily. 'Just tell Mr. Coakley that I'll see him at six.'

She hung up the phone, looked at her watch, and headed for the door. Two hours to kill. Well, that was just as well. She needed time to calm down and collect her thoughts before she met Arthur. Steady, dependable, levelheaded Arthur. He'd help her put things in perspective.

Yes, she thought as she made her way briskly along Madison Avenue, Arthur would get her back on an even keel. She broke the news to him just after they'd been served their main course.

'Arthur?'

He looked up. Something pink and gelatinous was poised on the tines of his fork.

'Yes, my dear?'

'I quit.'

Arthur looked at her untouched plate and frowned. 'Without so much as tasting your duck? Really, Dana—'

'My job,' she said, her voice steady. 'I quit it, this afternoon.'

She watched his expression go from puzzlement to disbelief. The forkful of pink stuff slid, unnoticed, to his plate.

'You're joking.'

She leaned forward, carefully avoiding the lit tapers in the center of the table. The last time they'd dined here, the decor had been about as romantic as a museum cafeteria. Now, the place seemed to be in a battle with Portofino for the title of Chapel of the Month. What was happening to Manhattan restaurants? she wondered idly. Had they been taken over by flower children from the sixties?

'I wouldn't joke about a thing like that, Arthur.' His face turned pale. 'You mean...'

'I mean what I said. I quit.' 'Just like that?'

Dana nodded. 'Just like that.'

She saw his bow tie slide up, then down, as he swallowed. The desire to reach over, rip off the silly tie and toss it away was almost overwhelming.

Stop it, she told herself fiercely. *Whatever is wrong with you, Dana?*

There was no sense letting her anger out on poor Arthur. It wasn't his fault she felt like an overwound spring. She'd walked the afternoon away, but it hadn't done a thing toward easing her anger. She'd have had to fly to one of the islands in the Caribbean to manage that and find a place where she could have had a little wax doll made in Griffin McKenna's smarmy image.

'Oh, my dear,' Arthur said. 'How did it happen?'

She sighed. Arthur was looking at her as if she'd just told him the world was going to end in twenty-four hours. Of course, now that she'd been fired, now that her employment records undoubtedly said she was a disaster as a programmer, now that she'd joined New York's legion of the unemployed, that might just be the reasonable way to view things.

'How does it usually happen? McKenna called me in to fire me, and—'

'I thought you said you quit.'

'Quit, fired…what's the difference? I'm no longer employed at Data Bytes.'

'Dana.' Arthur cleared his throat. 'There's a world of difference. Were you fired, or did you quit?'

'Both,' she said after a minute. 'It can't be both.'

'Yes, it can.'

Arthur frowned. 'Let's begin again, Dana. I thought we'd agreed, at lunch, that you would not quit your job.'

'We did. And I didn't.' 'But you just said—'

'It wasn't my idea, Arthur, but when McKenna told me I was fired, I had to say something, didn't I? So I said he couldn't fire me, that I quit.'

Arthur stared at her for a few seconds. 'I see.' 'You don't.'

'I do. You were upset—'

'I was angry.'

'Whatever. And so you thought to trump him by quitting.'

Dana sighed and picked up her fork. 'It was something like that, I guess.'

'Well, we'll have to think this through. Surely there's some recourse you can take.'

'I am not going to crawl back to the man and beg for my job, Arthur.'

'No, of course not. I simply meant that there's surely some positive action to be taken, even in view of the current turn of events.'

She looked at him. 'Do you really think so?'

'Certainly. We can't simply let this slide by without taking action.'

Dana smiled. 'Thank you,' she said softly. 'I wasn't sure you'd see this my way, Arthur.'

'Dana, my dear, you know how much you mean to me. Why wouldn't I back you at a moment such as this?'

'Well—well, I know you thought I was crazy for disliking McKenna. I mean, I know you think he's the god of takeovers, or something...'

'He's an acknowledged leader in his field. But that has nothing to do with what he did to you today. The only question is, who made the first move?'

Dana's heart skipped a beat. She saw herself in Griffin McKenna's arms, their mouths fused in passion.

'The first move?' she said in a croaking whisper.

'Yes. Did he make it, or did you?'

'Well—he did, but—'

'Did he give any warning?'

'Warning?'

'That's right. Warning. Some sort of signal, so you could attempt to discourage him?'

'Certainly, I tried to discourage him! If you think I simply let that man—'

'That's what we must determine. Because if he didn't give you any warning, Dana, the situation works to our benefit.'

A nervous laugh rose in her throat. 'It does?'

'It does, indeed.'

'I don't—I don't see how, Arthur. What does it matter? Besides, I know what he'll claim. He'll say that I—that I kissed him back. It isn't true, of course. I mean, it may have seemed... What's the matter?'

'Kissed?' Arthur said. His face had gone white. *'Kissed?'*

'Yes. It wasn't my idea. It was just as you said. McKenna started it, and I...' Dana's eyes widened. 'Wasn't that what you were talking about?'

'No.' Arthur's voice was wooden. 'It was not.' He leaned forward, the neat, center knot of his tie bobbing inches above the flickering candles. 'Let me understand this. You kissed Griffin McKenna?'

'Yes. No! He kissed me. He...' Dana swallowed hard. What an idiot she was! Of course, Arthur hadn't been referring to that kiss. How could he have been? Only she and the detestable McKenna knew he had kissed her...

...Knew she had kissed him back...

'Dana?'

She forced her gaze to focus on Arthur's face. Two red spots had appeared on his cheeks.

'What, precisely, went on in McKenna's office?'

'Nothing that had any meaning. He was angry. I was angry. And things just—they just...' She drew a shuddering breath. 'What were you talking about, then? If not—if not... You said it mattered, if I'd tried to stop him. What was that all about?'

Arthur sat back. He took off his glasses, polished them meticulously with his linen napkin, peered through first one lens and then the other, then put the glasses on again. The color in his cheeks had faded to a dull pink and, when he spoke, his tone was calm.

'Unemployment insurance.'

Dana blinked. 'Unemployment insurance?'

He nodded. 'If McKenna fired you without warning you that he was displeased with specific aspects of your performance, you might have a case. But if you quit before he had the chance to say anything, you probably haven't.'

'Unemployment insurance,' Dana said again. She nodded, put her hands in her lap and linked her fingers tightly together. 'Of course.'

'I realize the amount you'd get per week isn't huge, but it would help until you found another position.'

She nodded. Money. Arthur had been talking about money, and she'd thought... But why wouldn't she have thought? That kiss, that damnable kiss, was stuck in her mind. It had been nothing but deliberate humiliation. Griffin McKenna had wanted to make her look foolish, and he'd succeeded, and now she couldn't stop thinking about it, about how she wished she'd had the presence of mind to have reacted properly, but McKenna had timed the thing well. He'd grabbed her when she'd been in such a state of confusion that she hadn't known what she was doing.

'...phone them on your behalf Monday morning, first thing. If you approve, naturally. Dana? Do you agree?'

'Phone who?'

'Some people I know at Social Services. Haven't you been listening?'

'Of course,' she said blithely. 'Thank you, Arthur. By all means, phone them. I'd be grateful.'

And she would be. Arthur was good, he was kind, he would never treat a woman as Griffin had treated her...

...*Never take her mouth with his and make the earth move beneath her feet*...

Dana pushed back her chair and scrambled to her feet.

'Dana? My dear, what is it?'

'I—I need some air, Arthur. It's so stuffy in here. And—and I've had such a long, miserable day...'

'I understand.' Arthur rose, too. He took out his wallet, peeled off some bills, frowned, studied them, looked toward the ceiling as he did a mental count of what they'd ordered and what he owed.

'Sixty should do it,' he murmured. He hesitated. 'Actually, it should be fifty-eight seventy-five, but—'

Dana bit down on her lip. Griffin McKenna would never be so cautious. Griffin would peel off some bills, toss them down. Actually, he'd never have let things go this far. He'd have sensed her mood the minute he saw her; he'd have swept her into his arms, stroked her hair back from her cheeks, smiled into her eyes and kissed her until her worries were gone, until she could think only of him...

'And we both ordered the chocolate mousse.'

'Dammit all, Arthur!' She reached across the table, snatched the bills from under his nose and dumped them on the table. 'Just pay the damn thing,' she sputtered, and then she grabbed her jacket and her handbag and hurried from the restaurant, with Arthur following in her wake.

People said New York was a city that never slept.

It was the truth. No matter what the hour, day or night, you could find people, shops, businesses ready and willing to serve you.

That was why Dana could sit cross-legged on the floor in her living room at six in the morning with an open box from Picasso's Perfect Pizzas in front of her. There was a can of Diet Coke in her left hand and a half-eaten wedge of sausage, mushroom and onion pizza in her right. She'd already finished two pieces; they lay in her gut with all the delicacy of hippopotamuses tiptoeing through a field of tulips. She could almost feel the weight settling onto her hips.

A string of cheese oozed from the wedge of pizza. Dana tilted it up, slurped at the cheese before it dropped onto her Daffy Duck sweatshirt, chewed and swallowed. Before her, on the flickering television screen, a woman in a thong leotard stretched long, limber muscles in time to a pounding rock beat. Dana assumed that was what it was; she had the sound turned off.

'One, and two, and three,' the woman on-screen mouthed.

'One, and two, and three,' Dana said around her mouthful of pizza.

'Push, and pull, and breathe in deep,' the vision mimed.

'Push, and pull, and, oh...to heck with it!'

Dana swallowed the last bit of pizza, picked up the remote control, and zapped the exercise princess into oblivion. Who could believe that someone who looked like that needed to work herself into a sweat?

'Not me,' Dana muttered as she got to her feet.

Exercise had been Arthur's idea. He'd put her into a taxi and told her to go home and not worry about a thing.

'I'm not worried,' she'd said, looking at him through the open window as he shut the cab's door. 'I'm angry. To think that that man fired me...to think he believed all the garbage Forrester told him...'

'I'll take care of everything,' Arthur had said soothingly, and then he'd leaned in, given her a quick kiss, and told her to go home and work off her anger on the Exercycle he'd given her for Christmas, after she'd mentioned she'd been thinking about taking up running.

'You cannot run alone,' he'd said. 'It isn't safe.'

'I know Tai Chi and karate, Arthur. Remember? I told you, I took some classes in college.'

Arthur's frown had told her what he thought of such a sweaty sport.

'I'd worry about you, my dear,' he'd said. 'Really, you shouldn't run by yourself.'

She'd thought, just for a minute, that he'd meant he was going to run with her. But he hadn't. Arthur's heart wasn't into sports. Instead, on Christmas morning, a huge box had been delivered to her door. It had contained an Exercycle, but Dana had never used it.

She didn't like it.

Stupid as it was, the machine that sat in the corner of her living room seemed to be a constant reminder of Arthur's pasty-white body. They'd gone to Fire Island for a day, last summer; the sight of Arthur in his black trunks had not been cheering.

For shame, Dana!

Why would he be muscular? she asked herself as she dumped the rest of Picasso's Perfect Pizza into the garbage. Arthur worked with his mind, not with his hands. There was no reason for a man like him to have muscles.

There was no reason for Griffin McKenna to have them, either, but he did. His arms had been hard as steel, as he'd held her, his body against hers as hard as granite. No, not granite. Rock was cold to the touch but Griffin... Griffin was hot.

Dana gave herself a determined shake.

'Idiot,' she said.

Briskly, she peeled off Daffy Duck and her sweatpants and headed for the shower.

At seven, she'd exchanged Diet Coke for black coffee, jeans for sweatpants, and Daffy's smiling likeness for that of Lois Lane.

Lois Lane, though still much too dependent on Superman, was the preferable choice this morning.

Dana sipped her coffee. She felt better now, even though she hadn't slept all night. How could she have slept, with the knowledge of her humiliation at McKenna's hands to haunt her?

But it was the dawn of a new day, both literally and figuratively. It was time to put yesterday aside and concentrate on tomorrow.

In other words, she was going to begin the search for a job. Dana unlocked the door and looked on the mat for the newspaper. It wasn't there. Well, that was no surprise. The *Times* was delivered to her door each morning, but José was sometimes late. Usually, he dropped the paper off at six or seven, but once in a while, it would be later than that because she'd find it on her doorstep when she returned from work in the evening. She didn't have the heart to complain. José was a scruffy-looking kid, in perpetual need of a haircut, and when she'd confronted him about it, he'd told her he had to take care of his mother before he did his route.

His eyes had defied her to argue.

Dana sighed. Why would she have argued? She'd had a mother to take care of, too, and though she had no way of knowing if the situations were similar, she knew how rough it was for a kid to take on such a responsibility.

Okay. She'd go down to the coffee shop on the corner, pick up the paper, and go through the employment section. There wouldn't be much, not on a Friday, but it would be a start. And then she'd phone Jeannie, who had to be wondering what on earth had happened to her. The rumor mill at Data Bytes would be working overtime by now. Jeannie would have heard a dozen different versions of the firing. It would be vital to make sure the true one found its way into the pipeline.

In fact, she'd phone Jeannie, right now, tell her what had really happened in McKenna's office...

Tell her about that kiss?

Dana froze, portable telephone in hand, but it was too late. She'd already dialed, and Jeannie had picked up.

'Hullo?'

'Uh, it's me. Did I wake you?'

'No,' Jeannie said in a sleep-fogged voice.

'I figured you had to be getting up soon, to go to work.'

'Right, right. Jus' give me a couple seconds to focus here...'

'No, that's okay. I'll call back when you're—'

'Dana? Dana!' Jeannie's voice sharpened. 'It's you!'

Dana ran her hand through her hair. It was still damp from the shower and starting its usual, impossible tendency to curl.

'Yeah. It's me.'

'Thank God! I'd begun to think you'd been kidnapped by

gypsies or something. I must have phoned you a dozen times last evening. Don't you ever check your answering machine?'

Dana glanced at the machine as she paced past it. Its red light was blinking furiously. Arthur had bought it for her for her birthday, but she still tended to forget its existence.

'Sorry. I didn't mean to worry you.'

'Worry me?' Jeannie gave a throaty laugh. 'I see you yesterday, you're ripping off old Charlie's head.'

Dana winced. The pizza trembled in her stomach.

'Then, next thing I hear, you've been canned.'

'That isn't entirely accurate.'

'McKenna didn't fire you?'

Dana slicked the tip of her tongue along her bottom lip. 'In a way.'

'You got fired, but only in a way?' 'I quit.'

'Before or after he fired you?'

'What's the difference?'

'Well, if you want to collect unemployment—'

'For goodness' sake, is that all everybody can think about? Unemployment insurance?'

'Who's everybody?'

Dana waved her hand. 'You, Arthur…'

'Well, for once Arthur and I agree. Money's important at a time like this.'

'Other things are more important, Jeannie.' 'For instance?'

'For instance, what did McKenna say?'

'About what?'

Be careful, Dana… 'About—about how I left. I mean, did he say he fired me? Or that I quit?'

'I just told you. The word is that he fired you.'

Dana frowned and looked down at her slipper-clad toes. A bit of lint was clinging to one fuzzy sole. She bent and plucked it off.

'And?' she said.

'And, what?'

'And, is that all? McKenna didn't say…anything more?'

'McKenna didn't say anything, period. Not to me, anyway. You forget, I am female. I am not one of the chosen few who carries the wondrous Y chromosome. I do not get to sit at his feet and hear him pontificate. What I'm telling you is only what I heard via the ever-trusty grapevine.'

'Oh.'

'Oh, indeed. Why? Is there something more to the story?'

'No,' Dana said quickly, 'of course not.'

'You sure?' Jeannie's voice lowered dramatically. 'Tell me what he did, Dana. You can trust me.'

'He didn't do anything. I don't know what you mean.'

'Oh, come on. Did he do something totally outrageous?' Dana flushed. 'Of course not.'

'Something you still can't believe?'

'No! Why would you ever think—'

'He made a pass,' Jeannie said with delight.

'He did not!' It wasn't a lie. What McKenna had done had nothing to do with sex and everything to do with power.

'Oh,' Jeannie sounded disappointed. 'Well, what then?'

'I just told you, he didn't do anything.'

'Did he lose his cool?'

Dana closed her eyes. Had Griffin lost his cool? She'd thought so, just for a minute or two, when he'd been kissing her that second time, when he'd made that soft, growling sound and drawn her close.

But he hadn't. It had all been an act; he'd proved that when he'd put her from him and given her that arrogant, I'm-such-a-stud smile.

'No,' she said, her tone an icy match for the memory of that smile. 'He did not lose his cool. He told me he was letting me go, so I said I was quitting, and then he told me to collect my paycheck and never to darken Data Bytes's doorstep again.' She sighed and sank down on the sofa. 'Or words to that effect.'

'Wow.'

'Wow, indeed. Now, I have to look for another job and worry about what kind of reference I'm going to get from Data Bytes.'

'Yeah,' Jeannie said. 'Well, that explains a lot.' 'What does?'

'That he gave you the old heave-ho. And that old Dave, so they say, got *el stinko*.'

Dana's eyes widened. 'Really?'

'That's the rumor.'

'Did McKenna know?'

'He must have. Word is, he went ballistic.'

'What do you mean? What happened?'

'Well, today's the start of the big Miami Beach conference, remember?'

Dana sighed. 'How could I forget?'

'Dave's supposed to show everybody how the new program shines.'

'He couldn't have. The code is a mess.'

'Uh-huh. And the word is that McKenna finally knows it.'

'Don't count on it. I tried and tried to warn him—'

'I saw him at the keyboard, myself.'

'Are you serious? What keyboard?'

'At the computer. Dave's first, and then yours. He sat there, tap-tap-tapping away—'

Dana's doorbell rang. She frowned and glanced at her watch. It was almost seven-thirty. Who could be calling at such an hour?

'—Doing everything he could to get the code to work, but it was a no-go.'

'Hang on, Jeannie. There's someone at the door.'

'At seven-something in the morning? Be careful, okay? I don't think Jack the Ripper rings the doorbell when he comes calling, but you can never tell.'

Dana smiled. 'It's probably José,' she said as she rose to her feet.

Jeannie giggled. 'Dana, you devil. And all the time, I thought good old Arthur was the only guy who held the key to your heart.'

'José's my paper boy. He usually collects on Saturday morning, but sometimes…'

The bell rang again. José was certainly impatient today.

'So,' Dana said as she tucked the phone between her ear and her shoulder and undid all the locks but the final chain, 'tell me more about McKenna.'

'What's to tell? You know everything I do. There he was at quitting time, staring first at Dave's monitor and then at yours, doing a fast two-finger shuffle on the keys, cursing and muttering and slugging down cup after cup of coffee while he tried to coax the code's secrets from the system.'

Dana snorted. 'Griffin McKenna,' she said as she opened the door, 'could probably get a hundred women into his bed faster than he could get that code from the comp… Oh, my God!'

'Dana?' Jeannie said. 'Dana? What is it? Listen, I was only joking about Jack the Ripper…'

Dana stared through the door opening. Jack the Ripper would have been easier to accept than reality.

'You're wrong,' Griffin McKenna said tonelessly. 'I could get a thousand women into my bed faster than I can get that damned code out of that computer.'

'Dana?' Jeannie's voice was frantic. 'Who's there? Talk to me!'

'Open the door, Anderson.'

Maybe he wasn't real. Maybe he was an apparition.

'I assure you,' Griffin said coldly, 'this is strictly business.'

'Dana? Dana, say something!'

'Open the door. And you'd better say something, to silence that hysterical female on the other end of the line.'

He was real, all right. And really furious. She could see it in the way he stood before her, arms folded, eyes and mouth narrowed.

'Miz Anderson?'

Dana looked past Griffin's shoulder. José looked back at her. 'You okay, Miz Anderson?'

Griffin glanced over his shoulder. 'She's fine,' he said. His gaze locked on Dana's. 'Aren't you, Anderson?'

She looked from the man to the boy. Then, wordlessly, she undid the chain, took the newspaper from José's hands and let Griffin brush past her into the living room.

'Dana,' Jeannie screeched, 'talk to me!'

Griffin folded his arms over his chest. 'Talk to her,' he said. He looked at José. 'And to your would-be rescuer.'

Dana swallowed. Could she talk? Her lips felt numb. 'Everything's fine,' she said to José and to Jeannie. 'Honestly.'

José nodded and headed for the stairs. Jeannie was more persistent.

'Somebody's there,' she said. 'Right?'

'Yes. And I've got to go now.'

'You want me to call nine-one-one?'

Dana felt an insane desire to laugh. 'Nine-one-one can't help me.'

'No one can,' McKenna said. His smile was chill. 'Except for me.'

'Dana?'

Dana licked her lips. 'I'm fine, Jeannie.'

'Really?'

'Really.'

'Call me later, okay?'

Dana nodded. She took the phone from her ear, pressed the off button, and looked Griffin straight in the eye.

'You have two minutes to explain why you're here,' she said. 'And then—'

'And then,' he said with a chilly smile, 'you'll call nine-one-one?'

She dumped the phone and the newspaper on the table. Then she took a step back, feet apart, hands slightly lifted, palms angled out, and told herself there was no way McKenna could hear the thump-thump of her heart.

'And then,' she said, 'so help me Hannah, I'll give you a kick where it'll do the most good. And I promise you, McKenna, you won't be doing any boasting about how many women you can get into your bed after that. Not for a very, very long time.'

CHAPTER FIVE

IF IT WAS true that looks could kill, Griffin figured he'd have been lying at Dana's feet, breathing his last by now.

There was no mistaking the message in her eyes. If he clutched at his throat, gasped, and fell to the floor, the only thing she'd do would be applaud.

A muscle twitched in his jaw.

Her threat to kick him should have been a laugh, considering her size compared to his, but that steely-eyed expression couldn't be ignored. There were times that guts could make up for lack of expertise. He'd learned that the first few months he'd spent swimming in the shark-infested waters of Wall Street, and he'd learned it well.

On the other hand, she didn't hold a monopoly on anger. His was every bit as hot as hers. Hotter, maybe, considering that he'd spent most of the night slaving over a computer that might as well have been the Sphinx, considering its smug refusal to give up its secrets.

Griffin eyed Dana. She was still standing poised like a female martial arts expert, feet apart, arms outstretched, hands ready to chop him into tiny pieces.

She had no idea how easily he could get past that fancy stance of hers. Griffin almost smiled. He worked out a few hours a week at a gym used by amateur boxers. It was a place that smelled of sweat and liniment instead of cologne and air freshener. A long time ago, back in his college days, he'd learned that a guy could get a pretty good workout punching the big body bag, develop quick hands on the speed bag, and get all the aerobics he needed, skipping rope.

That was what he did now, a couple of times a week. His footwork wasn't fancy, but it was quick, and so were his jabs— quick enough so that one move would take him right inside her blocking defense. Then, using nothing but his size and weight, he'd have her where he wanted her, right down on the floor.

Down on the floor, with him on top of her.

Dammit, what was wrong with him? He did not like the Anderson woman. Never had, never would. She wasn't his type. Come to think of it, she wouldn't be any man's type, not the way she looked this morning. The prim and proper Ms. Anderson of the office had given way to an entirely different woman. Her hair was loose. It looked damp, as if she'd just showered, and it was drying in soft-looking curls. She was wearing a sweatshirt, faded jeans and a pair of slippers that had definitely seen better days. Whose picture was that on the sweatshirt? Griffin frowned.

His brows rose. Damned if it wasn't Lois Lane.

'Lois Lane?' he said without thinking.

'Yes,' Dana's chin lifted a notch. 'You want to make something out of it, McKenna?'

'No,' he said quickly. 'No, Lois Lane is...'

Is what? What was he doing? Who cared if it was Lois Lane? She could have Quasimodo on her sweatshirt, for all he cared. What mattered was that she'd screwed up the computer code, or maybe she was the only one who could unscrew it, or—or...

Was she braless? She seemed to be. He could see the high, rounded outline of her breasts move as she breathed. And those jeans. They clung to her like a second skin, outlining her gently rounded hips, accentuating her long legs.

'I know what you're thinking, McKenna.'

Griffin's gaze flew to meet Dana's.

'And I wouldn't try it, if I were you. I've got a black belt in karate.'

He nodded, knowing damn well that she had no idea what he was thinking because if she did, she'd have come at him like a wildcat.

'Really,' he said.

Dana nodded. It wasn't a complete lie. She'd have had a black belt by now, if she'd continued taking classes, but that was none of his business.

'If you don't believe me, just try something.'

Griffin thought back to the long night he'd put in. It cooled his passion a lot faster than Anderson's puny threat. How many hours had he spent trying to make that miserable code work?

'Y'll never do it,' Forrester had slurred, after Griffin had poured a pot of black coffee down the man's gullet. 'That Anderson broad ish one smart cookie.'

Griffin had looked up from the keyboard. 'I thought you said she was incompetent.'

'Yeah, that, too.'

'Which is it, Dave? Was she incompetent, or was she smart?'

'She's smart enough to have screwed up the program, thass for sure.'

Forrester had guffawed at his own wit, hiccuped loudly, curled up in the corner and fallen into the sleep of the dead. Disgusted, Griffin had left him there. At four, he'd given up trying to make the code work. Instead, he'd typed a letter informing Forrester that he was lucky he was only being fired, stapled it to the jerk's lapel, and then he'd headed home to shower and catch a couple of hours' shut-eye, after which he'd finally acknowledged that there was only one possible hope of saving Data Bytes—which was why he told himself, now, to calm down and remember that more flies had been caught with honey than with vinegar.

'You hear me, McKenna?' Dana narrowed her eyes. 'Give me the slightest cause, and I'll give you a very bad time.'

Griffin fixed a solemn expression on his face.

'I'm sure you could,' he said, lying without a blink.

Dana nodded. 'Damn right.'

'But there's no need to take this hard-line approach with me.'

She snorted in derision. 'There's every need. Did you think I'd forgotten what you did?'

She meant the kiss. He knew that, but swimming with the sharks had also taught him that there were times it paid to play dumb.

'No,' he said, 'of course not. How could I have forgotten such a memorable moment?' A delicate wash of pink flowed up under her skin. Good, he thought grimly. Let her suffer a little. She could use the practice. He dragged out the seconds as long as he could, before dropping the other shoe. 'I assure you, I never forget the sad moment when I'm forced to fire a valued employee.'

Her face was a study in total bewilderment.

'Fired?' she said. 'But I thought—I thought you were referring to—to—'

'Referring to what?' he said politely.

The color in her cheeks went from pink to rose. At last, she cleared her throat, straightened her posture, and folded her arms over her chest.

'What are you doing here, McKenna? Explain, and make it snappy.'

Touchy broad, Griffin thought, and smiled through his teeth.

'Do you think we could have some privacy, while I explain?' he said, jerking his chin toward the open door.

Dana didn't take her eyes off him.

'No.'

'You like having an audience?' Griffin smiled again. 'Hey, that's fine with me.'

Dana looked past him. Mrs. Gibbs, who lived across the hall, was standing in the open doorway to her apartment. She was wearing a pink robe, a headful of curlers, and a rapt expression that meant she already had enough gossip to last a week, down in the basement laundry room.

'Hello, dearie,' Mrs. Gibbs said. 'Who's your handsome visitor?'

'He isn't—'

'He certainly is.' Mrs. Gibbs batted her lashes in Griffin's direction. 'Hello.'

'Hello.'

'Ooh, look at that smile! Aren't you going to introduce us, dearie?'

Dana rolled her eyes. 'Oh, for God's sake...'

'I'm Griffin McKenna,' Griffin said pleasantly.

'Her boyfriend?'

'Her boss. Well, her former boss. Ms. Anderson is no longer—'

Dana slammed the door shut and glared at him. 'Why not rent a billboard?'

'Sorry. I didn't know your termination was to be kept a secret.'

'I quit, remember?'

'A matter of semantics, Anderson.'

'A matter of fact, McKenna. You have one minute to explain what you're doing here.'

'That's fifty seconds more than I'll need.'

'Good. Because when the minute is up—'

'What in hell did you do to my code?'

Dana's eyes widened. 'I beg your pardon?'

'I said—'

'I heard what you said, McKenna. Are you crazy? I didn't do anything to your code.'

'Forrester says—'

'Besides, that code isn't yours.'

'Really,' Griffin smiled tightly. 'And who, pray tell, owns Data Bytes?'

'You may have enough money to make you think you can buy the world, McKenna, but you don't have the brains to—'

He moved fast, so fast that she knew instinctively she'd been lucky to get away with the karate bit only moments ago. His hands clamped down on her forearms, not hard enough to hurt but hard enough to lift her to her toes.

'You've got brass, Anderson.' His blue gaze bored into her. 'Anybody ever tell you that?'

Dana's heart thudded. She could see a little muscle jumping just beside his mouth. That handsome mouth, that had been so warm, so hot, on hers.

'Let me go, McKenna.'

'Why?' His voice was low and just a little rough. 'A little while ago, you were busy making it clear you weren't afraid of me.'

'I'm not.'

His hands slid up and clasped her shoulders. His gaze dropped to her mouth. She could feel the weight of that gaze, the heat of it, as surely as if he were stroking her mouth with the tip of his finger. As surely as if he were putting his lips against hers.

'I think you are,' he said softly.

She pulled away from him and stepped back. This was a game for him, that was what it was. She knew that, and yet she was playing right into it.

'What I meant,' she said briskly, 'is that owning a software company doesn't necessarily make you capable of understanding computer code.'

'And what *I* meant,' Griffin said just as briskly, 'is that the code was developed by Dave Forrester, who worked for me.' His smile was pure arrogance. 'And that makes the code mine.'

Dana stepped around him, snatching her coffee cup from the table as she made her way to the kitchen.

'Fine. Believe what you want. It doesn't mean a damn to me, anymore.'

'Forrester says you screwed up.'

'So you said when you terminated me.' Dana dumped the remnants of her cold coffee into the sink and poured a fresh cup. 'I repeat, believe what you want.'

Griffin frowned, looked at the coffee that remained in the pot and then at Dana.

'Who makes the coffee that was in that mug in your office?'

Dana blinked. 'What?'

'There's a big yellow mug on the desk in your office. There was some cold stuff in it that was oily and black and smelled like it might have been coffee, in a former lifetime. Who made it? You?'

'No. SueEllen did. She works down the hall in—'

'In that case,' Griffin said, nodding toward the coffeepot, 'I'll take a cup of that stuff.'

'I beg your pardon?'

'I said—'

'I heard what you said, McKenna. What I didn't hear was me offering you some.'

Griffin shook his head, reached past her, took a cup from the shelf and filled it.

'Your hospitality leaves something to be desired, Anderson,' He took a long swallow from the cup. 'This is much better.'

Dana rolled her eyes. 'What are you, McKenna? A financial genius or a coffee connoisseur?'

'A survivor.' The corners of his mouth twitched. 'I couldn't decide if that coffee in your office was an experiment gone bad or a secret formula for motor oil.'

Dana laughed. She hadn't meant to, but when she thought

of all the times she'd shuddered and glugged down SueEllen's guaranteed-to-keep-your-eyeballs-popping coffee as she worked late into the night, the laugh just came bubbling up.

Griffin laughed, too. Her pulse rate danced. He was incredibly handsome when he laughed. Well, he was always handsome, but when he laughed—when he laughed, he was...

The telephone rang. Dana swung toward it, closed her eyes for a second, then picked it up.

'Dana.'

'Arthur.' Good old Arthur. Dear Arthur. Arthur, her ever-reliable anchor to reality. The feeling of relief was so intense that she almost felt giddy. 'Oh, I'm so glad to hear your voice.'

'And I'm glad to hear yours. Are you feeling better now?'

'Better?'

'You were so upset last night, that I wondered—'

'Anderson?' Griffin said.

Dana frowned. 'I'm sorry, Arthur. I missed that. What did you say?'

'I haven't got all day, Anderson. Tell whoever that is that you're busy.'

Dana clapped her hand over the mouthpiece. 'I am no longer your employee, McKenna. I don't have to take orders from you.'

'As if you ever did.'

'Dana?' Arthur said. 'Is somebody there?'

Dana sighed and put the phone to her ear again.

'Yes, Arthur. Griffin McKenna is here.'

'There? In your apartment?'

She sighed again. Arthur sounded as if she'd just told him the President had stepped out of the woodwork.

'That's right.'

'Why is he there, Dana?'

'I don't know, Arthur. He hasn't deigned to tell me, yet.'

Griffin frowned. 'Is that the Bow Tie?'

Dana made a face.

'He hasn't tried anything unseemly, Dana, has he?'

'No. It's nothing like that, Arthur.'

'I'll bet he's there because he's concerned you'll go to the unemployment people and demand a hearing.'

'What's he saying?' Griffin demanded, and moved closer.

Dana turned her back. 'You're probably right.'

'Excellent news, my dear, excellent. Perhaps you'd like to let me speak with Mr. McKenna.'

'No. No, Arthur, that isn't necessary.'

'What's the problem?' Griffin leaned over her shoulder, his breath warm against her temple. 'Is he afraid I'm poaching?'

'Well, then, Dana, let me give you some quick advice. Remember that your rights are governed by law—'

'Did you tell him that you kissed me?' he whispered.

Dana swung around and glared at him. 'I did not!'

'Did not what?' Arthur said. 'Dana, no matter what the man tries to tell you, your rights are—'

'I'll call you back, Arthur.' She slammed down the phone and looked up at Griffin. 'You said you'd tell me why you came here, McKenna. Well, I'm waiting.'

Griffin frowned. Why *had* he come here? He couldn't remember. The scent of Dana's hair was in his nostrils. He'd reminded her of that kiss just to annoy her and the Bow Tie, but that had turned out to be a mistake. The kiss was all he could think of now, the feel of her mouth, the little sound she'd made when he'd parted her lips with his...

He took a step back, and cleared his throat.

'I came here to ask about the code, Anderson.'

'What about it?'

'Is Forrester right? Did you screw it up?'

'How many ways do you want me to say 'no,' McKenna? Now, if that's all—'

'It isn't.'

Dana blew a curl from her forehead. 'Make it quick, okay? I have things to do this morning.'

'Like, looking for a new job,' Griffin said with a tight smile.

'Get to it, McKenna. What do you want?'

'How big a part did you play in the development of the code?'

She opened her mouth, prepared to give him a snide response, but something in the way he was looking at her stopped her.

'A major part,' she said.

'Fifty-fifty, with Forrester?'

She smiled coldly. 'He only wishes.'

'Let's put it this way, Anderson. Can you debug that code and make the program run the way it should?'

'You mean, rather than debate whether or not I developed it, you'll settle for knowing if I can fix it?'

'That's one way of putting it, I suppose.'

Dana banged down her coffee cup. 'You are the most chauvinistic, insolent, impossible man I've ever known!'

'Thank you,' Griffin said politely. 'But I didn't come here to be complimented.'

'Oh, for heaven's sake—'

Griffin caught her arm as she started past him.

'I haven't finished delivering my message, Anderson.' He looked up at her kitchen clock. 'The Data Bytes rep has to be in Florida by one this afternoon.'

'How nice,' Dana said with a glittering smile. 'He'll be just in time for lunch.'

'There are meetings scheduled from one-thirty until five this evening, and there's a dinner tonight with—'

'He'll be a busy little bee, won't he?' she said brightly.

'If this weekend's a fiasco, Data Bytes will probably collapse.'

She sighed and fluttered her lashes. 'And you'll lose money. But I'm sure you aren't thinking of that, not one little bit.'

'A lot of people will lose their jobs. Can you make jokes about that, too, Anderson?'

She looked at him, her eyes gone cold. 'You're right, they will. I tried to warn you, McKenna.'

'So you did.'

'Yes. So I did. And now you're in trouble.'

'The company is in trouble.'

'Forgive me for asking, but is there a difference?'

Griffin put down his coffee cup. 'Ask the people who stand to lose their jobs that question. See what they say.'

He had her there. It was true, as Data Bytes went, so went McKenna...but so went Jeannie, and Charlie the Custodian, and SueEllen, and a couple of hundred others.

'You're right,' she said after a minute.

'I know I am, and believe me, it gives me no pleasure.'

'I should hope it doesn't! If you'd only listened to the truth—'

'Meaning, I should have listened when you told me about Forrester.' He nodded. 'Yes. I should have.' Griffin jammed his hands into his pockets. 'I shouldn't have fired you, either.'

Dana shrugged. She couldn't gloat, not with all the jobs in the balance.

'It really wouldn't have made any difference. I could never have gotten the program up and running by this morning.'

'Neither could Forrester.'

'If he'd had a little more time, if he'd have been running on all cylinders, maybe...' She smiled ruefully. 'My mother used to say that if 'if' ruled the world, nobody would worry about getting to heaven.'

Griffin smiled. 'The lady was a philosopher.'

'A pragmatist,' Dana said with no smile at all. 'All right, McKenna. Apology accepted. Now, if you don't mind—'

'What were you going to say? About what would have happened, if Forrester were functional?'

Dana tucked a loose strand of hair behind her ear. She moved past Griffin, into the living room, and sat down on the sofa. She put her feet up on the planked coffee table and crossed them.

'Anderson?'

She looked up. Griffin had seated himself opposite her, in the wooden rocker she'd salvaged from a pile of trash at the curb.

It was old and beat-up looking, but it seemed to have taken on a certain elegance, thanks to its occupant.

'You were saying, about Forrester?'

Dana cleared her throat. 'I was just saying that if he were sober, there was a chance—a slim one, you understand—that he just might have gotten you through the weekend.'

'Get me through, how?'

Amazing. When Arthur sat in the rocker, it was just an ordinary, slightly beat-up chair, but Griffin—Griffin gave it a very different look. Had the chair always been this small? Or was it just that he was so big?

'Anderson?'

Dana blinked.

'How do you mean, he might have gotten me through the weekend?'

'Well, even though he didn't really develop the code, he did work with me. And he's really a genius—when he's sober, anyway. So, he could probably have made the code behave. Not completely, of course, but with a little luck, he might have at least gotten the demos to work.' She sighed and put her feet down on the floor, side by side. 'But he can't, so what's the point of talking about it?'

Griffin looked at her for a long minute. Then he sat back, folded his arms and began, gently, to move the rocker back and forth.

'So, what you're saying is that you developed the code...'

'For the most part.'

'... But only Forrester could have made it work this weekend.'

Dana's head snapped up. 'I never said that!'

'You did. You just finished telling me that—'

'I said, Forrester—a sober Forrester—might have pulled it off because Forrester is your employee.'

'Ah. I see. Someone else could manage, then.'

'Not really. Not unless that person had a couple of days to get up to speed on the ins and outs of the program.'

'But, if that were possible?'

Dana lifted one shoulder. 'A guy who's good, who understands the nuances of the code…a guy like that might be able to get you through the weekend.'

"A guy," Griffin said, and smiled.

Dana rose from the sofa. 'A figure of speech, McKenna. A 'he,' a 'she,' an 'it.' I'm referring to a hypothetical person who's a computer whiz. A person with ability, training, talent and—'

'And knowledge.'

'Exactly. And a sober Dave Forrester is the only person at Data Bytes who fits that bill.'

'There's only one problem with that reasoning, Anderson.' Griffin's eyes met hers. 'Forrester isn't with Data Bytes anymore. I fired that miserable drunk this morning.' He smiled, and Dana thought she knew how a caged canary would feel under the steady gaze of a sleek cat. 'No one at Data Bytes fits that bill,' he said softly. 'But you do.'

Dana shot to her feet. Was that what this was all about? Did McKenna think she'd go back to working for him? Did he think he could talk her into taking on a job that was damn near impossible? After he'd fired her, swallowed all of Forrester's damnable lies, accused her of everything from incompetency to sabotage?

'Forget it,' she snapped.

Griffin rose, too, his gaze locked on hers.

'I already apologized, Anderson. What more can I do?'

'You're breaking my heart,' Dana said coldly.

'It's not your heart I'm aiming for, it's your brain. Think about all those innocent people who'll suffer, just because of your hurt feelings.'

'Is that what you think? That you wounded my ego?' She glared at him. 'I've got a message for you, McKenna—'

'If I introduce that program in Florida this weekend, it'll be the end of the company, and you know it.'

'Oh, that's great! But it won't work. You can't lay this off on me, mister!'

'Dammit, are you dense? You're the one who has the best chance of getting us through this.'

'Us? *Us?* There is no 'us,' remember? I am not a Data Bytes employee anymore.'

'But you could be. And, if you were, you'd have the best shot anybody could have of pulling us out of this mess.'

'The best shot at saving your ass, McKenna, isn't that what you mean?'

'My, my, Anderson, how you do talk!'

'Spit it out, McKenna. What do you want from me?'

His grin was charming, almost boyish, but there was no mistaking the flat determination in his eyes.

'If Data Bytes goes under, everybody drowns.'

'We agree on something, anyway. So?'

'So, come back on board.'

Dana stared at Griffin. He was begging now... The hell he was. He was looking at her as if *he* were doing *her* a favor, as if he'd expected her to leap for joy, throw her arms around his neck...

'No,' she said firmly, looking straight into his eyes.

'No?' he said, looking stunned.

'That's right. No. I don't want my job back, and that's final.'

A smile tugged at his mouth. 'Ah, but I didn't offer you your job back, now, did I?'

Color flew into Dana's face. Damn the man! She'd let him make a fool of her again.

'Get out, McKenna,' she said, stalking past him. 'Just turn around, walk to the door, and—'

'What I'm offering you is a new position.'

She stopped dead. 'A new position?'

'Certainly. You'll take Forrester's spot.'

She turned, very slowly, half expecting him to laugh, but his expression was solemn.

'Forrester's spot?'

'Of course.'

Dana nodded, as if she'd understood that all along.

'I'd expect a raise in pay,' she said calmly.

'I've already told as much to Payroll.'

'You've already...' She rolled her eyes. 'Has anyone ever told you what an arrogant so-and-so you are, McKenna?'

'Many. And, before you get your feathers ruffled, I also told Payroll you'd be getting a forty percent pay raise.'

'Oh, really,' she said, her words dripping with sarcasm. 'And I suppose you think that a—that a...' Dana's eyes widened. 'Did you say, forty percent?'

'Not enough?' He smiled, but without humor. 'Fifty, then.'

Dana put her hands behind her back and crossed all her fingers. 'I want a contract with stock options. And the executive medical plan.'

He nodded. 'Done.'

'New furniture, in Forrester's office.' She smiled coolly. 'I'm not much for metal desks and old file cabinets stuffed with back issues of a girlie magazine.'

'Pick whatever you like.' He held out his hand. 'Is it a deal?'

Dana looked at his hand, then at him. 'Not quite.'

To her surprise, he laughed. 'Okay, get your pound of flesh while you can. What else do you want? A secretary of your own? Done. A staff to do the drudge work? Fine. Come on, Anderson. What more can there possibly be?'

'A title. Vice president in charge of research sounds just fine,' she said, and waited, because even she knew that now she had pushed him too far.

'If you were a man,' Griffin said softly, 'I'd say you had... guts.' His gaze moved over her with excruciating slowness. 'But if there's one thing you most definitely are not, it's male.'

Color flooded her cheeks again, but she held herself stiffly.

'Is it a deal, or isn't it?'

'You are some piece of work, Anderson.'

'I'm a piece of work you need, McKenna.'

He nodded. 'All right. You're the new V.P. of Research and Development. How's that sound?'

How did it sound? Like a miracle. Could she answer his question without letting him know that her heart was racing like an out-of-control train?

'It sounds fine,' she said with what she hoped was admirable restraint.

'Everthing's contingent on you getting Data Bytes through this weekend, of course.'

Dana nodded. 'Of course.'

'Let's shake on it, then.'

He held out his hand again. She looked at it. Then, slowly, she put her hand in his.

Their fingers touched. Clung. She felt the heat of his skin. His fingers tightened around hers...

Dana snatched back her hand. 'It's—it's getting late.'

Griffin frowned, shot back his cuff again, and his frown became a scowl. 'Bloody hell! Can you pack in twenty minutes?'

She laughed, and tried not to sound as giddy as she felt. 'Time me.'

He looked at her. Her face was flushed, her eyes were as bright as stars, and he had to fight back the overwhelming urge to take her into his arms and kiss her until that look of joy, of sheer delight, was for him and not for a job.

He stepped back.

'Get to it, then,' he said gruffly. 'My car's waiting downstairs.'

She turned on her heel and fled into the bedroom. The door slammed shut. He could hear the sounds of drawers opening and closing. Less than ten minutes later she reappeared, dressed in a tailored shirt, a tailored skirt, and low-heeled, sensible shoes, carrying a small carry-on suitcase and her portable computer.

Griffin nodded in approval.

'Eight minutes, Anderson, and here you are, dressed for success, as usual, and all packed. And I see you've even managed to find time to clamp your hair to your head.'

There was something in his tone. Dana frowned and touched her hand to the neat knot at the back of her head. 'Is there something wrong with it?'

'No,' he said, his face virtually expressionless. 'It looks just the way it always does.'

'Well, then.' She smiled. 'I told you I'd be ready in time, McKenna.'

Griffin reached for her carry-on. They wrestled over it for a couple of seconds before she gave up fighting and let him take it.

They rode the elevator to the lobby in silence. It had started snowing sometime during the early morning hours; the city streets seemed strangely hushed and almost pristine. Griffin put his hand lightly on Dana's elbow and led her to the Mercedes at the curb. His driver opened the door and she stepped inside.

'La Guardia Airport, please, Oliver,' Griffin said as he sat down beside her. 'And see what you can do to get us there as quickly as possible.'

They were almost at the terminal when Dana turned toward him.

'I'll be in touch, of course.'

'In touch?'

'Yes. I'll call you from Miami and keep you updated on the situation.'

Griffin thought of telling her that she wouldn't have to do that, but just then Oliver pulled the car to the curb.

'I want you to know that I won't fail you, Mr. McKenna,' Dana said as she scooted toward the door. 'I'm not promising anything, you understand, I simply mean that I'll do my best to get Data Bytes through the weekend.'

'I hope you succeed, for all our sakes.'

Oliver opened the door. Dana, then Griffin, stepped onto the sidewalk. 'There's no need to walk me inside, Mr. McKenna.'

'What's going on here, Anderson? You've taken to addressing me as Mr. McKenna again.'

'Well, it's the polite thing to do. After all, I work for you now.' She smiled as she reached for her carry-on. 'If things don't work out and you fire me again, I'll undoubtedly call you by other names. Goodbye, Mr. McKenna,' she said very politely, and held out her hand.

Griffin took her hand in his. 'Hello, Ms. Anderson,' he said just as politely.

Dana frowned. 'I don't understand.'

'It's simple.' He took his suitcase from Oliver, clasped Dana's elbow firmly, and turned her toward the terminal, knowing, even as he did, that he was probably about to hear some of those names. 'You and I are going to Miami together.'

CHAPTER SIX

GRIFFIN COULD ALMOST see the lightbulb go on over Dana's head.

She stopped, processed his statement, then swung around to face him.

'What did you just say?'

Amazing, he thought, how very calm she sounded. Ominously calm. He wasn't fooled, not for a second. He had seen that look in her eye only a little while before. He had the feeling she was seconds away from her karate imitation.

'You heard me,' he said, and took her arm. 'I'm going to this conference with you.'

'You are not!'

'Keep walking, please, Ms. Anderson. We're late.'

'We're going to be even later, unless you tell me you're joking.'

'Do I sound as if I'm joking?'

Dana looked up at Griffin as he hurried her through the terminal. He most definitely did not look as if he were joking, she thought, and her stomach took a tumble.

'Get this through your head, McKenna. You have as about as much chance of going with me as—as a pig has of flying!'

'A fascinating image, Anderson.'

'*Will* you let go of my arm?' she said furiously. 'I do not wish to be dragged through this terminal like a package.'

'And I don't intend to stand here and debate an issue that's not on my agenda. We're running late. How many times to I have to say it?'

'What's with this *we* stuff? I am going to Florida. You are not going with me.'

They had reached the security checkpoint. Griffin dumped their luggage on the counter.

'Put your computer on the belt, Anderson.'

'Like hell I will!'

'Oh, for... Put the damned thing down,' he growled, peeling the case from her grasp. None too gently, he put his hand in the small of her back, propelled her through the security gate and followed after. '*I* am going to Miami,' he said, snatching up all the luggage as it emerged from the X-ray machine. 'And *you* are going with me.'

'I am not! And I can carry my own stuff.'

'I'm sure that's true,' he said, ignoring her efforts to wrestle her things from his grasp. 'You can do anything a man can do, only a hundred times better,'

'You've got that right.'

'Gate seven,' Griffin said, nudging her to the left. 'That's us.'

'There is no 'us,' McKenna.'

'A figure of speech, I assure you.' Griffin shot her a cold smile. 'A man would have to have a death wish, to want a woman like you in his life.'

'Believe me, the feeling is mutual.' Dana glared at him. 'Will you slow down?'

'If I do, we'll miss our plane. I keep telling you, we're late.'

'And I keep telling *you,* it isn't *our* plane. It's my plane. And it isn't even board—'

'Attention, please. Passengers for East Coast Air, Flight 356 to Miami. Your flight is now boarding at Gate Seven.'

Dana grabbed Griffin's arm and swung out in front of him.

'You lied to me,' she said. 'You told me the Data Bytes rep had to be in Miami by one this afternoon!'

'And he will be, if you'll just shut up and keep moving.'

'You don't know a damn thing about computers. You admitted that yourself.'

'Precisely.'

'So what's the point in you being there?'

He laughed. 'I hate to point this out to you, Anderson, but I own the company.'

'And *I* hate to point this out to *you,* but that isn't going to impress those people one iota.'

Griffin shot her a smug grin. 'It will, when they realize we've got a great new program.'

'You hope,' Dana muttered.

'These are business people who'll be at that conference, Anderson. As far as they're concerned, I *am* Data Bytes!'

'My god, you are unbelievable! A walking ego, is what you are.'

'Going face-to-face with the guy at the top gives people a feeling of confidence.'

'Humph.'

'Trust me, Anderson. It's the truth. It's how I got where I am today.'

'You got there by being born with a silver spoon in your mouth.'

Griffin swung her toward him. 'I got there by working my tail off,' he said coldly. 'The same as you.'

'Oh, spare me, McKenna. You were born rich. Everything's come easy to you, while people like me...'

'While people like you, what?'

Dana shook her head. 'Nothing. You wouldn't understand.'

'You're a snob, lady. Anybody ever tell you that? You think that anybody who was born to money is useless.'

'That isn't true!'

'It damn well is.' His mouth twisted. 'Well, let me tell you something. Not that it's any of your damn business, but I worked my way through college, the same as you.'

'That's ridic...' Dana's eyes narrowed. 'How do you know I worked my way through college?'

'I checked your personnel file, that's how.' Griffin began hurrying her toward their departure gate. 'Did you really think I'd offer you a vice presidency without making sure you had the stuff to warrant it?'

'You didn't offer me the vice presidency. I demanded...' She looked at him and saw that same opinionated little smile on his lips again. 'Dammit, McKenna! You came prepared to give me this job, didn't you?'

'Let's just say I came prepared, period. Good planning's at the heart of success. That's how come I know you went to Harvard, made the Dean's List, all eight semesters, made Phi Bete...' He grinned. 'An impressive record, Anderson. Almost as impressive as mine.'

'I'll bet.'

Griffin laughed. 'Well, first I got tossed out of two different schools, but once I had to pay my own way, I settled down and... Ah. Here we are. Gate Seven.' He dropped the luggage and dug in his pocket for their boarding passes. 'Got 'em. Let's go.'

His story—his half-told story, undoubtedly invented for her, right on the spot—had taken Dana's mind off the present situation. Now, as he nodded at the boarding gate, she came to her senses.

'No way.' She took a step back. 'I am not going anywhere with you, McKenna.'

'I see I don't rate being addressed quite so formally anymore.'

'Damn right, you don't. Debug the code by yourself, pal. I'm not going.'

'Don't be an idiot!'

'You've got that right. That's why I'm not—'

'Okay, let's cut to the chase.' Griffin looked straight at her, his expression cool. 'Are you going to be my new V.P.or are you going to play it coy?'

'Coy?' Dana said angrily, glaring up at that stony face with its firmly set mouth and cold eyes. 'What's that supposed to mean?'

'It means I know why you won't go with me.'

'I hope you do, McKenna! I just hope you understand how insulting it is, that you have so little faith in me that you think you have to go along and ride herd.'

Griffin smiled. It was the kind of self-confident smile that made Dana want to wipe it off his face.

'You're scared,' he said very softly.

'Me?' Dana snorted. 'Don't be ridiculous! I'm not afraid of anything.'

'No?'

'No. I just don't like liars.'

His eyes narrowed. 'I'm a lot of things, Anderson, but I am *not* a liar.'

'You lied about going with me on this trip.'

'Why, if I may ask a foolish question, would I have done that?'

Dana hesitated. A faint wash of pink colored her cheeks.

'So you could—so you could—'

'So I could what?'

She swallowed dryly. So you could get me alone someplace, and seduce me, she'd almost said, and wouldn't that have been stupid? Seduce her? Why on earth would he want to do that? She wasn't his type, and that was definitely a relief because *he* was surely not hers. So what if he'd kissed her once? Well, twice, but that first kiss hadn't really counted. It had been a meaningless brush of the lips, nothing like that second kiss, the one that had made her knees buckle.

And that only proved what a master he was at the game.

He was an arrogant male chauvinist to the bone. He was everything women had fought against for generations in a battle still not won—and yet, she knew that there were females of the species who'd want him. Lots of them. Legions, probably, once they got to Miami. The bikini brigade would keep him busy from the time the plane touched down until the second it left.

'So I could what?' Griffin said.

His smile had turned even softer and more knowing; his deep blue eyes were fastened on her face. Her heartbeat stumbled. She'd adopted a cat once, when she was a little girl. Not for long, of course; her stepfather hadn't liked animals. But she could still recall the pleasure of that brief time when the creature had been hers to enjoy. Its sleek beauty, its velvet touch—and the brilliance of its gaze as it watched the drab little sparrows that had scratched in the tiny patch of dirt her mother had called a yard.

A shudder ran through her. Oh, yes, the cat had been a creature of incredible beauty, but once she'd stumbled across it, stalking one of the sparrows, not out of hunger but out of whatever fierce joy it found in the hunt...

She jumped as Griffin reached out and put one finger lightly against her mouth, tracing the fullness of her bottom lip.

'You're afraid,' he said, his eyes glittering. 'Afraid of what might happen if we spend the weekend alone together.' Dana didn't think, she acted. She dropped her computer, rose up on her toes, dug her hands deep into Griffin's hair and dragged his mouth down to hers.

'Hey,' he said, but whatever else he might have been about to say was lost against her mouth as she kissed him, hard.

What was good for the goose was good for the gander, she thought calmly. McKenna had kissed her to prove a point. Well, she could do the same thing...

Maybe not.

A jolt of electricity seemed to arc from his mouth to hers. Her blood sizzled. Oh, she thought, oh...

She pulled back, heart racing. Griffin had the stunned look

of a man who's just discovered that the ripsaw he'd been carelessly tinkering with was plugged in all along and could have
sliced him into sushi at will.

'Anderson?' he croaked.

Say something, Dana told herself fiercely. For heaven's sake,
say something intelligible!

'You see?' Her voice sounded scratchy. She cleared her throat.
'You see, Mr. McKenna? If I were afraid of you, fearful I might
succumb to your—to whatever, would I have kissed you? Would
I be standing here, feeling so cool, calm, and collected?' Stop
it, she told her pulse as it gave a hyperactive leap. 'No. I would
not. So I suggest you get this through your thick skull. I'm not
afraid of you, or of spending the weekend in your company.'
Eyes still locked with his, she reached down and fumbled for
the handle of her computer case. 'The only thing I'm afraid of
is that you'll get underfoot, show your ignorance and keep me
from debugging that program.'

Griffin opened his mouth, then shut it. For the first time in
his life, no words would come.

'Attention, please. This is the final call for Flight 356 to
Miami.'

Dana snatched her boarding pass from Griffin's hand and
brushed past him. 'Hurry up, or we'll miss our plane.'

A couple of seconds passed. Then Griffin cleared his throat,
straightened his tie, picked up his things and followed after her.

What had happened in that terminal?

Griffin sat in the corner of the taxi that was taking them
from Miami Airport to the Hotel de las Palmas and tried to figure it out. Hell, he thought uncomfortably, he'd spent the entire
flight trying to figure it out. What made him think he'd come
up with an answer now?

Cautiously, he shot a quick glance at Dana. She was seated as
far from him as she could get, her spine as straight as a board,
her knees primly together, her hands folded in her lap. Her pro-

file was serene. For all he knew, she was running code inside her head. That was what she'd done through the whole trip, sat with her computer in her lap and her fingers on the keyboard, angled toward the window in a way that had made it clear she was deliberately excluding him.

His mood took another ten-degree drop. Cool as the proverbial cucumber, he thought grimly. She was the very portrait of a genderless young executive.

No. Not quite.

Griffin's gaze moved over her again. Despite the rigidity of her posture, her skirt had hiked up over her knees, exposing a length of thigh. Her hair was coming out of that tight little knot, too. Soft curls were falling at her temple and against her ear. The last time her hair had come undone, he was the man who'd undone it. He could still remember the silky feel of it in his hands, the sweetness of her mouth as he'd kissed her.

Hell.

He looked away from her and stared blindly out the window.

In the blink of an eye, everything had changed.

That kiss in the office was one thing. But the kiss at the gate... That had been something else.

It wasn't just that she had kissed him, although that had been a shocker all by itself. It was the way she'd done it. So deliberately. So calmly. She'd just grabbed two fistfuls of his hair and hauled his mouth down to hers. He'd been stunned, yeah, but in the first shocked instant, he'd understood.

I'm in control here, she'd been saying.

Except, she hadn't been. And neither had he. In the span of a heartbeat, the kiss had gone from ice to flame. It had almost scalded him—but before he'd had the chance to react, she'd stepped back and fixed him with an unfeeling stare, as if kissing him had been about as exciting as shaking hands with his great-uncle Edgar.

So, which was it? Had she lost control, the same as him? Or was he just plain crazy?

Not that he gave a damn. If the world ran out of women, Dana Anderson would still have to wait her turn until he showed any interest. What intelligent man *would* show interest in a woman like her? She was sharp-tongued and mean-tempered as a shark with a toothache. She hated men; she was obviously sexually repressed and probably terrified of her own femininity.

She was, in other words, one very interesting challenge.

Griffin's scowl grew even darker. Challenge? Ridiculous! Turning Data Bytes around was a challenge. Turning Dana Anderson into a real, live woman was not. Let another man peel away all those outside layers.

The Bow Tie, for example.

But would she ever really let the Bow Tie feel the unexpected heat of that soft mouth? Would he ever know the gut-wrenching frustration of that instant when she fought for control and stumbled back from the edge of the precipice? Could the Bow Tie, or any other man but him, teach her that the fire of passion was far more dangerous than the heat of anger? That a woman could lie in a man's arms without giving up her soul?

Griffin frowned. Dammit, maybe he really was crazy! He leaned forward.

'Driver? Can't this cab go any faster?'

The driver glanced in his mirror and sighed. Another crazy New Yorker, come for the sun but too impatient to slow down and start to relax.

'*Si,*' he said, 'no problem,' and stepped down harder on the gas.

No problem, was right, Griffin thought. He sat back, folded his arms over his chest, and forced his thoughts to the business that lay ahead.

The Hotel de las Palmas was big, and new, and it was right on the beach.

It looked like an overly decorated wedding cake, awash in pink, cream and several tons of gold leaf.

Dana wouldn't have been surprised if Marilyn Monroe had come slinking down the wide front steps.

'Interesting,' Griffin said briskly as they made their way through the ornate lobby.

It was the first word he'd uttered since they'd boarded their plane. Was it a flag of truce? Dana considered, and decided it was. All right, she'd accept the offering. There was no possible way to get through the weekend without a minimum of conversation.

'Very interesting,' she said as she matched her steps to his.

Apparently the kiss had done its job. She'd shocked Griffin McKenna into submission. It was a warming thought. A weekend of hard work, making the new program perform, a couple of days spent enduring his company, and it would be over. They'd head back to New York and, after a couple of weeks, Data Bytes would be secure and he'd move on.

And she—she would be vice president. What a wonderful thing, to happen. Arthur would be so proud. He'd be so—

Dana almost groaned. He'd be so puzzled when he came by this evening to pick her up for dinner and she wasn't there. In all the rush and confusion, she'd never phoned to tell him about any of this.

Well, she'd remedy that the minute she got into her room.

The desk clerk had a pencil-thin mustache and an enormous smile. He wore a dark suit with narrow lapels, accented by a tastefully correct bow tie.

Griffin figured it was one bow tie too many for the week.

Besides, he didn't like the guy's smile. How could a man smile while he said no, there most certainly were no reservations made in the name of the Data Bytes Corporation?

'Check again,' Griffin said.

'There is no point, sir. I have searched my data bank. I have no res—'

'Check,' Griffin barked.

The clerk was a perpetual smiler, but he wasn't a fool. His fingers raced across the keyboard of his computer terminal.

'I am sorry, sir. We have no record of a reservation for the Data Bytes Corporation.'

Griffin glowered at Dana. 'Who made the reservations, Anderson?'

'How should I know?'

'That's true,' Griffin's tone ripped with sarcasm. 'How should you know, indeed? Just because you handled this project—'

So much for the flag of truce. 'I didn't handle it. Dave was in charge, remember?'

Griffin frowned and scraped his hand through his hair. 'Okay,' he said briskly, 'Dave probably screwed up and made the reservation in his own name. 'Forrester,'' he told the clerk. 'With two r's.'

'Forrester, Forrester...' The clerk shook his head. His smile had slipped and become little more than a grimace. 'I'm afraid there's nothing here under that name, sir.'

'McKenna, then.' Griffin tried not to sound as irritable as he felt. It wasn't the clerk's fault the reservations couldn't be found. 'Capital M, small c, capital K-e-n-n-a.'

'Let me see... I have reservations for a Macintosh, and for a MacDougal, but nothing for McKenna.'

Griffin pinched the bridge of his nose between two fingertips.

'I don't suppose it ever occurred to you to follow up on stuff like this, Anderson,' he muttered. 'Considering that you knew Dave had a problem, I mean.'

'Why would it?' She smiled sweetly.

He sighed. When she was right, she was right. 'Okay.' He looked at the clerk. 'So, we have no reservations.'

'That is correct, sir.'

'Well, we'll just have to remedy that, Mr... ' He looked at the man's brass name tag. 'Mr. Whitby.' Griffin smiled pleasantly. 'We'll need a suite.'

'Not in this lifetime.' Dana's smile was equally pleasant. She turned it on the clerk, who beamed in return. 'We'll need two rooms,' she said politely. 'Two separate rooms, on separate floors.'

'We need a corporate suite,' Griffin said, ignoring her. 'One with a large central parlor, where we can meet with clients, and two bedrooms, *separate* bedrooms, each with a private bath, adjoining the parlor on either side. Do you have such suites, Mr. Whitby?'

Whitby brushed a fleck of lint from his lapel. 'Of course, sir.'

'Great. That's what we want.'

'I'm sure you do, Mr. McKenna.' The clerk paused. Griffin could almost hear the drumroll in the background. 'Unfortunately, they're gone.'

'Gone?'

'The corporate suites went early, I'm afraid. They were booked months ago.'

Easy, Griffin told himself. Just take it nice and easy. Reaching across the counter, grabbing the clerk by the ends of his bow tie, wouldn't solve a thing. It was just that that damned smile was getting to him. Hell, the guy would probably keep smiling as he gurgled his last.

'Of course they were,' he said soothingly. 'In that case, I suppose we'll have to take my assistant's advice. Two rooms, please, Mr. Whitby.'

'His vice president's advice,' Dana said. 'Two rooms, on separate floors. In separate wings, if possible.'

'*Three* rooms,' Griffin said through his teeth. 'On the same floor. Connecting rooms. I assume Housekeeping can remove the bedroom furnishings from the center room and bring in a couch and some chairs, instead?'

'There'd be a fee, of course.'

'Of course. But it can be done?'

Whitby sighed. 'I'm sure it could, sir—if we had three connecting rooms. But we do not.'

Griffin gripped the edge of the counter. 'Three adjoining rooms, then.'

'I really am sorry, sir.'

'Okay, forget about having them adjoin. Just give us three rooms on the same...'

Whitby shook his head. 'I don't have three rooms, sir.'

'Two rooms, then,' Griffin said in a dangerously soft voice.

The clerk's smile was, at long last, beginning to fade. 'Sir, I don't have... All the rooms were filled weeks ago.'

Griffin's eyes narrowed. 'Let me be sure I understand this. You haven't got a reservation in my firm's name, or in my name, or in the name of anybody connected with me. And now you're telling me you haven't got one blasted room available in this entire hotel?'

'I'm afraid that is correct, sir. Well, we do have an accommodation, but—'

'We'll take it.'

Dana touched his arm. 'McKenna,' she whispered.

Griffin swung toward her. 'What?'

She looked at the clerk, then at him. 'We cannot share a room.'

'Did you hear what the man said? This room he's offering us is all there is.'

His tone was soft again. Ominously so, but she didn't care.

'I don't care. There is no way I am going to share a room with—'

'Oh, it isn't a room, madam.'

Griffin and Dana both looked at the clerk, who swallowed nervously.

'It's a suite.'

A slow smile edged across Griffin's face. 'A suite?'

'Yes, sir.'

Dana cocked her head. 'But you just said—'

'He made a mistake,' Griffin chuckled. 'We all make mistakes, Mr. Whitby, isn't that right?'

'Uh, yes, sir. Well, not exactly, sir. I mean—'

'Good job, Whitby. I'll be sure to write a letter to management, telling them how helpful you've been. The key, if you please.'

The clerk hesitated. 'Perhaps I should explain, Mr. McKenna. This suite is unique. Quite costly.'

'It's kind of you to show concern, Whitby, but we'll take it.'

'Yes, sir. But the reason it's unique is because—'

'Don't tell me.' Griffin grinned and leaned closer. 'What is it? The Presidential Suite?'

The clerk looked from Griffin to Dana. She could almost feel his distress, especially when their eyes met. Was that a bell ringing in the distance, or was the warning sound tolling only in her ears?

'Not exactly, sir,' Mr. Whitby said, and cleared his throat. 'It's—it's the Bridal Suite.'

'It's only a name,' Griffin said as he marched Dana across the lobby toward the elevator. 'It's meaningless.'

'It is not meaningless,' she insisted. 'If it were, they'd call it Room 2010 or Suite 2010. Something. Anything. But they wouldn't call it the Bridal Suite.'

'It's a hotel, Anderson. They call suites all kinds of things. If George Washington slept in every place named for him, the guy wouldn't have had time to be President.'

'I don't care what you say, McKenna. I'm not going to stay in a bridal suite with you.'

They stopped before a bank of mirrored elevators. Griffin pushed the call button.

'Who's going to know it's the bridal suite, unless we tell them? Look, we've been all through this. You heard what the man said. They have no other rooms.'

'There are other hotels.'

'Yes. Yes, there are. But the conference is being held at this hotel. The meetings will be here. The presentations. The people we've come fifteen hundred miles to see.' He shot her a cold smile. 'Startling as this may sound, this is the hotel we need to stay at.'

'Not in the Bridal Suite, we don't.'

'Will you forget that stupid name? You were there. You heard me ask Whitby what, exactly, that name meant. And he said it didn't mean a thing'

'He did not say that,' Dana said coldly.

'He didn't have to. I mean, he spelled it out, didn't he? He told us there's a bedroom—'

'One bedroom,' she said, glaring at him.

'One bedroom, and a big living room with a sofa.' Griffin's smile glittered as the elevator doors slid open. 'You won't mind sleeping on a sofa, will you?'

There wasn't a way in hell she was going to give him the benefit of a response. 'And there's only one bathroom,' she said as they stepped inside the car. 'One bathroom, McKenna, do you understand?'

'One bathroom's all we need,' Griffin said. An elderly couple tottered into the elevator. The doors whisked closed. 'Not that I like the thought of sharing it. Having to shove aside a curtain of unmentionables so I can take my morning shower isn't my idea of a good time.'

Dana shot a quick look at the elevator's two other occupants. They were facing straight ahead, but she could almost see their ears rotating in her direction.

'For your information,' she said in a low voice, 'I do not hang a curtain of unmentionables in the bathroom.'

'No?'

'No.'

'What do you do with them, then? Wash them and take them to bed with you?'

'I hang my things neatly on the towel rod—not that it's any of your business.'

'It's going to be my business, now that we're going to be sharing the bridal suite.' His smile glittered. 'Amazing, isn't it?

Here we are, about to spend the night together and until yesterday, I hardly knew you.'

The old couple turned and stared at Dana, who felt her cheeks begin to burn. 'It's not what you think,' she stammered. 'We aren't—we haven't—'

'For shame,' the woman said.

Her husband put his hand on her arm. 'Now, Maude, times have changed.'

'Some things *never* change, Harold. Young lady, you give that young man what he wants before he puts a wedding ring on your finger and you might as well forget about him marrying you.'

'But I don't want him to marry me!' Dana bit her lip. 'You don't understand. He and I—'

By some merciful twist of fate, the elevator arrived at their floor. The doors slid open. Dana rushed out of the car and spun toward Griffin as he followed after her.

'That was not funny! If you think I'm going to spend the weekend letting you make crude jokes...' Dana frowned. Griffin was looking over her shoulder, and the expression on his face made the hair rise on the back of her neck. 'What's the matter?'

'Look,' he muttered.

Dana turned around. A low moan rose in her throat.

There was a door at the end of the hallway. It was set in splendid isolation and flanked by a pair of tables that bore gilded vases overflowing with white and pink roses. Dana's eyes widened. Surely this was a joke. Nobody would really make tables that used chubby, rosy-bottomed cherubs for supports.

But somebody had, just as somebody had seen to it that the door bore a gleaming brass plaque. Even at this distance, the engraved words stood out.

'No,' Dana whispered.

Griffin gave a choked laugh. He held up the key to their suite, looked at the room number, then looked at the plaque.

'I'm afraid so,' he said. 'Welcome to the Bridal Suite.'

CHAPTER SEVEN

DANA STOOD ANKLE-DEEP in the white carpet that flowed from one end of the bridal suite to the other and told herself to try and stay calm.

Inhale, she told herself. Exhale. Harmonize the body, mind and spirit. Just the way *Sensei* O'Malley had taught her to do. The idea of Tai Chi Chuan, he'd told his students, was to find your center. Your inner core. Your source of strength and serenity.

She shut her eyes and put her hands on her diaphragm.

'Breathe in,' she whispered. 'Breathe out. In. Out. In…'

'What in hell are you doing?'

Dana blinked her eyes open. Griffin was staring at her as if she'd lost her mind.

'I'm—I'm centering,' she said.

'Centering.' His mouth twitched. 'It looks more like you're hyperventilating.'

'Don't be silly. I never…' The room began to spin and turn gray.

'Hey!' He reached out and encircled her waist with his arm. 'That's all I need right now, Anderson, is you passing out on me.'

'I am not passing out,' she said weakly. 'I, ah, I just felt—'

'Like passing out. It's what comes of puffing in and out like a locomotive. Here, sit down.'

Dana looked at the sofa he was leading her toward. It was shaped like a crescent, covered with a silky-white fabric and strewn with red, heart-shaped pillows. It looked deep enough to consume anybody who was foolish enough to dent one of its overstuffed cushions.

She shuddered and freed herself of McKenna's arm. 'I'm fine, thank you.'

'Yeah, well, see that you stay that way. The last thing I've got time for is a swooning female.'

'I am not a swooning female, McKenna. I'll have you know, I have never fainted in my life.'

'Good. Because—' Griffin's mouth snapped shut as he looked past her. 'Wow. Just look at this place! Did you ever see anything like it?'

'No,' Dana said. 'That was why I was, uh, centering.'

Griffin cackled. There was no other word to describe it. Not that she could blame him. She felt as if they'd followed Dorothy straight into the land of Oz.

'The guy who did the decorating must have been whacked out,' he said. 'It's incredible.'

Incredible was an understatement. Dana frowned. Maybe she was dreaming. Or hallucinating. She'd done that once, when she was a little girl. Her mother had taken her to a free dental clinic and the dentist—dental student, she'd realized, years after—had given her what he'd said would be a whiff of gas. But he must have given her too much because the next thing she'd known, blue monkeys had been hanging from the ceiling.

A simple hallucinatory episode, they'd told her, after they'd brought her around. Not so simple, Dana had thought, and not only because the fear in the student's eyes had contradicted his words but because she'd been terrified, seeing things she knew weren't really there.

Not this time. This—all of it—was real.

'Heart-shaped pillows,' Griffin said. 'Do you believe it?'

He was holding out one of the red pillows, grinning at her as if he expected her to share in the joke.

'Tacky,' she said with a little smile.

'Tacky's a start.' He tossed the pillow on the sofa and strolled through the room, pausing every now and then to take a closer look at one thing or another. 'Look at this, Anderson. Champagne flutes and a little card saying there's a bottle of bubbly in the bar refrigerator.'

'How nice,' she said politely. 'We can offer it to our first guests.'

'Yeah. And get this. A stereo, complete with CDs.' He chuckled. 'Mood music.'

'Mood music,' she echoed. 'How...lovely.'

'And a VCR,' Griffin bent down and peered at the videotapes lined up neatly on a shelf. '*Casablanca. An Affair to Remember.* And something called *The Way We Were*.' He frowned. 'Must be an old one.'

Dana nodded. 'Oh, it is. It...'

She swallowed hard. What was the matter with her? A suite, Whitby had said. A bridal suite. She'd known what to expect, something schmaltzy and saccharine. Well, the furnishings were all that, and more. The decor was overblown, and a little embarrassing, and she wanted to laugh it off, the way Griffin was doing—except she couldn't. If these were all just silly fripperies, why was her throat constricting as she listened to Griffin read the names of those romantic old movies?

'Oh, hell.'

She looked up. Griffin had made his way further into the living room. He'd opened a door, to what she supposed was a closet or maybe the bedroom, and stepped inside. Now, he looked over his shoulder at her.

'Wait until you see this.'

'What?' she said with false gaiety.

'Come look. Trust me, Anderson, there's no way I can do this justice.'

Dana pasted a smile to her lips. 'What is it? The bedroo... Ohmygod,' she said as she looked past his shoulder.

'My sentiments, to the letter. Can you believe it?'

She couldn't, no. She had never even imagined a bathroom could look like this. And to think she'd been concerned about the intimacy of sharing. Oh, it boggled the mind.

'Pink marble,' Griffin said. He whistled in admiration. 'A shower stall that could host a party of six.'

'Eight,' Dana said gaily, though her eyes were riveted not on the shower but on the tub—if you wanted to call the heart-shaped thing a tub.

Nobody would ever just take a bath in it, that was certain.

It was pink marble, too, sunk into a small jungle of flowers and ferns, and bathed in the soft glow of recessed spotlights. A second pair of champagne flutes was within easy reach of the rim, standing alongside an assortment of bath oils with names like—like—

'*Passion Flower,*' Griffin said. He bent closer to the bottles. '*Jungle Nights.*' He uncorked a bottle, took a sniff of the contents. 'Holy hell, Anderson. Get a whiff of this stuff.'

'No.' Dana jumped back, then gave a quick smile. 'I, ah, I'm allergic to things like that. You know, stuff with heavy perfumes.'

'Well, this is heavy, all right.' He closed the bottle and set it back down on the edge of the tub. 'Some layout.'

'Yes, isn't it? Well, we'll work it out. The times we get to use the shower, I mean.'

Griffin turned and smiled at her. It was a teasing smile, but her heart took a tumble.

'It might be more efficient to skip the shower and use the tub,' he said. 'There's plenty of room for two.'

She knew she was blushing and she hated herself for it almost as much as she hated him for making it happen, but she stood her ground and looked him in the eye.

'I'll draw up the schedule,' she said coolly, 'and post it on the door. Any objections?'

'Ah, Anderson, where's your sense of adventure?'

'I prefer to shower in the morning. You can shower at night.'

His smile tilted. 'When does the Bow Tie take his shower?'

Dammit, he was making her blush again!

'My fiancé's bathing habits are none of your business, Mr. McKenna.'

'You're engaged?'

'We're as good as engaged, and that's not any of your business, either.'

Griffin's eyes darkened. 'If you were my fiancée,' he said softly, 'I'd be damned if I'd let you go away with another man for a weekend.'

'I am not away with another man, I am away with you. This is strictly business. Arthur knows that. Well, he will, just as soon as I call him.'

'Yeah,' Griffin folded his arms and leaned back against the wall. 'I noticed.'

'Noticed what? Really, Mr. McKenna, I'd like to see my bedroom, and unpack.' She caught her breath as Griffin reached out his hand and lazily stroked a finger across her cheekbone.

'You never phoned ol' Arthur.'

'I just said—'

'I offered you a job, and all you could think of was upping the ante.' His smile was as lazy as the whisper of his hand against her throat. 'Now, if you were my fiancée, I'd expect you to think of me before you thought of hopping on a plane and heading out of state for a long weekend with another guy.'

'Will you stop that?' Dana said irritably as she brushed his hand aside. 'You were the one who kept saying there was no time to waste, McKenna. And, I repeat, I have not gone off for a long weekend with another man. You are not—'

'Careful, Anderson.' Griffin chuckled softly. 'If you're going to impugn my manhood, you'd better be prepared for me to prove you wrong.'

Their eyes met, their gazes locked.

'You enjoy this,' Dana said in a low, angry voice. 'You get a kick out of embarrassing me.'

'Is that what I'm doing? Embarrassing you?'

'You know you are!'

Griffin frowned. She had him there. That was exactly what he was doing. And she had every right to be ticked off. There was no reason to be teasing her. Teasing a woman, especially this kind of double entendre stuff, was just another way of flirting, and he didn't flirt with the women he worked with; he never had. It was a bad business practice. It was just that it was so damned easy to get a rise out of her.

Maybe it was because she was so serious, or because she had a kind of naïvetéhe hardly ever saw in a career-minded woman. In any kind of woman, in today's insane world.

'If this place makes you feel uncomfortable, McKenna, don't take it out on me!'

'Don't be ridiculous,' he said coldly, although he knew, instantly, that she was right. The suite *did* make him uncomfortable, which was silly, but he'd be damned if he'd let her know that. He was in charge. He was in complete control.

'It's time to get the show on the road.' He shouldered past her, collected their luggage from near the door, and strode the length of the living room. 'We'll unpack, hang our stuff away—'

'Forget the use of the plural,' Dana said as she hurried after him. '*We* are not unpacking. We are not hanging anything away. I get the bedroom, you get the living room.'

'Bedrooms have closets, Anderson.' Griffin paused outside the door of what had to be the bedroom. 'And,' he said, shouldering it open, 'the closet is where I intend to park my stuff. If you think...'

His voice died away.

'McKenna? What's wrong now?'

He gave a strangled laugh. 'Prepare yourself,' he said, and held out his hand.

Dana looked at the hand, ignored it, took a deep, centering breath and stepped inside the bedroom.

'Nothing could surprise me,' she said, 'after that bathroom...' Her breath caught. 'Oh, my,' she whispered.

'Uh-huh. That just about sums it up.'

He was wrong, Dana thought. Nothing could sum it up. If the living room was straight out of the land of Oz, the bedroom was—it was—

'The Arabian nights,' Griffin said softly.

Dana looked at him. 'Yes. You're right. It's—it's—'

Tacky, she'd almost said, but not even she could pull off such a lie. The simple truth was that this was the stuff of middle-of-the-night dreams. Two walls were draped in pale pink silk; one was all glass and overlooked the ocean. The fourth wall was mirrored and faced the bed—a bed covered in pale pink silk and shielded in yards of frothy white lace.

'Damn,' Griffin said very softly.

He turned to her. She could see him reflected in the mirrored panels, a dozen Griffin McKennas, each of them looking at her in a way that made her heart stand still. Their eyes met, and the room filled with silence. No, not silence. Dana could hear a roaring in her ears. It was like an ocean. Yes. Yes, it had to be the sound of the ocean, hurling itself against the beach down below...

'Dana.'

Griffin whispered her name. She felt it brush like a feather down her spine, and she knew that the roaring she heard was the sound of her blood racing through her veins.

'No,' she said...but as she said it, she was moving toward him, or he was moving toward her, she didn't know which, she only knew that suddenly they were in each other's arms.

'No, Griffin.'

The words were a lie. Even as he bent to her, she was lifting herself to him, slipping her arms around his neck, tunneling her hands into his hair, offering him her mouth.

Offering him everything.

He groaned, cupped his hand behind her head, and took her mouth. His kiss was hungry, hot and urgent. There was no tenderness to it, but tenderness wasn't what she wanted. She wanted him, had wanted him for days. For all the years of her life, and when he caught her up in his arms and took her to the bed, she sighed and sank down with him into the softness of the silk, her hands already under his shirt, her fingers hot against his hard, muscled flesh, her mouth open to his.

'Dana,' he whispered, as if her name were all he could manage. He tried to pull back, so he could undress her, but she clung to him, whispering his name, kissing him with a hunger she'd never known before. His hand closed on her blouse, tore it, ripped it from her, exposing her flesh to his mouth, his hungry, eager mouth...

Somewhere in the distance, bells began to ring, chiming out the opening notes of *Here Comes the Bride*.

It was the doorbell.

They went rigid in each other's arms. The bells rang again. Griffin cursed, rolled off the bed, and headed for the front door.

Dana sat up. She was trembling. What had she done? What had she *almost* done? She got to her feet, dragged the ragged edges of her blouse together and tried to think. She could hear voices in the living room. Griffin's, rough and angry. Another man's—Mr. Whitby's?—apologetic and unctuous.

A sob burst from her throat. Frantic, she spun in a tight circle. There had to be a closet. A hall. Someplace where she could hide, where she could fix her hair, her blouse...

'It was the manager.'

Dana swung toward the doorway. Griffin looked at her, his expression cool. She pulled her jacket over her gaping blouse, but his eyes were fixed to her face.

'He wanted to know...' He gave a harsh laugh. 'He wanted to know if we were satisfied.'

She felt color race up under her skin. 'Satisfied?' she said dumbly.

'Yes. You know, were the accommodations okay, did we have enough towels...' A muscle tightened in his cheek. 'I told him we couldn't stay here.'

Dana nodded jerkily. 'Good.'

'I told him that there was no way we could entertain clients in this setting.'

She nodded again. It was all she seemed capable of doing. Her brain felt numb; she stared at Griffin, wondering how he could manage to look so unruffled, sound so calm, as if they were having a meeting in the office, as if they hadn't—as if they hadn't just been—

'I said that I wasn't born yesterday, that I knew damned well that hotels always had a couple of rooms stashed away to take care of the overflow, or of some VIP who might come through the door at the last minute.'

'And?' Dana cleared her throat. 'And, what did he say?'

Just for an instant, something seemed to flicker under that calm facade.

'He was one step ahead of me. He said that these *were* the overflow rooms, and that if any VIP came along, they'd just have to put him in the broom closet.' He paused. 'So, I said that we'd do the best we could, under the circumstances.'

'No!' Dana almost shouted the word. 'Forget it, McKenna. I will not stay in this—'

'Listen to me, Dana.'

'There's nothing you can say that will change my mind. What just happened—what damn near happened...'

'Nothing happened.'

She stared at him. He looked as if he'd been hewn from stone, his face set, his eyes icy-blue. The man who stood before her was Griffin McKenna, the corporate raider, and for the first time, she understood why he was respected—and feared.

'Nothing happened,' he repeated.

It was silly, but the dismissive words stung her.

'You can't just pretend—'

'I'm not pretending.' He walked toward her and she told herself not to shrink back against the wall. 'I'm simply stating facts. We're both tired, and this damned pleasure palace isn't exactly conducive to sainthood.' His mouth hardened. 'In other words, you're a woman and I'm a man. And, despite what our politically correct pundits say, there are differences between the sexes.'

Dana drew herself up. 'Now just a minute, McKenna—'

'Spare me the dialectic, Anderson. I'm not about to debate the issue. The bottom line is that things got out of hand a minute ago, but it won't happen again.'

'You're damned right it won't.'

'Sexual attraction can be controlled, the same as any other emotion.'

'I agree, McKenna.'

Griffin smiled thinly. 'Do you suppose we might move on to addressing each other by our first names? Considering our relationship, I mean. Our business relationship,' he said when he saw her eyes flash a warning. 'I'll call you Dana, you'll call me Griffin. It's the practice I follow with the people who work with me. As for the rest...' He waved a hand toward the bed in a clear gesture of dismissal. 'Just put it out of your mind.'

'Just put it...'

'You can do that, can't you?'

His voice was hard, and dangerous. What was he worried about? Did he think he was so irresistible that he'd have to spend the weekend fending her off? Well, he could relax. What had happened a little while ago had been the price she'd paid for the highs and lows of the past couple of days. It wasn't all that different from looking up and seeing blue monkeys.

'Yes.'

'Good. I'm glad we have that out of the way.'

'Yes. So am I. And now, if you don't mind—Griffin—I'd like to unpack.'

'Certainly.'

'I'm sure you'll understand, though, if I suggest you unpack in the living room.'

'No problem.'

Dana smiled politely, and waited for Griffin to step aside. He didn't.

'Ah, if you wouldn't mind? You're standing in my way.'

'Oh.'

He didn't move. She cleared her throat. 'Griffin. Step aside, please.'

'You're sure you followed what I said? About there being nothing to be concerned about?'

'Of course,' she said quickly, looking up at him. Had he moved closer? His eyes were dark. So dark. Her heart gave a crazy thump.

'Sexual appetite,' he muttered. His gaze fell to her mouth. 'Easily controlled, especially since you're not my type of woman anyway, Anderson.'

'Well, you're not my type of man, McKenna.' Her heart thumped again. His hand was slipping up her throat, his fingers threading deep into her hair. What had happened to the clips that kept it off her face? What was happening to her knees? 'Not my type at—'

His mouth closed on hers, very gently. She made a soft little sound; she lifted her hand, almost touched his chest, then drew it back down to her side.

Griffin lifted his head.

'It was just an aberration,' he whispered. 'Understood?'

Dana nodded. 'Understood.' Her hand rose again and this time she touched him, lay her palm flat against his chest and felt the gallop of his heart. He hissed, caught her hand in his, and brought it to his lips. 'An aberration.' Her voice shook.

'Of course,' he said. He tilted her face up to his and kissed her again, slowly, passionately, his mouth open, the tip of his tongue playing against the tip of hers.

She shuddered. 'Of course,' she sighed, and sucked his tongue into her mouth.

He groaned. His hands slid down and down, cupped her bottom and lifted her into him. He was fully, excitingly aroused; she felt the thrust of him against her belly and she rose up on her toes and curled her fingers into his lapels.

They drew back at the same moment, the flush on her face mirroring on his. The seconds slipped by while they stared into each other's eyes, and then Griffin took a shuddering breath.

'I'm going to go down to the lobby. You know, look around, see who else has checked in.' He touched the back of his hand to the hollow of her throat. 'All right?'

'Yes.'

He nodded. 'Good. Good.' He spoke quietly, as if nothing had happened. But his hand was still at her throat, as if measuring the flutter of her pulse. 'Meet me in the bar at six. Can you manage that?'

'Seven,' she said. She could feel her heartbeat slowing as he took his hand away. 'That'll give me time to follow through on some of the code work I did on the plane.'

'Seven. Fine.' He stepped back. 'Anderson?'

Dana cleared her throat. 'Yes?'

For a long, long moment, he didn't speak. Then he cupped her face in one hand and kissed her again, with a sweet, yearning tenderness that made her dizzy.

'If that door has a lock,' he said gruffly, 'use it when you go to bed tonight.'

He walked from the room. She waited until she was sure her knees wouldn't buckle. Then, carefully, she shut the door. There was a lock. She looked at it, considered, and turned it, although she was no longer sure whether it was to keep Griffin out or to keep her in. Then she crossed the room, sat down gingerly on the edge of the bed and took a deep breath.

Finally, she reached for the phone and dialed.

'Mr. Coakley, please,' she said, and when she heard Arthur's familiar voice, she almost sobbed with relief.

'Arthur,' she began cheerfully, 'I'm afraid I won't be able to keep our dinner appointment this evening. You'll never guess where I am...'

CHAPTER EIGHT

GRIFFIN SAT IN the Coconut Lounge of the Hotel de las Palmas and wondered if he'd gone crazy.

How else to explain what he'd just done?

He was an adult male. Sophisticated. Intelligent. In full and complete control of his emotions, manners, and hormones.

That's what he'd been, anyway, until he'd come on to Dana with all the subtlety of a stallion in heat.

Griffin reached for his bourbon and water, lifted it halfway to his lips, then set it down. Booze was the last thing he needed. A bucket of ice water, was more like it. Or maybe a quick trip to a psychiatrist's couch.

Tell me, Doctor, why would a man who has his pick of women—hey, this was not a time for false modesty—why would such a man try and bed the one woman in the entire world who least appeals to him?

It was an excellent question. Griffin looked at his drink, frowned, picked it up and then put it down again.

Why, indeed?

He had no idea. And, he suspected, neither would the eminent shrink.

'Hell,' he muttered.

'Sir?'

Griffin looked up. The bartender smiled politely.

'Did you want something?'

'No. Yes.' Griffin frowned. 'I suppose people sit here day after day, telling you the damnedest stories.'

'Oh, they do, sir. They do, indeed.'

'Men probably talk about women, women about men...?'

'It's the men who do most of the talking, sir.'

Griffin nodded. 'Women are almost a different species, aren't they?'

The bartender chuckled. 'You can say that again.'

Griffin sighed. He pushed his drink aside. 'Ditch the bourbon,' he said. 'Bring me a club soda, with a twist of lemon.'

'Very good, sir. Anything else?'

A functional brain, Griffin thought. 'No, just the club soda.'

He nodded his thanks when the soda was set before him, lifted the glass and took a long swallow.

What had happened, up there in the bridal suite? Why had he kissed Dana Anderson?

Kissed her? Griffin almost laughed. He hadn't kissed her, he'd damn near ravaged her, or he would have, given another thirty seconds.

No. Ravaged wasn't the right word, not unless Dana wanted to admit that she'd done her share of ravaging, too. Touching her had been like touching a ribbon of flame. He'd never experienced anything like it. The way her mouth had clung to his. The way she'd melted into him, uttered those soft little cries that had almost driven him past the point of no return.

The glass shook in Griffin's hand. He put it down, carefully, and took a deep breath.

Back to square one. Maybe he *was* crazy. Or maybe she was. For all he knew, they were a scientific phenomenon, two seemingly rational human beings who'd suddenly gone over the edge together.

The only certainty was that he'd never done anything like that in his life. He was a man who liked women; he took great pleasure in uninhibited, passionate sex—but he was always in control. Always.

Until the Anderson woman came into his life.

Bringing her here had been dumb. He should have remembered how things had gone in his office yesterday. He hadn't been any more in control then than he had in that ridiculous bedroom just now. If he had any brains at all, he'd have...

Hell.

If, if, if. Should have. Would have. Could have.

Griffin picked up the glass and drank some of the club soda. What was it Dana had said? Something about everybody making it to heaven if 'if' ruled the world?

She was right. What was done, was done. The thing to do now was put the foolishness behind him and get on with business.

So she was attractive, once you got past the funny hair and the shapeless outfits. Big deal. He had the numbers of most of New York's most beautiful women in his address book. What was attractive, compared to that?

'Nothing,' he muttered. 'Nothing at all.'

Was she sexy? Was she flirty? Did she look at him with stars in her eyes?

'No,' Griffin muttered.

No, she sure as hell didn't. Wasn't. Whatever. She'd said he wasn't her type, and she certainly wasn't his. Okay, maybe she had possibilities, but so what? Basically, she had about as much femininity to her as an audit report.

'Hi.'

Griffin looked around. A woman was sliding onto the stool beside his. Nice, he thought. Very nice. Long, straight red hair.

An oval face. Big, dark eyes and a pouting mouth that made his imagination sit up and take notice.

She smiled. 'Are you here for the conference?'

Her voice was low and sultry. She was wearing a black dress, some sort of backless, sleeveless thing. Her breasts oozed from the bodice like ripe fruit. She smiled, leaned back a little and crossed her legs.

A little obvious, not as subtly sexy as Anderson, but...

Griffin frowned, emptied his head of such nonsense and told himself that he was about to be a very lucky man.

'Yes,' he said, smiling back at her. 'And you?'

She nodded. 'I'm with Omniplex Computers.' She held out her hand. 'Julie Everett.'

He took her hand, held it a second longer than manners required. A weight seemed to lift from his shoulders. It was going to be a pleasant weekend, after all.

'Hello, Julie Everett. I'm—'

'Sir?'

Griffin looked up. The bartender held out a telephone. 'Sorry to interrupt, Mr. McKenna.'

Griffin sighed. 'A call?'

'Yes, sir.'

'Yeah, okay.' He took the phone and shot the redhead a quick smile. 'You just hold that thought, Julie Everett.'

Her brows lifted. 'What thought?'

'The one I hope we're sharing, about the rest of the evening.'

She laughed. It was a nice laugh, soft and musical, and pleasant to hear. Griffin felt his spirits lift. This was the way women were supposed to be. Sweet. Compliant. Eager to please...

'McKenna?'

Dana's angry bark sounded in his ear. He winked at the redhead, turned away, and spoke into the phone.

'Anderson. What's the problem?'

'I'll tell you the problem. You are the problem.'

Griffin scowled at the phone. 'Listen, Anderson, is this really important? Because if it can wait—'

'You had to have things your own way, didn't you?'

'I already apologized for that,' he said, lowering his voice. 'There's no need to—'

'I'll put my carry-on under my seat, I said. 'Oh, no,' you said. 'Give it to me,' you said. 'I'll put it into the overhead compartment.'"

'What the hell are you talking about?'

'My luggage. What does it sound like I'm talking about?'

'What about your luggage? Dammit, Anderson—'

'It isn't.'

'Isn't what?'

'Isn't my carry-on,' Dana said impatiently. 'It looks like mine. It's the same size and color, but when I opened it up, it was full of some guy's dirty laundry.'

Griffin sighed. Just what he needed. A luggage screwup.

'Okay,' he said, 'okay, I'll report it to the airline.'

'I'm not helpless, McKenna. I already did that.'

'And? I assume they've already heard from the guy who took your carry-on by mistake. Let them send somebody over to make the switch.'

'Assuming anything is a mistake, McKenna. Didn't the screwups with the code and the hotel reservations teach you that?'

Griffin felt a faint hammering begin in his temples. 'You're right. Forget what I said. Just get to the bottom line.'

'The bottom line is that I don't have my luggage, and neither does the airline. The flight continued on to Bogota. My clothes are probably sitting inside a hut beside the Amazon River by now.'

He shut his eyes, blinked them open, and looked toward the ceiling. 'The Amazon doesn't come anywhere near Bogota.'

'Dammit, I don't care! I want my luggage!'

'All right, calm down. These things happen. Look, I saw

a shop in the lobby where I'm sure you can pick up whatever you need. Come down, buy what you want, and bill it to me.'

'I can't do that.'

'Don't be an idiot. It's not as if I'm offering to set you up in an apartment.'

The redhead chose that instant to move into his line of vision. One glance, and he knew she'd heard the last sentence.

Griffin slapped his hand over the telephone.

'It's not what you think,' he said quickly.

'You just hold that thought,' she said with a little smile. Dana's voice buzzed from the handset. Griffin ignored it. He watched the redhead's slow exit and the collapse of his plans for the evening. Jaw set, he turned his back to the door and jammed the phone against his ear.

'You have five minutes to get your tail down to that shop, Anderson. Five minutes. If not, your job is history. Do I make myself clear?'

'Whatever you say, McKenna.' Her voice trembled with anger. 'I just hope you're ready to explain to anybody who asks why I'm down there, walking around in clothes that look like they've been ripped off.'

'All right. Okay, you've made your point. Stay where you are. I'll take care of everything.'

'I don't want you to take care of everything. I just want you to get me something to wear.'

'I'll do that, and I'll have it sent up.'

'Thank you.'

Griffin almost laughed. Anne Boleyn must have said the same kind of 'thank you' to the executioner who'd assured her that the blade of his ax was razor-sharp.

'Tell me what you need,' he said.

'I need everything. Toothbrush. Toothpaste. Comb.'

'Try that stage set of a bathroom. There's bound to be an assortment of toiletries in there.'

'You're right. I'm using the portable phone. Let me just walk down and check… Okay, scratch the toothbrush and stuff. Just get me something to wear for this evening. I'll stay here and work on the code until it's time to meet you, and I'll do the rest of my shopping tomorrow.'

'Sounds good,' Griffin signaled to the bartender for a pencil and paper. 'Size?'

Dana hesitated. He could almost see her trying to find a way not to give him such personal information.

'Come on, Anderson. What's the matter? Are you afraid I'll make a wax doll in a size twelve and stick pins in it?'

'Eight,' she said coldly. 'I'm size eight.'

He grinned. 'Eight. Fine. I'll pick out a feed sack and have it sent up.'

'Very amusing. Just get me something simple, please.'

'I'll do my best.'

'A man-tailored blouse. White, with long sleeves.'

'I just said, I'll do my best.'

'And a suit. Or a skirt and a blazer, if they don't have a suit. Something conservative.'

'Anderson, I am not the Saks Personal Shopper.'

'Tell the salesclerk I want a skirt that falls below the knee. Either that, or trousers. Tweed is good, if they have it, or a lightweight wool. Oh, and I prefer a dark color—'

Griffin hung up.

The Shoppe de Mer was just off the lobby. The display window held an assortment of gold and silver balloons, a stuffed flamingo and a couple of bathing suits that gave him pause. He'd seen stuff like that on the Cote d'Azur, but could a woman really wear two circles of silk and a thong in the good old U.S. of A. and get away with it?

Regretfully, he thought about how terrific Julie Whatever-Her-Name-Was would look in something like that…

Dana would look even better.

Griffin frowned and stepped inside.

The salesclerk, ageless and elegant, went with the territory. He doubted if the word 'tweed' would be either in her vocabulary or in the shop's back room, but he gave it his best shot.

'Tweed?' she said as if she'd just gotten a mouthful of lemon juice.

'Tweed,' he said pleasantly. 'You know—scratchy wool, the kind favored by spinster great-aunts. In a size eight.'

Her smile assured him that she was willing to share in the joke.

'I know the fabric, sir, but I'm afraid there's little call for something so—traditional, in South Beach.'

Griffin nodded as he strolled around the little shop. Surprisingly enough, he'd never been in a place like this before. He never bought his women gifts of clothing. Flowers, yes, and perfume, and jewelry sometimes, but never clothing.

Clothing was far too personal…but it surely was interesting.

'What's this?' he said, nodding at a bit of pale blue silk.

'That's a camisole, sir. Does the lady in question prefer camisoles to bras?'

Did she? Griffin thought back to the morning. He was pretty certain Dana hadn't been wearing anything under that Lois Lane sweatshirt. She wouldn't need to—he'd felt the round fullness of her breasts against his chest, felt their lush firmness…

'Sir?'

Griffin blinked. 'I'll take it,' he said gruffly.

'We have matching panties, too,' She held up two snippets of silk. 'Which would madam prefer, do you think? The tap pants? Or the thong?'

Madam would prefer to club me over the head, Griffin thought, especially if I buy her undies.

'Oh, the thong,' he said. 'Definitely.'

'There's a matching garter belt, of course.'

'Of course,' he said calmly.

'And hose. Would madam wish a pale shade? Nude, perhaps?'

Damn, what had he gotten himself into? Nude was not a

concept he wanted to consider right now. He could almost see Dana wearing nothing but the camisole, the thong panties, the garter belt and the sheer-as-a-cobweb stockings...

'Nude.' His voice cracked, and he cleared his throat. 'Nude, would be fine.'

The clerk nodded. 'You did say madam prefers suits?'

'Suits,' Griffin said, forcing his attention back to the business at hand. 'Uh, yes. She likes suits, but I believe we've already established that you have nothing in tweed.'

'I have a silk suit that might be just right.'

'In a size eight?'

'Indeed. Let me show it to you.'

The clerk drew something from a rack. The sexy underwear, the bathing suits in the window, the clingy, soft garments hanging all around the shop had put Griffin's brain into overdrive. The thing on the hanger brought him quickly back to reality. It was a suit, made of silk but in a flat white that reminded him of the underbelly of a dead fish. The skirt was long enough to please a nun, and the jacket was big enough to shelter at least two people.

He hated it on sight. Dana would love it.

'Would you call this suit conservative?' he asked.

The clerk gave him a strange look, but he figured she had the right, considering that a man with his taste in underwear would ask such a thing.

'I suppose so,' she said slowly.

He nodded. What was the sense in fantasizing? Dana would sooner wear a blanket than anything he might buy in this shop. She wanted conservative? She could have conservative.

'Great. Send it to—' To the Bridal Suite, he'd almost said, but his lips wouldn't form the words. 'To Suite 2010. And put it on my account.'

'What about shoes, sir?'

'Shoes?' He looked blank. 'She—the lady has shoes. Black

ones, if I remember right. Conservative, like the suit. You know, those things with chunky, low heels... What?'

The clerk cleared her throat. 'If I may suggest, sir...' She held up two scraps of leather, the same shade as the suit. 'These would be preferable.'

'Yeah, sure.' Griffin was starting to feel uncomfortable. Maybe he should have told the clerk what he needed, let her pick out everything instead of doing it himself. 'If you think she needs shoes, toss 'em in.'

'Size?'

He ran his hand through his hair. 'I don't know. She's tall. Well, not too tall. She's...'

'About my size, perhaps?'

'Yes. A couple of inches taller. And a little, ah, curvier...'

Dammit all, the clerk was trying not to smile. And he—he was blushing! Blushing, and all because a woman who didn't like being a woman had sent him to do a chore no man should ever have to do.

A scowl spread over his face.

'Send up an assortment of sizes,' he said in the same tone he used when he ordered his broker to buy ten thousand shares of stock. 'One is sure to be right.' He glanced at the little pile of silk wisps that Dana would never call underwear. 'As for that stuff...'

'Sir?'

Forget about it, he'd been going to say, but hell, a man could dream, couldn't he?

'Send it up, too,' he said, and then he scribbled his name on the bill and beat a quick retreat.

He called Dana on a house phone, told her the shop would be delivering the things she needed, and that he'd drift around the conference floor for the rest of the afternoon and meet her in the lobby at seven, as they'd planned.

At six forty-five, he settled in to wait. She'd been fast as lightning this morning, and he had no reason to expect otherwise now. Women didn't tell time the same way men did, that was a fact of life, but Dana didn't live by female rules.

The minutes slipped by. Griffin glanced at the big wall clock over the elevators and frowned. Twenty after seven. Where was she? There was a cocktail party this evening, for the conference attendees, followed by a rubber-chicken dinner. It was the kind of thing he hated but he knew it had to be endured. He'd do some networking and leave the computer talk to Dana. He wondered if she'd made any headway with the code. She'd only been at it a couple of hours, but still...

Griffin felt his heart stop. A woman stepped hesitantly from the elevator, one he'd never seen before—one he knew he had wanted, all his life.

Dana.

No wonder the salesclerk had looked at him as if he were crazy when he'd asked her if the silk suit was conservative. Conservative? He'd have laughed at his own stupidity, if he could have trusted himself to do anything more complicated than to get to his feet and stare.

Everything he'd thought about the suit had been wrong. It was ivory, not white, a shade that brought out the rosy blush in Dana's skin and made her tumble of loose curls gleam like gold. The jacket he'd thought was big was, instead, clingy and sexy. It tied at the waist—such a sweet, slender waist—and the single tie was all that held the jacket together. Beneath, he could see the creamy length of Dana's throat, and the gentle rise of her breasts.

And the skirt. Griffin's throat tightened. What an idiot he was to have thought it concealing. The skirt was long, yes... long and clinging. It was slit all the way from the narrow hem to her thigh.

A hush fell over the lobby. People were looking. Griffin felt his heart swell with anticipation as he started toward Dana. He wanted to sweep her into his arms and tell every man whose eyes were popping that this beautiful woman was his.

His? But she wasn't his. He didn't want her to be his.

Did he?

'Griffin?'

Her voice, soft and wonderfully sweet, made his pulse quicken. They were standing only inches apart. Dana's head was tilted back. Her eyes were glittering, her lips were parted. Griffin gave up the fight. Of course, he wanted her. And she wanted him. He could see it in the way she was staring at him, with an intensity that sent a tingle right down to his toes.

'Yes,' he said softly, and flashed a killer smile.

It could work. First this long weekend, then a lazy affair back in the city. A month, maybe even two...

'Griffin,' she said, 'if we were alone—'

Every muscle in his body tightened. He could feel the eroticism of the moment, sense the words of need and desire she was going to whisper right here in this crowded, public place.

'If we were alone, Griffin, I'd smile while I killed you.'

He blinked.

'I asked for tweed.'

'They didn't have tweed.'

'I asked for conservative.'

'They told me this was conservative.'

'I've never worn anything so—so—'

'Feminine?'

'Revealing. I'm positive everyone is staring.'

'They are.' Amazing, he thought, that he could carry on such a rational conversation when what he wanted was to sling this gorgeous creature over his shoulder and carry her off. 'You look—you look—'

Her hand snaked out between them and she jabbed him in the gut.

'And what's with the...' Her cheeks turned crimson. 'The underwear?'

Griffin slid an arm around her waist. 'Could we discuss this someplace else?'

'We can discuss it right here.'

'Well,' he said pleasantly, 'in that case, you need to speak just a little bit louder. That gentleman to your right is having trouble keeping up with the conversation.'

Dana looked to the side. Her cheeks turned a deep crimson, and she let Griffin lead her through the lobby to an alcove hidden behind a pair of potted palms.

'Answer the question,' she snapped, twisting out of his encircling arm. 'Why on earth did you buy me that underwear?'

He shrugged. 'I figured you needed some.'

'I didn't. I was wearing perfectly adequate...' The wash of color swept over her face again. 'You know what I mean. What you selected was—outrageous.'

'It was the only stuff they had.' It wasn't really a lie; it was the only stuff he'd seen, but why mention that? His gaze moved over her, lingering for a heartbeat on her mouth before rising, again, so that their eyes met. 'So, tell me.'

'Tell you what?'

He smiled lazily. 'Do you have those things on?'

'Do I have...' Dana lifted her chin. 'It's none of your business.'

He smiled, and her breath caught at the dangerous promise in that smile.

'Meaning, you do.'

'Meaning just what I said, McKenna. It's none of your business—but if I do, it's only because I showered, and I couldn't just put on the stuff I'd worn all day.'

'Showered?' He lifted a hand, touched it to her shoulder. The silk of the suit sighed under his fingertips. He could feel the heat of her skin, burning like fire through its softness. 'I figured you'd use that big tub.' His hand stroked across her shoulder, slid gently under her hair and around the nape of her neck.

Dana swallowed hard. 'Don't change the subject! You had no right to buy me any of that stuff.'

He grinned. 'Wanted to murder me the second you saw it, did you?'

'It won't work, McKenna.'

'What? The underwear? But you already admitted you were wearing—'

'This—this childish plan of yours.' His fingers moved lightly against her skin. Oh, she thought, how good it felt, having him touch her. She wanted to shut her eyes, tilt her head into his palm, purr like a kitten...

'What childish plan?'

'I am an intelligent woman, McKenna. I know what you're doing.'

'Really?' Griffin's eyes were dark, almost blurred with passion. He moved closer to her; she took a step back until her shoulders were against the wall. 'That's good, Anderson. That's very good, because I sure as hell don't know what I'm doing.'

'You do. You're trying to... Don't do that!'

'I'm just sniffing you, that's all.' He bent his head. His nose, then his mouth, brushed the sensitive skin just behind her ear. 'What's that scent?'

'It's...' God, her knees were buckling! 'It's bath oil. It was in that basket in the bathroom.'

'I thought you said you didn't use the tub.'

'I didn't. I rubbed the oil on after I...'

'Rubbed it on?' He moved again, so that his body was pressed lightly against hers. She could feel the heat coming off him, and the hardness of his arousal against her belly. 'All over?' His voice was low, so low that it seemed to thrum through her blood. 'I could have done that for you, if I'd been there.'

Dana closed her eyes. 'Please,' she whispered, 'don't.'

'Don't what? I'm just trying to impress you with my usefulness.'

A low moan broke from her throat. His hand was in her hair,

and he was tilting her head back. Her heart was beating so quickly she was sure he could hear it pounding against her ribs.

'McKenna...'

'Griffin.' He bent his head, brushed his lips over hers. 'A man and a woman sharing the Bridal Suite should at least be on a first-name basis.'

'Listen to me,' she said desperately. 'I showered because I was running late. I spent the afternoon working on the code, trying to fix it.'

'Did you?'

'Yes. No. I'm not sure. I'll have to try it again, later.' 'Much later.'

'Dammit, Griffin! This isn't fair. I'm trying to tell you that I made progress on the code and you—you're trying to seduce me.'

There was a silence, and then he drew back, just enough so he could look down into her eyes.

'You're right,' he said softly. 'I am.'

Dana blushed. 'I—I didn't expect you to—to admit it so—so—'

Griffin cupped her face in his hands. 'It's too late to lie about it, Dana. We're not children. We both know what's happening.'

Logic, and whatever remained of self-preservation, told her to deny the statement, but how could she, after this afternoon? How could she, when she was staring up into his eyes and trembling with longing?

'It's wrong,' she said in a breathless whisper.

'Why is it wrong?'

'Because...' Why? Why was it wrong? 'Because—because of that woman I saw with you in the restaurant.'

'Cynthia?' He shook his head. 'She's a friend, that's all,' His eyes darkened. 'What about the Bow Tie? Have you really got something going with him?'

'Arthur? No. I mean, he's never said...'

Griffin drew her into his arms and kissed her. 'I've never

wanted a woman as I want you,' he whispered. He looked into her eyes. 'Be honest, Dana. You want me, just as much.'

She did, he was right. And that was why it was wrong, because if she went to bed with him, she would never be able to forget him...

Griffin put his arm around her. 'Come with me.'

'Where?'

To bed, he wanted to say—but not yet. He wanted to draw out the pleasure, prolong the anticipation until the both of them were dizzy with hunger and wanting for each other.

'I don't know. We could take a walk, on the beach.' The image blazed to life in his mind. 'Maybe we could build a fire,' he whispered. 'And we could dance, on the sand. Do you like to dance?'

She looked up at him and smiled. 'Yes. I love to—'

He bent and kissed her hungrily, and this time she rose toward him, wound her arms tightly around his neck and opened her mouth to his.

'Griffin,' she whispered, and buried her hot face against his chest. 'Griffin...'

She felt the swift quickening in his body. 'The hell with this,' he growled, and then he was turning her toward the lobby, leading her out from behind the palms. 'The only place we're going is to—'

'Ohmygod!' Dana stumbled to a halt, her face suddenly as pale as her ivory suit. 'Look,' she whispered, and pointed a trembling finger toward the registration desk.

'What?' Griffin said irritably—and then he groaned. A woman stood at the desk, looking flustered and lost.

'Cynthia?' he muttered, his voice rising in disbelief.

Dana shoved free of his encircling arm. 'Just a friend, huh?' Her voice shook. She swung toward him, eyes flashing fire. 'You—you rat! What kind of man are you? Trying to seduce me when all the time, you knew that—that woman was on her way to join you for the weekend! What were you going to do? Play musical bedrooms?'

'Dana, I swear to you, I had no idea she'd be here.'

'No?'

'No. Honest to—'

'So you figured you'd take a shot at me, instead?'

'She must have decided to surprise me.'

'Oh, yeah. She surprised you, all right.'

'Will you listen to...' Griffin's eyes narrowed. 'Well, I'll be damned.'

'That goes without saying!' Dana slapped her hands on her hips. 'There are names for men like you, McKenna. If I weren't such a lady, I'd—'

'I suggest you get down from the pulpit, Anderson.' Griffin gripped her shoulders, and swung her towards the lobby door. His voice had gone flat and icy. 'You're in no position to give me sermons on morality, considering what just came waltzing in.'

Dana's mouth dropped open. 'Arthur?' she said, in a choked whisper.

'The Bow Tie, in the flesh.' Griffin shook his head. 'Hell, lady, I had you pegged all wrong.'

'You don't understand. I never...'

'Yeah, I'm sure you didn't, but that's the risk you run, if you play the game. Getting caught is always a possibility.' Griffin's hand closed around her wrist. 'Time to face the music, babe,' he said, and Dana hardly had time to paste a smile on her face before he set off across the lobby, towing her after him.

CHAPTER NINE

GRIFFIN COULDN'T BELIEVE IT.

The lobby was like a stage set, just before the curtain rises. No action. No sound. Just all the principal characters on their marks, poised and ready to speak their lines in what was rapidly becoming a farce of epic proportions.

There was Cynthia, standing at the desk. And there was the Bow Tie, standing just inside the lobby door.

And here was Dana, bristling with fury.

'Now see what you've done,' she said, pulling free of his grasp and hurrying towards Arthur.

Griffin stared after her. What *he* had done? It was such a typically female thing to do, put the blame for this mess on him when he was as innocent as a baby. God knew, he hadn't invited Cynthia to come here. Had Dana invited Arthur? It didn't seem possible, considering the way she'd been kissing him behind the palms a minute ago, but women were unpredictable creatures, yet another reason why they didn't belong in the business world.

'Griffin!'

Griffin pasted a smile to his lips. Cynthia had spotted him.

She waved as enthusiastically as a cheerleader at a football game and rushed towards him.

'Cynthia. What a surp—'

'Oh, Griffin,' she said, as she flung herself into his arms. It was something she had not done before and something he wished she hadn't done now. He hesitated, then put his arms around her.

Over by the door, the Bow Tie was doing the same thing to Dana.

Bloody hell, Griffin thought bloody *damn* hell!

Cynthia drew back, linked her hands with his, and smiled.

'Are you surprised, darling?'

Surprised? Stunned was a better word. And what was with the 'darling' business? Something new had been added.

She laughed gaily. Too gaily, he realized, as her hands turned icy in his.

'I know it's terribly bold of me, and if you want me to leave, you've only to tell me and I'll fly straight home, but I thought— well, Marilyn and I had brunch together, and one word led to another, and she said—'

Griffin felt his blood pressure move up a notch. 'My mother suggested this?' he asked, very gently.

'No,' Cynthia replied, backtracking quickly, 'of course not. We were chatting, that's all, about how some men seem to prefer their women to—to be a tad less conservative in, you know, in their relationships.' Color rose in her cheeks. 'And I suddenly thought how—how exciting it might be, if I flew down to see you.' Her color deepened. 'I've done something stupid, Griffin, haven't I? Forgive me. I'll get right into a taxi and—'

'Don't be silly.'

'Are you sure?'

There were times in a man's life that a lie was an act of kindness. As for the weekend he'd been anticipating, only moments ago... His gaze focused narrowly on Dana. She was smiling at the Bow Tie and clinging to his arm as if he were Prince Charming.

How could he have ever thought he wanted her in his bed?

'Positive,' he said briskly.

Cynthia smiled. 'That's wonderful, darling. And I promise, I won't get in the way. I know you have business to transact.' Her smile dimmed as she looked past him. 'I see I've already taken you away from a meeting. Such an attractive woman. It's hard to imagine she'd be knowledgeable about computer programs.'

Griffin looked at the happy couple again. They were deep in conversation. The Bow Tie's hands rested lightly on Dana's waist, her face was lifted to his in rapt concentration.

'Yes,' he said tightly. 'It is, isn't it?'

'What does she do?'

Drives me crazy, he thought, and frowned.

'Griffin? Is she here for the conference?'

He nodded. 'Actually, she's with Data Bytes. The company I took over. She's the vice president in charge of research and development.'

Cynthia's eyes widened. 'Really? Oh, I'd like to meet her, Griffin. I always marvel at women who don't mind giving up their femininity to succeed in a man's world,' She took his arm and smiled up at him. 'Introduce me, darling, would you? Although, perhaps we should wait for a better time. Your vice president does seem to be rather busy, at the moment.'

Busy wasn't the word for it. The Bow Tie was playing kissy-face.

'On the other hand,' Griffin said, clasping Cynthia's hand, 'there's no time like the present.'

He reached Dana's side just as her boyfriend was puckering up for another smooch.

'Ms. Anderson,' he said with a chill smile, 'how nice. I see you've stumbled across an old friend.'

Dana's smile was every bit as icy as his. 'And so have you, Mr. McKenna. Small world, isn't it?'

'Miniscule.' Griffin slipped his arm around Cynthia's waist. 'Cynthia Gooding, this is Dana Anderson.'

'Delighted, Miss...' Cynthia hesitated. 'Haven't we met before?'

'I don't think so,' Dana said. It was almost the truth. They hadn't met, officially, they'd simply slipped past each other, in *Portofino.* She held out her hand. Cynthia looked at it, then extended hers. 'It's very nice to meet you, Ms. Gooding.'

'Oh, please, don't call me Ms.' Cynthia laughed gaily and tucked her hand into the crook of Griffin's elbow. 'It's Miss. I don't subscribe to all that feminist nonsense, do I, darling?'

Three darlings, or was it four, in just a handful of minutes? A muscle ticked in Griffin's jaw. 'No, Cynthia, you do not.'

'Well,' Dana said briskly, 'since I do, why not make it easy on ourselves? I'm Dana, you're Cynthia.'

'And I'm Arthur,' Arthur said brightly.

'Oh.' Dana blushed. 'Oh, I'm terribly sorry. Arthur Coakley, this is Griffin McKenna. He's my—'

Arthur laughed. 'I know who he is, my dear. Everyone knows Mr. McKenna.' He held out his hand. 'It's a pleasure.'

Griffin nodded as the men shook hands. 'How do you do, Coakley?'

'I've followed your career with great interest, Mr. McKenna.'

'Griffin,' Griffin said. 'Or McKenna. Either one. Ms. Anderson never mentioned that she was expecting you.'

Arthur chuckled. 'She wasn't. I thought I'd surprise her.'

'Isn't that lovely?' Cynthia said happily. 'I thought I'd surprise Griffin, too.'

'An evening filled with surprises,' Dana said gaily.

The little group fell silent. After a moment, Griffin spoke.

'Well,' he said briskly, 'why don't we all have a drink?'

'Lovely,' Cynthia said. 'But...' She blushed. 'I've run into a bit of a problem, darling. At the registration desk. They've just told me there are no rooms. I—I told them... I asked them...'

She gave a tinkling laugh. 'I said I'd come to spend the week-end with you.'

'Isn't that sweet?' Dana's smile could have cut steel.

Griffin smiled back at her. 'Sweet,' he said, blithely ignoring the fact that his relationship with Cynthia had never progressed beyond a goodnight kiss. 'It is, isn't it?'

'...and the clerk was just about to look your name up in the computer, darling, to see what room you were in—'

'Room 2010,' Griffin said quickly.

Arthur frowned. 'Are you sure? I thought Dana told me that was her room number, when we spoke this afternoon. She said I could call her there, direct, instead of going through the desk.'

'No,' Dana said.

'No,' Griffin said, at the same instant. He cleared his throat. 'That's the number of the Data Bytes' corporate suite.'

Arthur looked even more perplexed. 'I don't understand, Dana. Are you and Mr. Mc... Are you and Griffin staying in the same suite?'

'No,' Griffin said.

'Yes,' Dana said. She gave a trill of laughter as they all turned towards her. 'I mean—I mean...'

'She means,' Griffin said smoothly, 'that we share the parlor room of the suite.'

'And that's room 2010?' Arthur shook his head. 'I really am confused, Dana. If the parlor is number 2010, then what's the number of your bedroom?'

Dana flashed Griffin a desperate look. 'I forget,' she said. 'Mr. McKenna? Can you—'

'Hell, no.' Griffin gave a hearty laugh. 'I'm terrible with numbers, Ms. Anderson. You know that.' He beamed at Cynthia, who was looking at him with a puzzled expression. 'Amazing, isn't it? That a man who's so bad with numbers would be at a computer software conference?'

'It's more than amazing,' Arthur said slowly. 'I just can't

imagine that someone who's made such a killing on Wall Street would be bad with numbers.'

'He didn't mean that.' All heads turned towards Dana. 'I mean…he's bad at remembering simple ones. Unimportant ones. Numbers without dollar signs.'

Hell, Griffin thought with disgust, between the two of them, they were digging the hole deeper and deeper.

'I have an idea,' he spoke briskly. 'Cynthia? Coakley? Have either of you had dinner? Wonderful,' he said, before anyone could utter a word. 'Ms. Anderson and I were just about to eat. Why don't we continue this conversation in the dining room?'

'All four of us?' Dana said. Her voice came out in a squeak, and she blushed as all eyes fixed on her. 'I mean—isn't there some sort of dinner tonight, Mr. McKenna? For conference attendees?'

'We'll skip it.'

'But…'

'We'll skip it, Ms. Anderson.' Griffin's tone left no room for argument. 'Cynthia? Is that all right with you?'

'Why, that would be lovely,' Cynthia said. 'But first…' Two pink splotches appeared on her cheeks. 'The room arrangements, Griffin,' she whispered. 'So I can have the bellman put away my luggage…'

'Yes, Mr. McKenna.' Dana smiled, but her eyes shot angry sparks. 'Do let's discuss the room arrangements.'

'Well,' Arthur said with a coy smile, 'there's no need to fuss. Dana and I…'

'This is a business trip, Coakley.'

Griffin spoke coldly. What he really wanted to do was punch the Bow Tie in the nose, but what would that solve? The situation was shaping up pretty clearly. This was the man Dana wanted, the man she loved. And it didn't matter a damn to him. She'd have been a weekend's diversion, nothing more.

'Griffin?' Cynthia gave a nervous little laugh. 'Griffin, you're hurting my hand.'

He looked down. Cynthia's fingers were trapped within his. 'Oh. I'm sorry, Cynthia. I...'

He let go of her hand and, as he did, his head lifted and his eyes met Dana's. Suddenly, he was back hidden behind the potted palm, with her in his arms. Her face colored. Her breathing quickened. He knew she was remembering the very same thing, and he took a step back.

'Ms. Anderson, why don't you take everyone on through to the dining room while I stop at the desk? I'm sure the clerk will be more than happy to reserve rooms for Cynthia and Arthur at another hotel.'

He heard the swift intake of Cynthia's breath. 'Oh,' she said softly, and turned towards him, so that her back was to the others. 'Then—then I'm not going to—to say with you, Griffin?'

His smile tilted. 'No, Cynthia,' he said gently. He touched her cheek. 'I'm sorry, but you're not.'

Okay, so McKenna wasn't going to let Cynthia sleep with him.

Well, she wasn't going to let Arthur sleep with her, either. What on earth had gotten into Arthur? Flying down here, without telling her. Making it clear he expected to share her room. Dana frowned. Even if she'd had a room, she wouldn't have let him do that. Their relationship hadn't progressed that far. They'd only known each other a few months.

You know Griffin McKenna a couple of weeks, but you damn well were going to sleep with him, Anderson. If Arthur and Cynthia hadn't shown up...

But they had shown up. And a good thing, too. Sleeping with McKenna would have been the worst mistake of her life. She knew what happened when people who worked together ended up having sex. Their on-the-job relationships fell apart. Why, she could have lost her title...

She could have lost more than that.

No. No, she wouldn't have. Griffin McKenna was exciting,

yes. And okay, so she was human. She'd succumbed to his charm, his sexuality...

Almost succumbed. Oh yes. It was a good thing this Cynthia person had come along.

And an even better thing Griffin wasn't going to share his bed with her.

Dana bit her lip. She couldn't have survived that, lying in the darkness through the endless night, knowing that Griffin was making love to another woman, touching her, kissing her, doing all the things he'd been about to do to her.

Would he have slept with Cynthia, if he'd had his own room?

Of course he would have. Cynthia was his—she was his...

What? Not his fiancée. The gossips would have said so. Not his mistress. There was something too untouchable about her for that.

What was she, then?

Dana peeped over the edge of her oversized menu. Cynthia sat quietly beside her at the dining room table, her menu held just so, her head carefully tilted. She was dressed in a pale peach suit, with tiny pearl studs at her ears and a rope of pearls at her neck. She looked serene and elegant and as perfectly bred as a French poodle.

'So,' Dana said brightly, laying her menu on the table, 'how long have you known Griff—Mr. McKenna?'

Cynthia looked up and smiled. 'Oh, forever. His mother and mine are old friends. Griffin and I went to school together.'

'Ah.' Dana thought of his silly tale about having worked his way through college. 'I'll bet you and he were homecoming king and queen,' she said with a false laugh.

'Well...' Cynthia blushed prettily. 'I was queen, actually, but by then, Griffin had—left.'

'Left?'

'Yes. He went to a different university.' She laughed. 'Well, a couple of different universities, actually. I don't know the details.'

'But you said you went to school together.'

'Nursery school. And kindergarten. After that, of course, I attended Miss Livingston's School for Young Ladies, and Griffin went away to board at the Essex Academy. Everyone in our crowd did. You know how it is.'

'Of course,' Dana said airily, thinking back to the red brick schoolhouse in the middle of Jersey City. 'I know how it is.'

'And what about your Arthur? Have you known each other long?'

Dana shrugged. 'A few months.'

Cynthia smiled. 'I'll just bet there's a June wedding in the making.'

'Well, he hasn't actually asked me to marry him yet...'

'But he will. And, when he does, you'll say 'yes'. It's what every girl wants, isn't it? To have a man take care of her?'

Dana bristled. 'I don't need a man to take care of me! No woman does.'

'I suppose there are some who feel that way.' Cynthia sighed. 'I'm afraid I'm quite old-fashioned. So is Griffin. We both agree that a woman should center her life around her husband.'

Dana's heartbeat stumbled. That was what Cynthia was, then. Not a lover. Not a mistress. Not even a girlfriend.

Cynthia was the Wife Designate.

'How nice.' She forced a smile to her lips. 'Then, you should be very happy together.'

'Well, as you just said about your young man, Griffin hasn't actually proposed yet, but—'

'But, he will.'

'His mother thinks so.'

Not just the Wife Designate. Dana's smile wobbled. The Wife Designate, complete with the McKenna Maternal Blessing.

Not that it mattered.

'That's—that's wonderful,' she said brightly.

Cynthia sighed. 'I just wish—'

'What do you wish?'

Both women looked up. Griffin stood alongside the table. Dana's heart turned over. He was so handsome. So exciting. And he was going to marry Cynthia Gooding, who'd obey his every command, accede to his every wish, bore him to tears for the rest of his life instead of standing up to him, arguing with him, making him so angry that the only way to soothe that anger was to go into his arms...

'What do you wish, Cynthia?' Griffin said again, and Dana leaped to her feet.

'She wishes Arthur would hurry up and come back, so we could get this meal over with.' She shot them a wobbly smile, and rushed off in search of Arthur.

In search of sanity.

'They dance well together, don't they, Griffin?'

Griffin's eyes narrowed. Dana and the Bow Tie were waltzing. He'd have laid ten to one odds that the Bow Tie had taken dancing lessons. Well, Griffin had, too. It was one of the things you had to do, at Essex, but he'd moved past that silly one, two, three, thank God. A man could waltz and still manage to hold a woman close to him, feel her body move against his, smell her scent.

Cynthia lay her hand on top of his. 'Griffin? Don't they dance well together?'

'Yes,' he said, and bared his teeth in what he hoped was a smile.

'The band's quite good, don't you think?'

He nodded. 'Yes,' he said again, his eyes riveted to Dana and the Bow Tie.

'Griffin.' Cynthia moved closer. 'You haven't danced with me once this evening.'

'Maybe later.'

'Just one da—'

'I'm not in the mood, Cynthia.'

'Oh.'

Griffin sighed. The single word was an accusation that trembled in the air. Hell, he thought glumly, he was being an insensitive bastard, but whose fault was that? Why didn't Cynthia stand up to him? Why didn't she jab her finger into his chest and say, listen, McKenna, you are treating me like dirt and if you don't stop, I'll go someplace where I'm appreciated.

Because she wasn't Dana, that was why.

Dammit, he thought, and turned his back to the dance floor.

'Cynthia.'

'Yes?'

Unshed tears glittered in her eyes. Griffin reached out and cupped her face with his hand.

'Cyn, I'm sorry.'

She smiled tremulously.

'You've nothing to apologize for, Griffin.'

'I do.'

'No. No, you don't.'

'Dammit!' Griffin snatched back his hand. 'Don't make me out to be a saint when I've been an S.O.B. I know I've been rotten to you, all evening.'

'Not all evening. Anyway, you're preoccupied with business. I understand. I never should have dropped in on you.' She smiled again, but one perfect tear rolled down her cheek. 'I just wanted to do something that would surprise you.'

He sighed and blotted the tear with his fingertip. 'Yeah, well, you certainly did that.'

Cynthia looked towards the dance floor. 'She's very pretty, your Miss Anderson.'

'Is she? I hadn't really—'

'Smart, too. She has strange ideas, though. She's one of those feminists.'

'She's very independent, Cynthia.'

'Did you see how she took over? Pulling out her chair without waiting for Arthur to do it, telling the waiter what she wanted to eat instead of letting Arthur do it for her.' Cynthia shook her head. 'I never saw such a thing.'

'Well, the Bow... Coakley should have said something, if he didn't like it.'

'A man shouldn't have to say something. A woman should be feminine and wait for the man to make certain decisions.'

'Dana is feminine.'

'Well, I suppose she looks feminine enough, though, actually, that outfit is—well, it's—'

'Yes?'

'Obvious, you know? That slit in the skirt. That neckline. I'm sure her beau would prefer her to dress in a more discrete fashion.'

Griffin looked across the dance floor. The band had segued into a tango. The Bow Tie was dipping Dana back over his arm. Her hair trailed out behind her, like a golden flame; her out thrust leg was exposed from ankle to thigh.

'She looks...' He cleared his throat. 'She looks all right.'

The music changed yet again, became soft and dreamy. The lights dimmed. The Bow Tie tried to draw Dana closer but she didn't seem cooperative. Then her eyes met Griffin's. Her chin lifted, and she melted into the Bow Tie's embrace.

Griffin's vision clouded.

The Bow Tie's hands slid down Dana's back and settled at the base of her spine. Dana slid her arms around his neck.

'Enough,' Griffin snarled, and shot to his feet.

'Griffin? Darling, what is it?'

'It's late,' he said, dumping bills on the table. 'Tomorrow's a long day.'

'I haven't finished my—' Cynthia blinked as Griffin dragged back her chair, pulled her to her feet and hurried her across the dance floor. 'Griffin.' She gave a little laugh. 'If you'd just slow down...'

Dana and the Bow Tie were swaying to the music. Dana's

head was on his shoulder; her eyes were closed. Griffin muttered something under his breath and tapped her on the shoulder.

'Time to call it a night, Anderson.'

She lifted her head and stared at him. 'I beg your pardon?'

'I said, it's late, and we have to get an early start in the morning.'

'But—'

'Coakley?'

He thought, just for a minute, that Coakley was going to protest. Something masculine and primitive stirred deep inside him. Come on, he thought, and almost smiled, come on, man, just give me an excuse…

'Yes,' Arthur said. He let go of Dana and his bow tie slid up, then down, as he swallowed. 'Dana, Mr. Mc—I mean, Griffin is right. We've all had a long day.'

Griffin took Dana's elbow. 'Indeed,' he said, and strode from the nightclub with one woman on each arm.

Dana spun towards him as soon as they reached the lobby.

'Let go of me, McKenna!'

'I told you, it's late.'

'I am your employee, not your property. When I decide it's time to call it a night, I'll—'

'You should have done that hours ago. You have to finish working on that code, Anderson, or have you forgotten your responsibilities?'

'I told you, I'm almost done with the code. Another half an hour—'

'Well, I want that half an hour put in tonight, not tomorrow morning.'

Dana took a step back. 'You are, without a doubt, the most selfish son of a—'

'Griffin!' Cynthia's face was white. 'Are you going to let her talk to you that way?'

'Now, Griffin.' Arthur's face was even whiter. 'Surely, you can speak a little more politely.'

'Stay out of this, Coakley.'

'Yes, Arthur.' Dana's eyes flashed. 'Stay out of this. This is between Simon Legree and me.'

Griffin let go of Cynthia and moved towards Dana. 'Go to your room,' he said in a soft, cold voice.

'I am not a child, McKenna!'

'You are an employee, and this is not a vacation. If you want to keep your job, you'll do as you're told.'

'My room?' Dana's voice shook with rage. '*My* room? Don't you mean that travesty they call the br—'

Oh God. The Bridal Suite, she'd almost said, and then she'd have lost everything. Her job. Her promotion. Arthur's respect, because he'd never believe the truth. Who would? Not even Cynthia, the limpet, who just stood there with her silly mouth open and her hands pressed to her cheeks, would believe the truth, that she and the Mighty McKenna were sharing the Bridal Suite when the only thing they should have been sharing was ten rounds in a boxing ring.

'I hate you, McKenna,' she whispered shakily.

'Oh, Dana.' Arthur was almost moaning with anguish. 'Mr. McKenna. She doesn't mean—'

'She does,' Griffin said coldly, 'and that's fine, Coakley. I demand results from my employees, not affection. And now, if you and Cynthia will come with me, I'll have the doorman call a cab.'

'Dana?' Arthur said. He licked his lips. 'Dana, shall I leave?'

Dana jerked her chin up. 'If you have to ask such a question, Arthur, you don't need me to give you an answer.'

She turned on her heel, marched across the lobby and into the waiting elevator, holding back her angry tears until the doors slid shut on the sight of Griffin McKenna clasping both his charges by the arms as he herded them to the door.

CHAPTER TEN

DANA RAMMED HER electronic key-card into the lock on the door of the Bridal Suite. The little light in the panel blinked green and she pushed the door open, then slammed it shut.

'McKenna,' she said, flinging the key-card across the empty room, 'you are a first-class, dirty, rotten skunk!'

Her shoes went sailing after the key-card...shoes McKenna had chosen, shoes no sensible woman would have gone near except in a teenage boy's fevered dreams. Skinny straps, skinny, spike heels... Walking in shoes like that could become an Olympic event. Sexist stilts, she thought coldly, just the sort of thing a man like McKenna would like.

The nerve of him.

'The nerve,' Dana said, storming into the bathroom, peeling off the ivory silk suit and drop-kicking it into the corner. Ordering her around. Telling her what to do. Telling *everybody* what to do! Buying her an outrageous outfit, buying her underwear—*underwear*, for heaven's sake, and then asking if she were wearing it.

Of course, she'd worn it. What else could she do? She couldn't have worn her own things under the ivory silk, not when the top was cut down to her whatsis and the skirt was cut up to her whosis...

...Not when she could close her eyes and imagine McKenna seeing her in it.

Dana snatched one of the terry-cloth robes from its hook and put it on.

What a ridiculous thought! She'd sooner find herself the love object of a baboon! McKenna had been right about one thing, anyway. It had, indeed, been a long day. What she needed now was a good night's sleep, and to hell with his ordering her to get to work on the code tonight. What did he know about codes and programming, anyway?

'Nothing,' she muttered as she marched through the living room again. Not one miserable thing. So far as she could tell, the only thing Griffin McKenna knew was how to run a dictatorship.

Dana opened the sliding-glass doors that led onto the terrace. The air was warm, rich with the scent of the ocean that foamed against the shore below. She sighed, leaned her elbows on the terrace railing and gazed out over the dark water.

Such a sweet thing Arthur had done, flying down to join her. She'd never have imagined him doing something so impulsive.

'Whatever possessed you?' she'd asked him as they'd danced, and Arthur had blushed and replied that he'd just wanted to surprise her.

'You see?' he'd said with a little smile. 'I'm not always a cautious stick-in-the-mud.'

The evening had been so nice, until McKenna had—

Oh, hell.

Dana turned her back to the night, sank down into a wicker chair and rubbed her hands over her eyes.

Why kid herself? The evening had been horrible, from the minute she'd spotted Arthur in the lobby, straight through to when McKenna had sent her packing.

What a farce! Pretending it was fun to watch Arthur damn near clicking his heels and saluting each time McKenna opened his mouth.

'Yes, Griffin.' Dana dropped her chin, and her voice, to her chest. 'Whatever wine you prefer is fine, Griffin. You're going to have the red snapper? Well, then, I'll have it, too.'

Cynthia's performance had been even worse. The little-girl voice. The demure looks. The way she'd hung on McKenna's every pronouncement as if he were giving the Sermon on the Mount.

Not that he'd said much. What he'd done most was glower. That was why, when Cynthia had nervously suggested it might be fun to peek into the hotel's nightclub, Dana had jumped at the chance.

Anything, she'd figured, was better than sitting around like a bunch of mourners at a wake.

'Let's,' she'd said quickly, before Griffin could frown and cast his royal veto.

But when not even the noise and the music in the small, artificially darkened room had been enough to lift the gloom, Dana had grabbed Arthur's hand and said she wanted to dance. 'Dance?' Arthur had replied as if she'd suggested they go parasailing over the Atlantic.

'Dance,' she'd said firmly. 'Remember those lessons you told me about? Why let them go to waste?'

It had been an argument Arthur could not resist. He'd followed her onto the stamp-size dance floor, where she'd practically had to beg him to put his arms around her.

'I already have them around you,' he'd insisted.

It was an accurate assessment, by his reckoning. His right arm encircled her waist, hand planted neatly in the middle of her back. His left arm was upraised, elbow out, so that his hand could hold hers. A chaperone at a high school prom would have applauded, but Dana wanted something else.

'Hold me as if you meant it,' she'd said, trying not to make it sound like a command. 'Look around you at other people, Arthur. See what I mean?'

He looked, he saw, but he went on leading her around the floor with enough space between them to have parked a bus. In the end, she'd resorted to a pure, unadulterated lie.

'I want you to hold me close,' she'd whispered, batting her lashes.

Dana groaned at the memory.

Oh, what a rotten thing to have done! She hadn't wanted Arthur to hold her at all. She'd wanted to drive McKenna crazy.

And she'd succeeded.

Her pulse quickened at the memory of Griffin's face once Arthur's arms had finally enfolded her. The narrowed eyes. The flared nostrils. She'd read a description once, of a stallion preparing to defend his mares against an interloper...

In another time, another place, she knew he'd have come for her, torn her from Arthur's embrace, carried her off to his castle and made passionate love to her until she pleaded for mercy, until she clung to him and whispered the truth, that she wanted him, that she'd never stop wanting him.

Dana bowed her head. She sat still for a long moment. Then, slowly, she rose to her feet.

She was tired. That was why she was thinking these wild thoughts. What she needed was a good night's rest, without sight or sound or thought of Griffin McKenna, and there was only one way to guarantee that.

Resolutely, she marched to the door of the Bridal Suite and pulled the Do Not Disturb sign from the knob. Let him sleep in the lobby. Let him sleep on the beach. Let him curl up outside the door, like the cur he was.

The one place he was not going to sleep, was here.

She felt a weight lift from her shoulders. Of course, he wasn't going to sleep here. Why hadn't she put her foot down when this craziness all began? He could take a room at another hotel.

So what if he had to gallop back and forth once the conference began?

Dana's chin rose as she opened the door. She was the programmer, not Griffin. He might like to think he had to be available every minute of every hour, but the simple truth was that she was the indispensable one, this weekend, not—

The elevator doors whooshed open. Griffin stepped into the corridor.

'Dana?'

She froze, but only for an instant.

'Griffin,' she said politely, and then she looped the Do Not Disturb sign over the knob, slipped inside, and slammed the door.

His footsteps pounded down the corridor.

Safe inside, she fumbled for the security chain. She heard the swish of his key-card in the lock, but she was quicker. The chain fell into place and, triumphantly, she pushed the door closed.

'Dana.' The doorknob rattled. 'Open this door.'

'No.' She shook her head and flattened her palms against the door. 'I'm not opening it.'

'Don't be an idiot. Open the door.'

'That's how you've been treating me, as if I were an idiot.' She drew a shuddering breath. 'Well, I'm through letting you get away with it, McKenna. You think you can boss people around, have your own way all the time—'

'Open the door, Anderson.'

Dana shut her eyes. Oh, that voice. She could just imagine the face that went with it, the burning eyes, the thinned mouth...

'Anderson!' Griffin's fist slammed against the door. 'Do you hear me? Open it, I said.'

'Try hearing me for a change,' she said. 'I loathe you. I hate you. I despise you. Am I getting through to you, McKenna?'

'Anderson. If you want to keep your job—'

'You can't fire me. Not now, anyway. You need me to debug that program.'

'I'm going to count to ten. And then you'd better open this damned door because if you don't—'

'I'm not listening,' she said, and turned the lock. 'Go away.'

'Look, I don't know what you're so ticked off about, but—'

'That's exactly the point. You don't know. You should, but you don't.'

He sighed. With her ear to the door, she could hear it as clearly as if he were in the room with her.

'Is this about my suggesting Cynthia and the Bow—and Coakley leave, so we could call it a night?'

'Suggesting?' She stepped back and folded her arms. 'Suggesting?' she said, and gave a little laugh.

'Okay. Okay, maybe I was a little abrupt—'

'It's too late for apologies. You're a horrible person, Griffin McKenna, and I hate you.'

'You already said that.'

'I despise you.'

'That, too.'

'Well, it's worth saying again.'

Griffin shut his eyes and leaned his forehead against the door. 'Dana, for God's sake, be reasonable. Where am I going to sleep?'

'What do I care? Sleep on the beach. Sleep in a telephone booth. Sleep with Cynthia.' Her voice quavered, though there was no reason for it. 'Why miss a night, if you don't have to?'

'I don't sleep with—' He heard a door crack open somewhere behind him. Oh, hell, he thought miserably. 'I don't sleep with Cynthia,' he said in a low voice. 'Not that it's any of your business.'

'You're right. It's absolutely none of my business. Why don't you?'

How many times had he asked himself that same question? 'What kind of question is that? I don't know why I don't sleep with her. Why don't you sleep with the Bow Tie?'

'How do you know I don't?'

'I just do,' he said, and wondered why he felt so damned relieved. 'Why don't you?'

Why, indeed? 'Our relationship's on a higher plane than that.'

'Well, I'm delighted for you both, but I still need a place to bunk for the night.'

'Try the lobby. Some of those chairs looked pretty comfortable.'

Another door creaked open down the hall.

'Anderson.' Griffin did his best to sound like the very voice of reason. 'Let me in.'

'I don't want to.'

'Dammit, Anderson, I'm telling you for the last time—'

'What's the problem, young man?'

Griffin stepped away from the door and looked around. A woman was peering out from behind the door of her hotel room. She had curlers in her hair and a look of perplexity on her face.

'Problem?' he said.

'Yes. Why are you talking to that door?'

'I, ah, I'm not. I'm talking to, ah, to—'

'What does it say there?' The woman peered nearsightedly at the brass plaque on the door of Room 2010. 'Brindle Suit? What's a brindle suit?'

Griffin cleared his throat. 'No. I mean, it says—it says—' He gestured helplessly. 'I'm sorry we disturbed you, madam. Why don't you just—'

'Ah, I can make it out now.' The woman's wispy brows lifted. 'It says Bridal Suite.'

'Yes. Yes, it does. Look, just go on back to bed. I apologize if—'

'My, oh, my, did you forget your key? Are you locked out?'

Oh Lord, Griffin thought, why me? 'Madam, really, I appreciate your concern, but really—'

'You just wait there, young man. I'll phone the desk and have them send someone up to open that door for you.'

'No,' Griffin said...and then he cocked his head. 'Why, yes.

Yes, thank you, madam. If you'd just wait a second, while I tell my—bride—the good news... Darling?' He leaned closer to the door. 'Dana, dearest? Did you hear that? One of our neighbors has offered to call the desk. They'll send someone up to open the door.'

'No one's going to open this door, McKenna. I've got the chain on, remember?'

Griffin sighed. 'You say the chain is stuck? Well, I'll tell our Good Samaritan to have the desk send up a maintenance crew. They can take the door off the hinges.' He folded his arms and stared at the door, his face a study in concern. 'That should draw quite a crowd.'

A second passed. The chain rattled free, the lock turned and the door swung open. Griffin looked at the woman with the curlers in her hair.

'Isn't that remarkable? My bride's managed to open the door, all by herself.'

She smiled. 'Sweet dreams, young man.'

'The same to you, madam,' Griffin said, and stepped inside the Bridal Suite. The door slammed shut, and he came face-to-face with Dana.

'The only thing more horrendous than spending the night in the same suite as you,' she said, 'would be having everyone on this floor *know* that I was spending the night in the same suite as you.'

Griffin's jaw tightened. He'd never been so angry at a woman in his life. It seemed impossible to think that this—this undersize wraith in an oversize robe had kept him cooling his heels in a hotel corridor. He could have pushed her over with one finger, if he'd been into pushing women, and, dammit, he wanted to do exactly that. Hell, he thought, jamming his hands into his pockets, he most certainly wanted to do exactly that!

'For once,' he said, 'we agree. You ever try and make a public spectacle of me again, you'll pay the price.'

'Oh, give me a break, McKenna! If there's anybody into making public spectacles of people, it's you!'

'I beg your pardon,' he said coldly.

'Bossing me around. Telling me to go to my room, as if I were a ten-year-old!'

'You have a job to do, in case you've forgotten.' He stalked past her, yanked off his jacket and tossed it on a chair. 'I know you'd rather pretend this is a holiday weekend, that the only thing you've got to do is—is climb all over that boyfriend of yours on a public dance floor, but—'

'I was not climbing all over anybody!' Dana skidded around Griffin and stopped in front of him, her hands on her hips.

'No?'

'No.'

'Did you finish working on that code?'

'Are you kidding? I just got up here. I haven't even had time to take off my makeup.'

But she'd had time to get undressed. The long robe kept gaping open. Not even the slit in the skirt of the ivory silk suit had showed as much long, luscious leg as the robe was showing now.

Griffin felt a sudden tightening in his groin.

'Get out of my way,' he growled.

'First, we talk. Then, I'll be happy to oblige!'

Did she have to do that? Tilt back her head, so that her hair slid down over her shoulders?

'Dammit,' he said through his teeth, 'step aside!'

'I have no wish to see your face or hear your voice, McKenna.'

'Amen to that. Now, get out of—'

'As for the code, I'll be up at dawn to work on it.'

He pulled off his tie and tossed it after the jacket. 'I expect as much.'

'Now that that's settled, I'm going to bed.' She glared at him. 'And I promise you, I'm going to take your advice and bolt my door.'

'Why?'

'Why? What do you mean, why? Because…' She hesitated. He was undoing his shirt, peeling it off his shoulders, and dropping it to the floor. 'What are you doing, McKenna?'

'I'm getting undressed.'

'Well, stop.' She swallowed, glared, snatched up his shirt and held it out. 'Would you please put this on?'

He looked at the shirt, then at her. 'What for? I'm getting ready for bed. I don't sleep in my clothes, Anderson. Do you?'

'No. Of course not. I mean…' What did she mean? She couldn't think, not with him standing around shirtless. Such golden skin. Such beautiful muscles. And that curling dark hair, stretching over his chest, down his flat, taut belly, into the waistband of his trousers…

'What do you sleep in, then?'

Her gaze flew upward. He was looking at her, his eyes dark and heavy-lidded.

'That's a ridiculous question.' 'Is it?'

Those eyes. So dark. And so focused. So tightly fixed on her…

'Why are you so angry at me, Anderson?'

His voice was soft, caressing. She felt a flutter along her spine.

'You know why. You treated me like—like a slave. 'Anderson, do this. Do that…"

'You were all over him on that dance floor.'

Dana colored. 'I wasn't!'

'He's in love with you, the poor bastard.' Griffin moved toward her, his steps slow and deliberate, his eyes never leaving hers. 'But you're not in love with him.'

'Don't be silly. You don't know anything about… What are you doing?'

His smile was slow, dangerous, and heart-stoppingly sexy. 'You never did answer my question, Anderson.' He reached out and took hold of the sash on the robe. 'Did you wear the lingerie I sent up?'

'I told you I didn't. McKenna, what are you...?'

'I want to see for myself.'

Dana's heart thumped crazily. He was undoing the sash, letting the ends slip through his fingers.

'Are you calling me a liar?' she said unsteadily.

'Are you asking me not to do this?' he said just as unsteadily.

Time seemed to stop. The robe fell open, but Griffin's eyes remained locked on hers.

'Dana,' he said, his voice a husky whisper.

'Yes,' she said, 'oh, yes...'

And then she was in his arms. She had expected him to undress her, there in the living room.

He didn't. He swept her up into his arms, carried her swiftly through the suite to the bedroom, where the soft light of the moon teased the darkness.

He kissed her then, with a hot, sweet abandon that made her heart pound.

Slowly, so slowly that it seemed to take an eternity, he lowered her down his body, until her feet touched the floor.

'Let me see you,' he said, and she held her breath as he drew the robe back from her shoulders.

Her heart thudded even harder as he looked at her. She had never had a man look at her this way before. Not touching, not stroking, but touching and stroking just the same, with his gaze. She felt her breasts swell, her nipples harden.

'Beautiful,' he whispered, and she knew that she was, if only for this night. If only for this man.

The robe slipped to the carpet. He looked at her for a long moment, his face barred by moonlight, and then he reached out, undid the laces on the camisole, and drew it from her.

His breath caught. She saw his features grow taut with desire.

'My beautiful Dana.'

He knelt before her, drew off the wisp of lace that were her panties. His hands lingered on her skin, caressing her, touching her, until she cried out his name. Then he leaned forward, his breath fanning her thighs, and put his mouth on her.

The shock of the kiss sent a white-hot lick of flame through her blood. She felt herself shatter and she cried out, half in passion, half in disbelief. No, she thought, no, it couldn't end so quickly. She wanted what was about to happen to last forever.

He kissed her again. A sob burst from her throat. She swayed, clutched at his shoulders for support.

'No,' she sobbed. 'Griffin, please...'

'Yes,' he said fiercely, and he caught her up in his arms again and carried her to the bed. Down, spiraling down in want and need, she tumbled into the softness of the silk sheets.

She watched as he undressed. How beautiful he was. The broad shoulders, the ridged chest and belly. The narrow hips and long, muscled legs...

And the part of him that was pure, unadulterated male.

He came down to her, and she went into his arms, opening her mouth for his kisses, lifting herself to him so that he could taste her breasts, lick her belly, inhale her scent as she was inhaling his.

'Griffin,' she whispered, 'I want... I want...'

'Everything,' he said, and entered her on one long, deep, heart-wrenching thrust.

She came apart instantly, shattering like crystal even as he sheathed himself in her heat, and her last thought, before she could think no more, was that if hating Griffin McKenna was like this, what would happen when she admitted that she loved him?

Griffin awoke hours later with Dana still asleep in his arms.

She lay on her side, turned toward him, her head nestled against his shoulder, her mouth inches from his throat. Each soft breath she took sent a whisper of warmth along his skin.

It was late. Very late. The moon had slipped across the sky, submerging the bedroom in the velvet darkness of the night.

Griffin shifted his weight just a little. Dana sighed, and nestled closer. Her hair, soft as silk, brushed against his lips. He tilted his head and buried his nose in her hair. It smelled of flowers. Lilies? Lilacs? He wasn't very good with flowers. The only ones he knew by sight were roses. Long-stemmed, hothouse roses, the kind he'd sent, over the years, to dozens of women.

He smiled. Somehow, he didn't think the woman in his arms would be impressed by hothouse roses. Griffin drew her closer. Wasn't there something called a desert rose? If there wasn't, there ought to be. A rose—perfect, sweet-smelling, beautiful... and surrounded by prickly thorns.

Dana murmured in her sleep. Griffin put his hand against her cheek, stroked the pad of his thumb over her silky skin.

'What is it, love?' he whispered.

She sighed, and his name slipped from her lips. She was dreaming, and of him.

A feeling like none he'd ever felt before seemed to expand inside his chest.

Of him, he thought, and he rolled onto his side, gathered her tightly into his embrace, and let the warmth of her, the feel of her, draw him down into deep, deep sleep.

When he awoke again, it was morning.

Bright sunlight streamed across the room. Griffin groaned a protest, reached out for Dana...

But he was alone in the bed. If he hadn't known otherwise, he'd have thought he'd been alone all night. There wasn't a sign of her. The covers had been smoothed back where she'd lain, the pillows plumped.

He sat up and ran his hands through his hair. He was the one who usually made an early retreat. Not that he ran out, right after making love. Women liked to be held. He knew that. He even liked to hold them, to make that feeling of completeness that came after good sex last just a little while longer. So, he stayed in a woman's bed for a while. Half an hour, an hour—once in a very great while, he stayed until early morning.

He didn't believe in one-night stands. He always phoned the next day, sent flowers, whatever, suggested dinner and the theater and kept things going for a civilized stretch of time, until he lost interest, which he invariably did...

Griffin frowned and swung his feet to the floor.

Where the hell was Dana?

He pulled on his trousers, zipped the fly, and strode from the bedroom.

'Dana?'

He stopped halfway through the living room. She was out on the terrace; he could see her clearly through the glass, sitting cross-legged on the chaise with her portable computer in her lap. That she'd gone to work straight from bed was obvious: she was wearing the terry-cloth robe, she'd pulled her hair into a curly tumble on top of her head, and her face was scrubbed and shiny-clean.

Griffin felt as if a hand had closed around his heart.

She was so beautiful.

He must have made a sound because suddenly she looked up and saw him. Her eyes lit; pink swept into her cheeks and she lifted her hand to her hair in a gesture so feminine, so unaware, that it made his throat constrict.

She smiled, and mouthed 'hello.'

He smiled, and mouthed it back, when what he really wanted to do was go to her, take her in his arms, tell her—tell her...

She tapped the keyboard, then rose, the computer tucked under one arm, and slid open the terrace door.

'Hi,' she said.

'Hi.'

'I've got good news.'

He nodded. Her feet were bare, her toenails unpolished. He couldn't recall seeing a woman's toenails without polish before.

'Griffin?'

He looked at her face. Her beautiful face. She was smiling.

'I solved the problem with the code.'

'Ah.' Slowly, he started toward her. 'That's great.'

'It just took a little… Griffin? What are you doing?'

Gently, he took the computer from her hands and put it on the table.

'Griffin?' she said, her voice suddenly husky. 'Don't you want to hear about the code?'

He nodded, his face solemn. 'I want to hear all about it,' he said as he undid the belt of her robe. 'Every last detail.'

Her head fell back as he bent and kissed her breasts. She moaned, and clasped his head.

'Griffin… Griffin, I can't—I can't think if you—if you…'

He swung her up into his arms. She lifted her face for his kiss, and he carried her through the Bridal Suite, back to bed.

CHAPTER ELEVEN

Guilt.

That was what Dana felt. Guilt, as drowning-deep as the ocean that beat against the shore below, as hot and suffocating as the heat of the late morning.

She stood on the terrace of the Bridal Suite, her hands clutching the railing, and tried to convince herself that she had nothing to feel guilty about.

She was not committed to anyone. Neither was Griffin. They were adults, and unencumbered. What they had done could hurt nobody.

Her fingers curled more tightly around the railing.

Who was she kidding? There were two people in a hotel moments from here who'd be devastated if they knew that she and Griffin had made love. Arthur had flown all this distance to be with her. He was in love with her, and she knew it. Just because he'd never said it didn't make it less true.

And Cynthia. Cynthia, who looked at Griffin with her heart glowing in her eyes...

'Sweetheart?'

Dana closed her eyes at the sound of Griffin's voice. She heard the terrace doors slide open, then felt his body brush lightly against her.

His arms went around her, and he drew her back against him. Don't, she told herself. Oh, don't. This is wrong. It's wrong...

'Dana.'

He put his mouth to her throat, and her breath caught. I love you, she thought, oh, Griffin, I love you. What was the sense in trying to deny it?

But he didn't love her. This was a weekend's amusement for him, and that made what they'd done even worse. To deceive two perfectly nice people, just so she could lie in the arms of a man who would never whisper those magic words...

'Where'd you go? I woke up and you were gone.' He nuzzled her hair aside and lightly nipped the tender skin just behind her ear. 'I missed you.'

'I—I felt restless.'

'Restless?' He laughed softly and turned her toward him. Her throat tightened at the sight of him—his tousled hair, his sexy, unshaven face. 'I've got a cure for that,' he said, tilting her face up to his. 'All you had to do was wake me.'

'Griffin.' Dana put her hands on his chest. 'Griffin, I've been thinking...'

'So have I.'

He smiled and sought her mouth, but she turned her face away.

'Please. Listen to me.' She took a deep breath. 'I—I was thinking about—about Arthur.'

'Thinking about what?' His smile tilted. 'You're not accountable to him.'

'I know. And you don't owe anything to Cynthia. But—'

Griffin lay his index finger against her lips.

'We didn't ask them to fly here, Dana.'

'No, of course not. Still—'

'And we didn't plan what happened to us.'

She smiled. It was so ridiculous, even to suggest such a thing.

'You're right, we didn't.' She laughed softly. 'Actually, if I'd thought about us being together, I'd have bet on one of us tossing the other into the Atlantic.'

'Into the Atlantic, huh?' Griffin chuckled. 'If I'd known my new V.P. was entertaining murderous thoughts, I'd never have agreed to share a suite with her.'

Dana's smile faded. 'We shouldn't have agreed to share it, Griffin. If we hadn't—'

Griffin bent his head and kissed her. She tried to hold back, but how could she, when his mouth was so sweet? She groaned, lifted her arms and put them around his neck.

'We could have stayed on two different floors,' he whispered, 'and it wouldn't have mattered. This was inevitable, Dana. You must feel that, the same as I do.'

She nodded, and leaned her forehead against his chin.

'I do. But I keep thinking about Arthur. And—'

'I know a way to solve that problem,' Griffin said as he swung her into his arms and carried her inside.

'No.' Dana put her hand gently over his lips. 'We have to go downstairs. The presentations are going to begin soon. The demo—'

'To hell with the demo.'

'You don't mean that.'

He sighed. She was right. Data Bytes was in a precarious state, and close to collapse. But, as he lowered her gently to the floor, it occurred to him that it was his heart that should be worrying him.

All of a sudden, it felt as fragile as glass.

The computer software section of the conference hall was crowded with representatives from more than a dozen companies, but most of the crowd had gathered around the Data Bytes exhibit.

The program demo wasn't just up and running, it was running perfectly. Griffin couldn't remember the last time he'd shaken so many hands and accepted so many congratulations.

'Don't pat me on the back,' he kept saying. 'The program's the brainchild of my Vice President, Dana Anderson.'

At last, the crowd thinned. Griffin pretended to heave a sigh of relief. 'We made it,' he said, 'Thanks to you.'

'Agreed.' Dana grinned and wrinkled her nose at him. 'But you're the reason the program is selling. Much as it pains me to admit it, you were right. You're the guy everybody wants to meet.'

'I think we should go somewhere and celebrate.' He took her hand in his and played with her fingers. 'How about lunch?'

'Lunch.' Dana sighed. 'Good idea.'

'Lobster salad and a bottle of chilled white wine?'

'Umm. Even better.'

'Good.' He moved closer and smiled into her eyes. 'We can order in.'

'Order in?'

'We'll have it upstairs, in our suite.' His fingers laced through hers. 'Lunch—and a long, relaxing soak in that tub. How's that sound?'

Dana flushed. There was no mistaking his meaning. 'Now?'

Griffin gave a low, sexy laugh. 'Right now.'

'But isn't there some sort of speech in half an... Griffin. Don't look at me that way.'

'Come upstairs with me, Dana. Let me get you out of that dress, take your hair down and—'

'McKenna? Hey, man, great program.'

Griffin looked up. A guy he'd gone to school with, the rep from a major Boston banking conglomerate, was beaming at him. For one wild minute, he thought of telling him that his timing was lousy, but Dana had already discreetly disengaged her hand from his and moved away. So he sighed, did his best to look pleased, and stuck out his hand.

'Evans,' he said. 'Nice to see you again.'

'Same here. You know, I read about you buying up this company, but I had no idea you'd...'

Evans droned on. Griffin tried to pay attention. He smiled, nodded, managed an occasional, 'Is that so?' but his thoughts weren't on the conversation, they were on Dana.

She was standing a couple of feet away, explaining the program to some guy who obviously didn't know the difference between a computer chip and a potato chip. Griffin's eyes narrowed. It didn't take much to see that they guy's interest was less on the program and more on Dana, but she kept demonstrating the program, pointing out its strengths with such care that, after a while, the guy began to focus on the monitor. At last, you could almost see the lightbulb going on over his head.

'I get it,' he said, and Dana smiled in a way that had to make him feel as if he'd won an Olympic gold medal.

The guy said something. Dana smiled again, and they shook hands. Griffin relaxed. Amazing. The guy had gone from seeing her as an object of desire to accepting her as an intelligent human being. It wasn't an easy transition for most men, himself included. The truth was that she was right. Nobody wanted to admit that it was still pretty much a man's world.

God, she was wonderful. He'd never known anyone like her. The hardest thing he'd ever done, in his life, was to let her leave his arms this morning and come down here, where he had to share her with a couple of hundred people. How long would it be before he'd be alone with her again?

'... Fair warning, McKenna.'

Griffin tuned in just in time to see Evans give him a wink.

'I'm dead serious, you know.'

'Uh, I'm sorry, Tim. I must have missed something. Fair warning about what?'

'About hiring away that Veep of yours. She ever wants to make a move to Massachusetts, all she's got to do is say so. Brains and beauty, McKenna. That's one hell of a combination.'

'Yes. Yes, I suppose it is.'

'We can use a gal like that in our company.'

'A woman like that,' Griffin said easily.

Evans punched him lightly in the arm. 'Will wonders never cease? Affirmative action's finally gotten to you, has it?'

'Have to keep up with the times,' Griffin said, smiling as the men shook hands. 'And, Evans—don't hold your breath. Dana Anderson isn't about to leave Data Bytes.'

She sure as hell wasn't, he thought as Evans strolled away. Not for Boston, or anywhere else that would take her away from New York, and from him. Griffin folded his arms, leaned back against the display table and watched as she explained the new program to yet another interested conference attendee. No way, he thought. He'd found himself a miracle, and he was going to hold on to it.

He watched as she fielded a tough question about the new program with a dazzling combination of charm and reason. Evans was right. Beauty and brains, all in one package. Her hair was loose today, a concession he'd won only after telling her, straight-faced, that if she pinned it back, he'd take it down right in the conference hall. She was wearing a butter-yellow dress, very simple and proper, but feminine and pretty, too. She'd ordered some things by telephone from the little shop where he'd bought the ivory silk suit last night. To his relief, her request for 'something businesslike' had led not to the shapeless stuff he'd always seen on her until now. Instead, the shop had sent up two dresses, this yellow one and another in pale violet.

Griffin had watched her place the order just a few hours ago. 'I'll need two outfits,' she'd said crisply. 'Simple lines, no frills, something suitable for business, in size eight.'

Her tone had been the only no-nonsense thing about her, considering that she'd made the call while she was sitting cross-legged in the center of their rumpled bed, wearing nothing but one of his shirts, with him sitting just behind her.

'And a dress to wear tonight,' he'd whispered, kissing her temple.

'I don't need a dress for tonight,' she'd whispered back. 'There's that dinner, and a guest speaker...'

'Something black and slinky,' he'd said, slipping his hand inside her shirt.

'Griffin,' she'd said breathlessly, clapping her hand over the phone, 'I can't—you have to stop...'

And he had stopped, after she'd ordered something black and silky, and then he'd taken the phone from her hand and tumbled her back onto the sheets.

'Stop what?' he'd murmured, and then she was in his arms again and he was on fire...

Griffin frowned, shifted his weight, and told himself to think about something else before he became a public embarrassment.

Think about tonight, and the dinner reservations he'd made at a little place on the water the concierge had told him about. Think about later, when they got back to their suite and the door closed behind them. Think about...

Oh, hell.

Think about Cynthia and Arthur, who'd just come through the door at the far end of the room.

Somehow, he'd managed not to think about them after he'd called Cynthia at her hotel, shrugged off a guilty twinge at the sound of her voice, and explained he'd be tied up most of the day.

'That's all right,' she'd said. 'I understand.'

No, he'd wanted to tell her, no, you don't understand...but in the end, he hadn't because he didn't understand, either. Something was happening to him, and he knew it, something that was as terrifying as it was exhilarating. He was feeling an emotion he couldn't quite identify, one he wasn't ready to examine too closely but one he wasn't about to walk away from, either.

One thing was certain. He had to tell Cynthia that they had no future together. He'd known it , and he'd done his best to let her see it, but either he'd been too subtle or she hadn't been listening, or maybe, if he took a good, hard look at himself and was brutally honest, maybe he'd been content to let her stand around while he toyed with the possibility that someday he might care enough to want to marry her.

He wouldn't. He knew that now. Cynthia was a nice woman, with a good heart, but she wasn't the woman for him and she never would be. If he married, it would be for love. That was something else he'd finally figured out. His father had married the same way he'd done business, the same way he'd raised his son. Coldly, expediently, measuring what he'd invested in his relationships against what he'd expected to gain. With an attitude like that, he'd gotten exactly what he'd deserved.

Griffin supposed he'd always known that was the wrong way to go about marriage, but it had taken a feisty computer programmer with a defiant tilt to her chin to make him acknowledge it. Marriage had nothing to do with expediency and everything to do with love, and love had nothing to do with gain and everything to do with the loss of yourself in another person.

When a man took a wife, it ought to be because he'd found the one woman who could enrich his life, bring him passion and joy, share his interests, and his dreams.

His dreams? What about the Bow Tie's dreams? Wasn't that why Coakley had flown down here, because he was in love with Dana and wanted to marry her?

Griffin's heart pounded. He had to do something, fast. He had to grab hold of Dana, tell her that—tell her that—that *if* he ever fell in love, *if* he ever decided to marry—

'Griffin?'

Dana turned toward him. Her face was white. She'd spotted Cynthia and Arthur.

'Dana.' He took her hand. It was icy cold. 'Sweetheart, listen to me—'

'Griffin. I can't face them! I thought I could, but I can't. How could I have—how could we have—'

She was breathless; her panic terrified him. She was going to say the wrong thing, do the wrong thing, agree to anything Coakley asked and spend the rest of her life making up to him for having fallen in love with another man because, dammit, she *had* fallen in love with another man. That was why she'd gone to bed with him. Because she loved him. Only him.

And he loved her. Adored her! He'd been too dumb, too scared to admit it.

'Dana.' He knew he sounded angry; he couldn't help it. It was fear that roughened his voice; he wanted to tell her that, but there wasn't time. 'Keep quiet. Do you hear me? When they get here, let me do the talking. Don't—'

'Griffin,' Cynthia said, 'at last. We've been looking everywhere for you two!'

'Cynthia.' His heart was pounding but his years of putting a good face on disaster in corporate boardrooms from New York to California came to his aid. He smiled easily, bent down and kissed her on the cheek.

'How did your meetings go?'

At least she'd stopped calling him 'darling.' Maybe that was a good sign. Hell, he thought desperately, he was willing to read tea leaves for a good sign.

'The meetings were fine,' he said with false good humor. 'Just fine.'

'That's wonderful.' Cynthia looked over her shoulder. 'Isn't that wonderful, Arthur?'

Arthur nodded. 'Wonderful,' he said, but his eyes were darting from Griffin to Dana. Did he suspect something? He looked as if he did. Griffin spoke fast. He had to get Dana out of here and talk to her.

'Well,' he said, 'we'll see you late—'

'Dana?' Arthur's voice rolled right over his. This was definitely not a good sign, not from a man who'd been afraid to look him in the eye last night. 'Dana, my dear, I want to talk to you.'

'No,' Griffin said. 'You can't. Dana and I were just about to—we have an appointment, Coakley.'

'Your appointment will have to wait. I have to talk to her now.'

Dana clutched the table for support. Arthur knew. He knew!

She didn't know how, but he knew. How else to explain his standing up to Griffin?

What a terrible thing she'd done! Arthur had flown all the way here to be with her, and what had she done in return? She'd slept with Griffin, even though she knew that Arthur was hoping that, someday, she'd fall in love with him. And the truth was, she never would, not in a million years, not even if—not even when—her affair with Griffin ended, and oh, what an ugly word that was, affair...

'Dana?' Arthur said.

Dana wrapped her arms around her middle. 'Yes,' she said quietly, 'all right. Let's go someplace quiet. I have to talk to you, too.'

Everyone looked at her, Cynthia with polite curiosity, Arthur with concern, and Griffin with a look that said, don't be an idiot.

'I do,' she whispered. 'Really. I can't—I can't... I mean, I have to tell you—'

'Anderson.'

Griffin's voice was blade-sharp. Dana turned toward him.

'I need to talk to Arthur,' she said. 'Alone.'

'I'd advise against it.'

'This doesn't concern you, Griffin.'

'The hell it doesn't!' He leaned toward her, his eyes dark with rage. 'Of course, it concerns me!'

Dana's mouth trembled. It was all so pitifully obvious. Griffin was afraid she'd tell Arthur what had happened, and Arthur would tell Cynthia, and then Griffin's chance to have his cake and eat it, too, would be lost.

Oh, Griffin, she thought, and her heart broke.

'You have nothing to worry about,' she said. 'This is between Arthur and me.'

'Will you listen to me, dammit?'

'No.' She cleared her throat, and worked hard to keep back the tears. 'No, I won't. I know what I have to tell Arthur, and I'm going to do it.'

Griffin's jaw tightened. 'Then save it for New York, when you're not on the Data Bytes clock.'

'Oh, my,' Cynthia said nervously, 'Griffin, really!'

'Keep out of this, please, Cynthia. Ms. Anderson is my employee. It's unfortunate that I have to remind her of that fact again, but if I must, I will.'

'Listen here, McKenna, you can't talk to Dana that way. You have no right—'

'Who's going to stop me, Coakley? You?'

'Are you crazy?' Dana's voice rang out, loudly enough to stop conversation around them, but she was beyond caring. 'What's wrong with you, McKenna? Can't you tolerate it if people don't knuckle under at the sound of your voice?'

'Dana.' Griffin tried to take her arm, but she shook him off. 'Dana, take it easy. You don't know what you're saying. You're upset.'

'You're damned right, I'm upset! I should never have let you talk me into taking this job, McKenna. Never!'

'Now, wait just a minute, Anderson. I didn't talk you into anything. *You* damn near blackmailed *me* into offering you a vice presidency.'

'Hah!' Dana glared at him. 'Maybe you've forgotten that you admitted to me, *boasted* to me, how you'd checked me out, gone through my résumé, set things up so I'd ask for a promotion you'd already decided to give me! But that's the way you are, isn't it? Always looking out for number one.'

'Dana.' Griffin spoke quietly, his eyes locked on hers, trying to turn things around before it was too late. 'Dana, I'm asking you to listen to me.'

'Say something worth hearing, then.'

I love you, he thought... But there was Cynthia, looking bewildered, looking as if it would take little or nothing to make the tears start to flow, and he owed her better than this, dammit, better than telling her that he felt nothing for her in a room filled with strangers.

'You see, McKenna?' Dana's voice trembled. She had hoped, just for a moment... Oh, she had hoped... 'You don't care, not for anybody but yourself. All right, then. I can see I've no choice but to tell you this, right now. I hadn't planned to. I'd intended to wait until we were back in New York, but...'

Griffin felt a coldness seeping through his bones. The Dana he'd held in his arms last night had vanished. The woman he saw in front of him now was stony-eyed with determination. She was the woman he'd known in New York.

'Go on, then,' he said quietly. 'Tell me now.'

'Very well.' She smiled, reached out to Arthur and curled her hand around his arm. 'Timothy Evans offered me a position with his company.'

The room seemed to become very still. 'And?'

'And...' She hesitated, then plunged ahead. 'And, I intend to accept it.' She smiled brightly, even though it was the hardest thing she'd ever done, even though she was about to compound one lie with another she'd have to live with for the rest of her life. 'All I have to do now is convince Arthur that we'll both be happy, living in Boston.' She saw the shock on Griffin's face, saw it give way to rage, and she smiled at Arthur, before she could do anything as stupid as weep. 'We will, won't we?' she said.

And Arthur, poor dear, sweet Arthur, hesitated only briefly before saying yes.

CHAPTER TWELVE

HOW LONG DID it take a sensible man to admit he'd come within a whisper of disaster?

A couple of hours, at the most.

Actually, not even that because Griffin had sorted it all out by the time he and Cynthia were on the six o'clock flight to New York.

What had happened between Dana Anderson and him had been—to put it down and dirty—good, hot sex. And that was no big surprise. The old horizontal tango was the inevitable result when you took a pair of healthy, attractive, unencumbered adults, dropped them into a tropical paradise, then stirred the mix by locking them into something euphemistically called the Bridal Suite.

But love? Griffin almost laughed. Love, as the song said, had nothing to do with it. Lust was the operative word here, and there was nothing wrong with that. He'd just let things get out of hand, that was all. His emotions. His behavior. And his treatment of Cynthia.

Poor Cynthia.

She sat beside him in the first-class compartment, eyes closed, hands folded demurely in her lap. His expression softened. Dear, gentle Cynthia. You'd never catch her putting on a display of temper, snarling and snapping like a cat with its back up. She hadn't once complained about the way he'd treated her, either.

Of course, she hadn't been in any position to complain. Flying down to join him had been her idea...

Griffin took a deep breath. Why try and blame this mess, or any part of it, on Cynthia? Okay, she'd delivered herself at his doorstep like a surprise package, but it had taken a lot of courage for her to do that. He should have let her know how much he admired that courage. And she shouldn't have been subjected to Dana's unladylike display of temper.

What a study in contrasts the two women were; Cyn with her eagerness to please, Dana with her tendency to bristle like a porcupine. Only a fool wouldn't have seen the difference, and known instantly which woman was one a man would want.

Cynthia was right for him. Of course, she was.

What an unholy mess he'd made of things. And for what reason? Why had he tried to put such a stupidly romantic spin on what had been nothing more than a weekend in the sack?

'Ridiculous,' he muttered.

Cynthia looked at him. 'Did you say something, Griffin?'

Her voice was gentle and ladylike, as always. He smiled, took her hand and patted it.

'It was nothing. Close your eyes, Cyn. Try and get some rest.'

'Griffin. About this weekend...'

'I know,' he said gently. 'And I'm sorry. I promise, I'll make it up to you.'

Cynthia gave a deep sigh. 'Yes. I'm sure you will.'

And he would.

It just amazed him that he'd been attracted to Dana at all. She was beautiful, yes, but so was Cynthia. Cynthia reveled in being feminine. Dana would probably sock a man in the eye if he so much as breathed the word in her direction.

Dana hadn't lied; he had to give her that much. She'd made it clear, right from the start, that she could play a man's game in a man's world. And she had. She'd gone after a better job right under his nose, as readily as she'd gone to bed with him. Oh, sure, she'd talked about feeling guilty but when you came right down to it, who wouldn't have felt guilty, considering the way they'd gone at each other even after Cynthia and the Bow Tie had turned up?

Sex. That's what it had been. But love? Love? No way. Dana hadn't fallen in love, and that was a damn good thing because neither had he.

Griffin's throat tightened.

Neither had he, he thought, and he turned his head and stared blindly out into the clouds.

Arthur and Dana couldn't book last-minute seats to Kennedy Airport, so they took a seven o'clock flight that would land them in Newark.

'We can take a taxi into Manhattan,' Dana said, knowing that Arthur would probably tell her it was more efficient to take the bus, knowing, too, that she'd have to work at keeping her temper when he did because the last thing she gave a damn about just now was efficiency.

But he just nodded and said, yes, that would be fine.

As they buckled their seat belts, he turned and looked at her.

'Dana? Are you sure this is what you want to do?'

His face was ashen, but then, that was to be expected. She knew that she'd stunned him by accepting the proposal she'd spent so much time trying to avoid.

'I'm sure,' she said, and gave him a quick smile.

Poor, dear man, she thought, and sighed. He must have been hoping she'd want to stay the rest of the weekend, to celebrate their engagement. Well, they would celebrate it. Certainly, they would…but not now. Not here, in the place where she'd behaved like just the sort of female she'd always despised, a round-heeled idiot who fell over backward the minute a man like Griffin McKenna gave her a smile.

What a self-centered, manipulative bastard he was! She'd gone into this knowing that he was a man who could have any woman, who thought women had been put on this earth for only one purpose—his pleasure—and what had she done? Played right into his hands, that was what! She'd let him talk her into sharing that damned suite, let him seduce her…

Dana's throat constricted. Who was she kidding? Griffin hadn't had to seduce her, she'd gone to him willingly, wantonly. She'd have stayed in his arms forever, if he'd wanted her.

No. No! She was romanticizing what had happened, rather than face the ugly truth, that she'd been sexually attracted to a man who might as well have been a stranger, a man whose beliefs were the opposite of her own…

'Dana?'

…A man she'd wanted, with all her heart.

'Dana. About this weekend…'

No, that was nonsense. Her heart had nothing to do with this. It was a different part of her anatomy that had ruled her behavior the past couple of days. She'd had a sleazy liaison with Griffin McKenna, and she'd treated Arthur—sweet, dear, kind, dependable Arthur—in a way he didn't deserve. But she'd make it up to him. She would. She'd spend the rest of her life, making it up to him.

'Dana,' Arthur said again, and she turned to him, smiled, and took his hand.

'I know. It was an awful weekend, Arthur. But I promise, I'll make it up to you.'

'No,' he said quickly, 'see, that's just the point. You don't need to—'

'I do,' she said firmly, and managed a wobbly smile.

Arthur hesitated, as if he didn't quite believe her. Then he sighed.

'Yes,' he said. 'Yes, I'm sure you will.'

He closed his eyes and, after a minute, Dana closed hers, too.

She *would* make it up to him. She'd marry him, become a good wife, learn to love him...

...*Learn not to think about Griffin.*

Tears seeped from under her lashes, and she turned her head away.

A month later, the special meeting Griffin had called at Data Bytes was drawing to a close—and not a minute too soon, as far as Jeannie Aarons was concerned.

Jeannie loved the elegance of computers, not the dullness of business reports, but that was what she'd been subjected to this morning, she and all the company's A-level employees. Slide shows from Sales. Pages of figures from Accounting. Brochures from Support. Jeannie had yawned and fought to stay awake through a litany of Projections, Predictions and Proposals... and what for?

The bottom line was simple enough.

Data Bytes was operating in the black.

Not that the information came as any great surprise. Things had turned around right after the Miami Beach conference. Griffin McKenna had brought back a stack of new clients, and Dana had brought back a big new job in Boston—and the announcement that she was engaged to marry Arthur.

Jeannie sighed. Married to Arthur. Dear, sweet, dull-as-dishwater Arthur.

A smattering of applause rolled through the boardroom, then grew stronger. McKenna was making his way to the microphone. Somebody whistled and McKenna grinned and held up his hands.

'You know,' he said, 'not very long ago, I had the feeling

some of you people were figuring on throwing rotten tomatoes at me the next time we got together.'

Everybody laughed.

'So, I'm doubly pleased that the news we've heard today is so good.' He smiled. 'And now I've got more good news. With the company on its feet again, I'm going to be pulling back from any hands-on management.'

There were a couple of whistles, even an exaggerated, 'No, not that!' McKenna laughed, along with the crowd.

'Yeah, well, I'm sure you'll get along just fine without me poking my nose where it doesn't belong—but before that happens, I want to tell you about your stock options.'

The place erupted in cheers. Jeannie cheered, too. She'd have to tell Dana all about this when they had dinner together tonight. Not that stock options, or news about Data Bytes and McKenna would mean anything to Dana, considering her exciting new job in Boston, and the plans she was making for her future as Arthur's wife. Each time they spoke, Dana babbled on and on about how great things were—although, so far, there'd been no mention of a wedding date.

McKenna finished his announcement. People started to applaud.

'Champagne's on me,' he said, and waved, but after shaking a few hands, Jeannie saw him slip out the door.

Ever since that Miami weekend, people said, he seemed to be all business.

She sighed. That Miami weekend. Sun-filled days, moonkissed nights, in the company of a hunk like Griffin, and Dana had come back engaged to Arthur?

Heck. There was just no accounting for tastes.

Macy, the Dragon Lady, rang Jeannie at her desk and said McKenna wanted to see her.

Well, Jeannie thought, that was pleasantly unexpected. Maybe he'd finally noticed her. She fluffed up her hair, checked her makeup, and went down the hall to his office. Macy sent her straight in.

McKenna was standing with his back to his desk, looking out the window. Jeannie took a couple of seconds to admire the width of his shoulders before she spoke.

'Hi,' she said brightly. 'You sent for me?'

McKenna turned around. Jeannie frowned. She hadn't seen him close-up in weeks. Now that she did, she was kind of surprised. He was still as gorgeous as ever, but there were little lines around his eyes and a harsh set to his mouth that she didn't recall seeing before.

He had the general look of a man who needed a good night's sleep.

He motioned her to a chair, then wandered through a long explanation about wanting to be sure R and D was operating smoothly before he took off. Jeannie was even more surprised. He needed to query somebody on her level about as much as a dog needed to advertise for fleas.

Eventually, the peculiar conversation wound to a halt.

'Well,' he said, and hesitated.

'Well?' Jeannie said, and waited.

McKenna shook his head. 'Nothing. That's it, Ms. Aarons. That's, ah, that's all.'

She nodded, and rose to leave. She was almost at the door when he called her name.

'Ms. Aarons?'

Jeannie turned and gave him her very best smile. 'Jeannie,' she said.

McKenna nodded. He was standing behind his chair and now he wrapped his hands around the back of it. She could see his knuckles whiten, and then he took a deep, deep breath.

'Jeannie. I was just wondering... I, ah, I mean...'

The phone on his desk buzzed. He frowned and punched a button. 'What is it, Miss Macy? I thought I asked you to hold my calls.'

'Yes, sir. But Miss Gooding is on the line. She wants to confirm your dinner appointment and tell you she may be a bit late.'

'What dinner...?' Griffin sighed and ran his hand through his hair. 'Of course. Tell her that's fine. Chez Maude at seven, and if she's late, I'll wait. Now, hold any other calls, please.' He punched the button again, then looked at Jeannie. 'What I'm trying to ask you, Ms. Aarons... Jeannie. What I'm trying to ask is—is...'

'Yes?' Jeannie said, trying not to let him see how puzzled she was. McKenna, stumbling for words? It didn't seem possible.

'I understand that you and Dana Anderson were good friends.'

'Yes, sir. We still are.'

'Do you hear from Ms. Anderson, then?'

'Oh, sure. We keep in touch. I'm meeting her for drinks this evening, as a matter of fact.'

'She's in New York?'

Jeannie frowned. McKenna had said that the way she figured somebody might say, 'You mean, there are life jackets on this boat?'

'Uh-huh. Dana's in on business. She and I are getting together, and then she's having dinner with her fiancé.'

McKenna's mouth twisted. 'Of course.' He walked to the window, stuffed his hands into his trouser pockets and stared outside. 'And what does she say? Is she happy?'

'Happy?' Jeannie relaxed. She understood now. Dana was good at what she did, and McKenna was wondering if he could hire her back. 'Well, as far as I know, she likes her new job well enough...'

'To hell with her job!' Griffin swung around. His eyes were dark. 'I'm asking you about Dana. About her life. Is she happy?'

Wow, Jeannie thought. McKenna's face was like an open book. It was there, right there, in his eyes, a need—a painso raw and undisguised that it took her breath away. Whatever had happened in Florida, it had to do with lots more than new clients, job offers and Arthur's marriage proposal.

'Happy?' Jeannie echoed stupidly.

'Yes.' Griffin glared at her. 'Dammit, aren't I speaking English? It's a simple question, Ms. Aarons. Please answer it.'

Jeannie considered. It wasn't such a simple question, now that she thought about it. Dana said she was happy. In fact, she said it all the time. Maybe she said it too often...and maybe there was a darkness in Dana's eyes, too.

'I—don't know,' Jeannie said. 'That's the truth, Mr. McKenna.'

'Is she married yet?'

Jeannie hesitated. Then she tucked one hand into the pocket of her skirt and crossed her fingers.

'Not yet,' she said. 'But the wedding's next month.'

McKenna nodded. She waited for him to speak, but he didn't. Instead, he walked back to the window and looked out. The seconds rolled by. After a while, Jeannie tiptoed out of the office and shut the door quietly after her.

She'd told McKenna a lie, a big one. And yet, somehow, it had felt more as if what she'd told him was that yes, there *were* life jackets on this boat, and tossed one to him.

Right or wrong, whatever happened now, it was out of her hands.

Dana hurried along Third Avenue toward the place where she'd agreed to meet Jeannie, and wished she'd canceled the appointment.

It wasn't that she didn't want to see Jeannie. She did. It was just that there was so much to do back in Boston. Her new job, her new apartment, her plans for the future...

How could she deal with all that, if she was in New York?

Besides, New York wasn't part of her life anymore. Her job, her old apartment...it was all in the past.

And so was Griffin.

Dana's pace quickened. As ridiculous as it was, he'd been on her mind all day. And that *was* ridiculous, because she never thought about him anymore. Why would she? Her memories of him, of that weekend, were an embarrassment. Not just what she'd done with Griffin, but what she'd told herself she felt for him.

Love. Love? What a joke. She'd given in to some very basic sexual urges, and then she'd lied to herself about it. *That* was the real humiliation, that she, of all people, should have found it necessary to justify her behavior by trying to bathe it in the pink glow of romance.

All right, so she did still think about him. Not often, though, just every now and then, when she saw a man with a walk like Griffin's, or heard a laugh like his. And there were times she dreamed about him, too.

Silly, when sex was all it had been, all it could ever have been.

Except, it wasn't sex she dreamed about. She dreamed about lying safe in his arms. About doing all the things they'd never had time to do—walking along the beach or going for a drive in the country. Talking, strolling hand in hand, sharing their lives and their hopes…

'Hey, lady, watch where you're goin'.'

Dana murmured an excuse as somebody maneuvered past her. Great. Just great. Here she was, so caught up in her own pointless thoughts that she was bumping into strangers on the street. Why hadn't she flown back to Boston? That had been her intention when she'd phoned Jeannie to cancel their appointment late this afternoon, but Jeannie hadn't given her the chance.

'No time to chat,' Jeannie had said briskly. 'We can talk later, at this great new place. Chez Maude. Meet me there at seven, okay?'

Dana sighed. Another pretentious restaurant. Flowers. Candles. A menu that was impossible to decipher. And there it was now, just ahead. She'd told Arthur to meet her here, too. Seven-ish, she'd said, because she wanted to give Jeannie a chance to get to know him and like him. Arthur was a good person. And perceptive. He seemed to understand that she needed time to get used to the idea of marrying him. He hadn't pressured her at all. He hadn't even mentioned marriage since that night they'd flown back from Florida.

Arthur had his good points. Really, he did.

It's just that he wasn't Griffin.

The tears, and the despair, came without warning. Dana started to cry just as she reached the restaurant door. She couldn't see Jeannie tonight, nor Arthur. And she knew, with stunning certainty, that she *couldn't* marry Arthur, not like this, not ever. She started to step back, but it was too late. The door to the restaurant opened, a man stepped out, they collided...

...And Dana stumbled straight into Griffin's arms.

Griffin had been standing in Chez Maude's tiny entryway, as uncomfortable as a prisoner waiting for the jury's verdict, telling himself that no matter how bad it was, he'd manage to tough it out.

It seemed dead wrong to be meeting Cynthia for dinner when his mind was filled with Dana, and that made him angry as hell.

Why should he be thinking about Dana? There wasn't a reason in the world. And what an ass he'd made of himself today with Jeannie Aarons. Asking those silly questions about a woman he was never going to see again. Never wanted to see again. He had to put Dana aside and get on with his life, and the way to do that, he knew, was to leave the past behind him.

It was time to make a commitment to Cynthia.

She was right for him. She'd fit into his life without causing a ripple. She was easy to get along with, gentle, kind, amenable to his every wish. She'd never give him a hard time or argue with his decisions.

And he'd never love her.

Well, so what? A good marriage should be structured like a good corporation. It needed a solid base, and he would surely have that with Cynthia. Their lives would be comfortable, pleasant...and dull.

Life with Dana would never have been dull. It would have been filled with the spark of disagreement and the joy of reconciliation, with a passion so intense it could make his heart sing just to remember what it had been like to hold her in his arms.

'Bloody hell,' he muttered, and he swung around and pulled open the restaurant door.

He didn't want a comfortable life, he wanted a joyful one.

He wanted Dana.

She was out there, somewhere. And he wasn't going to rest until he found her and made her admit that she loved him and not the Bow Tie, even if he had to force the admission from her with his kisses, if he had to find out where she was going to be married and abduct her from the altar.

'Yes,' he said as he stepped onto the sidewalk—and Dana stumbled into his arms.

They stared at each other in stunned silence.

'Griffin?'

'Dana?'

Oh, she thought, how she had missed him! Her legs were weak, just at the sight of him. If only—if only, by some miracle...

Yes, he thought, oh, yes. This was the other half of his own soul. His heart was already hammering against his ribs. She had to love him, dammit, she had to.

'I...' She made a little fluttering motion with her hands. 'I didn't expect—'

'No,' He cleared his throat. 'Neither did—'

'Griffin,' she said breathlessly, 'Griffin, I—I—'

Tell him. Tell him the truth, Dana, that you love him with all your heart. Because you do. You know you do. You know you'll always love him...

'Dana.' Griffin stared at the face he'd dreamed of, at the woman who held his life in her hands. 'Dana,' he said... *Hell, man! Don't be an idiot.* 'You can't marry Arthur,' he said, rushing the words together. 'I won't let you.'

'You won't...?' Dana stared at him. 'Really, McKenna, you can't just...'

'I can,' he said, 'and I will. Dammit, Anderson, you are not going to marry that man!'

'Of course I can. I mean, I could. I mean...'

'You can't.' Griffin's eyes narrowed. 'You're going to marry me, instead.'

'What?' Dana whispered. 'What?'

Griffin took a deep breath. 'I said...oh, hell, Anderson! Come here.'

He reached out and took hold of her. For one long, endless moment, she held back. Then, just when he feared he had lost her forever, a smile began to tremble on her lips.

'Oh, Griffin,' she whispered, and then she was in his arms. He kissed her and kissed her, and she kissed him back. His arms tightened around her, until she could hardly breathe; her arms rose and she twined them around his neck.

'Dana,' he said against her mouth, 'my darling Dana.'

'Griffin, I missed you so much—'

He kissed her again, his hands clasping her face. 'I love you,' he whispered. 'With all my heart.'

Dana sighed. 'Tell me again.'

He did, with another kiss that left her swaying against him.

'When you said you were going to marry Coakley,' he murmured, 'I almost went crazy.'

'Me, too. When I realized you were trying to protect Cynthia—'

'Protect Cynthia?'

'Uh-huh.' Dana touched the tip of her tongue to her lips. 'You know, keep her from knowing about us, because you loved her.'

'Oh, sweetheart. We've got some talking to do. Cyn's a nice girl, but I never loved her.'

'And I never loved Arthur.'

'Didn't you?'

Dana shook her head. 'You're the only man I've ever loved, Griffin McKenna.'

'Damn right,' he said gruffly, while his heart swelled with joy. 'Not just the only, but the first and the last. Any arguments about that?'

'Not a one,' she said softly.

Griffin's arms tightened around her. 'When I think of all the time we wasted…'

Dana went up on her toes and put her mouth to his, kissing him with a tenderness and a passion that he'd known only in her arms.

'I thought I'd lost you,' he whispered.

'I know. I thought what we'd had—what we'd found…that those memories would be all I had to live on for the rest of my life.'

Griffin drew back, just far enough so he could see Dana's face. Her eyes glowed with joy and with tears. He kissed them away and thought how close he'd come to losing her. The realization made his own eyes feel suspiciously damp.

'Anderson,' he said gruffly.

She smiled and touched a fingertip to his mouth. 'Yes, McKenna?'

He lowered his head and leaned his forehead against hers.

'I am not an easy man to live with,' he said.

Her smile tilted. 'Do tell.'

'I'm opinionated. And maybe just a little bit egotistical.'

'A little bit,' she said agreeably.

'I tend to be very protective of what is mine.'

'That's quite a speech, McKenna. Are you telling me, perhaps, that there's a hint of male chauvinism in you?'

'Me?' A grin spread across his handsome face. 'Well, it's possible.' Their eyes met, and his smile faded. 'Anderson?'

'Yes?'

'When are we going to get married?'

'When? *When?* There you go, McKenna. You haven't even asked me if I *want* to marry you. Here you are, taking charge, barking out orders, assuming...'

'Shut up, Anderson,' Griffin said, and kissed her. After a while, Dana sighed and leaned back in his encircling arms.

'Next week,' she said dreamily. 'Is that too soon?'

'Well, I didn't want to rush you...' He smiled. 'How about this weekend?'

'This weekend sounds wonder... Oh, Griffin.' Dana's face fell. 'Griffin, we forgot.'

'What, sweetheart?'

'How are we going to break the news to Arthur and Cynthia?'

'Hell.' Griffin sighed and rested his hands on Dana's shoulders. 'It's going to be rough.'

'Arthur will be devastated.'

'Yeah, so will Cynthia.'

'I know.' Dana frowned and gazed past Griffin's shoulder. 'Well, we'll just have to do what has to be—what has to be...' Her breath caught. 'Arthur?'

'Where?' Griffin looked around. 'Be brave, sweetheart. Let me handle...' Griffin jerked back as his bewildered gaze fell on a couple locked in embrace a few feet away. 'Cyn?'

Cynthia and Arthur turned toward Griffin and Dana.

'Hello, Griffin,' Cynthia said shyly. 'We—we just... Arthur and I happened to come along at the same time. And we saw you two—I mean, we couldn't help but overhear...'

'Cynthia and I fell in love that weekend in Miami Beach,' Arthur said. He stood tall, his arm locked around Cynthia's waist. He blushed. 'Love at first sight, you know? We've been waiting and waiting to tell you, but—'

'But there just never seemed to be the right moment to do it,' Cynthia said. 'And we didn't want to hurt you.'

'We finally decided we'd each break the news tonight.' Arthur cleared his throat. 'We were concerned how you'd react, but—'

'But,' Cynthia said, leaning her head against his shoulder, 'it looks to us as if everything's worked out just fine.'

Dana smiled as she turned to Griffin. 'I think that's an understatement.'

'Oh,' Griffin said lazily, 'I don't know, Anderson. For instance, I've changed my mind about getting married this weekend.' He lifted her face to his. 'What would you say to tomorrow?'

Dana laughed, but her eyes filled with tears of happiness. 'I'd say it's the best idea you've ever had, McKenna,' she said.

Griffin didn't argue. He knew she was right.

The merger of Anderson and McKenna paid its first dividend three years later.

It was a boy, a healthy, beautiful son, weighing seven pounds, six ounces. He had his father's blue eyes, his mother's golden hair, and when he was old enough to leave for a long weekend with his proud grandmother, his parents celebrated the occasion with a joyous return visit to the Bridal Suite at the Hotel de las Palmas on the sands in Miami Beach.

* * * * *

LET'S TALK ABOUT BOOKS!

JOIN THE CONVERSATION

MILLSANDBOON
AUSTRALIA

@MILLSANDBOONAUS

ESCAPE THE EVERY DAY AT
MILLSANDBOON.COM.AU